S0-BCQ-132

PHOTO BY: STEVE GONZALES

Parris Afton Bonds

ALSO BY PARRIS AFTON BONDS

Deep Purple

Lavender Blue

Mood Indigo

Blue Moon

BLUE BAYOU

PARRIS AFTON
BONDS

Fawcett Columbine · New York

A Fawcett Columbine Book
Published by Ballantine Books
Copyright © 1986 by Parris Afton Bonds

All rights reserved under International and Pan-American Copyright Conventions. Published in the United States by Ballantine Books, a division of Random House, Inc., New York, and simultaneously in Canada by Random House of Canada Limited, Toronto.

Library of Congress Catalog Card Number: 85-90743

ISBN: 0-449-90153-X

Book design by Amy Lamb

Cover painting by Oliviero Berni

Manufactured in the United States of America

First Edition: August 1986

10 9 8 7 6 5 4 3 2 1

FOR G. W. AND MARY SUMMERS
You light up the night

and

LINDA LUCAS
For the good times!

PART

I

CHAPTER

Versailles-au-Val-de-Galie   *May 1683*

"Seven thousand pistoles, madame," Damien du Plessis said. He pushed his wager onto the gaming table before the king's former favorite, La Montespan.

The painted face of the still beautiful courtesan remained impassive, but then she was accustomed to the loss of one hundred fifty thousand pistoles in a single evening at cards or *cavagnole*.

Damien knew what to look for. When uncertain, she gave herself away by the unconscious tapping of the little finger of her left hand, that particular nail grown longer, as was the court custom, for scratching on a door at Versailles, where knocking was considered rude because there were simply too many doors in the immense palace.

As a matter of course, the cynical young man scrutinized his opponents' little habits—the absence or intensification of their movements under stress—because he made his expenses at Versailles, living on the losses of the royal relatives and attendant nobility at the *appartements* held three nights a week.

Tonight, though, he was distracted by the young girl costumed in pale pink silk damask who stood behind La Montespan. A new face among the *dames du palais*, he was certain, for it was a face one did not easily overlook. Hers was not conventional beauty, though the features were certainly arresting. It was simply that her whole being radiated surplus energy.

Damien was the most knowledgeable of young men when it came to seduction and to women in general. Twenty-six years before, he had been born to a prostitute in prison. At five, after he and his mother were released, he was taught to rob the customers with whom his mother had just lain. In the bagnios, he first encountered sexual pleasure and would endlessly reencounter it.

Street life had taught the roughly handsome young man to laugh when others fretted and to remain at ease when most shouted their rage. Court life that past year had developed for him a catholic taste in women—from bored wives of noblemen to a scrub maid from the palace's fifth kitchen, from a Moorish servant woman to her mistress, the wife of the Turkish ambassador.

None of these adventures had prepared him for this young woman, who could not have been more than twenty. She watched him with laughing eyes, the deep, sparkling blue of the Zuider Zee, that challenged his agatelike brown ones.

"Monsieur?" La Montespan said, her overripe lips compressed at his distraction. "I said, I am at the moment unable to match your wager."

Damien drew his attention back to the opulently beautiful blonde across from him. It was whispered that the marquise had submitted to the Black Mass, offering her naked body on the altar to Satan and drinking menstrual blood in exchange for the promise of the king's affection; that now, with the king's waning interest, she had become involved in an affair of poisoning. Nevertheless, she still wielded some power through the illegitimate children she had borne the king.

"Madame," Damien said, "I would accept a wager of equal value. Your lady-in-waiting." He inclined his powdered dark head toward the enchanting demoiselle behind La Montespan.

The young woman's blue eyes widened, then fired salvos of disgust and indignation at him. Courtiers gathered about the table gasped at the young man's audacity. One of the players, the old Comte de Polignac, tittered gaily behind a beringed hand.

La Montespan glanced over her shoulder at the woman, then said indifferently, "She is not mine to wager, or I would."

Her gaze returned to her opponent and flickered over the span of his shoulders beneath the dark green velvet coat that had faded in the creases, before lifting to linger on his sensitive, wind-marked face. Here was no court fop but a former soldier with the physique of a gladiator, as evidenced by the turn of calves that needed no padding to fill his white silk hose with powerful muscles.

Vaguely, she was aware that he had seen service with the *Mousquetaires* and been promoted to captain of the Guards. For the past four or five years, he had served as Louis's grand equerry. Her calculating smile revealed teeth well tended by silk thread. "Perhaps I could interest you in a wager of a similar nature?"

Damien returned her smile, understanding her meaning. He wasn't interested in bedding the woman, for no other reason than that his experience had taught him that silvery blondes didn't age well, but he wasn't so stupid as to offend her. "Madame, I accept your wager."

He took up the dice, applying himself to the *cavagnole* diligently. When next he looked up, the enchanting vision he had beheld so fleetingly had vanished. Fortunately for him, the Comte de Po-lignac won the round.

During the following days, Damien searched for the young woman incessantly, questioning those who had been in attendance at the entertainment that night. However, in a palace as vast as Versailles, with its apartments behind apartments and its secret corridors, one could go weeks without seeing the same face among its thousands of inhabitants.

Her face.

That single sighting had captivated him. Her worldly inex-perience attracted his peasant's lustiness, and her lack of coquetry appealed to his courtier's jaded senses. He had become obsessed by her image and was beginning to think he had imagined her. He didn't know her name and couldn't even remember the color of her hair. Was she a brunette, a redhead, or a blonde?

Could he be slightly mad, to have become so infatuated by a single glimpse of the young woman? At night, he lay in his attic room, which was little more than a hot and stifling closet, and tossed from one side of the narrow bed to the other, thrashing in a tangle of sweat-dampened linens. He fantasized about the mys-terious young woman, then cursed his foolishness when he knew he could have a selection of women yet wanted none. He succumbed to fantasizing again until fatigue drew him into a restless sleep.

Invariably, dinner at Versailles was served at one in the afternoon: a ceremonious affair normally *au petit couvert*, restricted to court attendance, though if open *au grand public*, the bourgeois would drive out from Paris for the spectacle.

Louis sat alone at the table, seldom talking to those standing in attendance, while he appeased his enormous appetite with his fingers. In the king's presence, only the Dauphin and his family and the princesses, but not the princes, of blood might sit—and then only on a *tabouret*, a three-legged stool. Everyone else stood. Things were different at the gaming table: any who could afford the stakes was allowed to sit.

The pecking order was inviolable, from black-velveted gentlemen of the chamber pot to the last lucky courtier who held the candle lighting the royal performance of the *couché*, when the king went through the nightly ritual of undressing for bed before he took himself to another, more private bed.

A day at court was worth a month's income; to live at court could cover a lifetime of debts, with fortunes spent on costumes alone. Damien's meager, full-dress wardrobe of brocades and silks and velvets, lavishly trimmed or embroidered, was meticulously cleaned and mended by himself in order to make do as long as possible at court.

Le Grand Louis had polished court etiquette as if it were a silver mirror in which daily life, so often dull, glittered like a medieval pageant. To be close to the king, to speak to and to be spoken to by him, to take precedence over others in closeness to him was an honor and ecstasy. The king was France incarnate.

To experience this contrived drama of court routine, noblemen and their wives mortgaged estates and hastened to the village of Versailles, which was little more than a cluster of four hundred huts, a rude inn, and a crudely constructed twelfth-century church. They lived in the village while hoping and scheming to obtain even an attic room at the palace. Their debts made them more beholden to the king for his favors, so he encouraged their extravagances.

If Damien was bored by the protocol and ritual of Louis XIV's entourage, if life at court did not wholly satisfy him, at least it kept him from being easily satisfied by anything else.

It was all a charade, of course, but for a courtier suddenly to declare it foolishness would be to declare his own worthlessness. Damien was certainly no fool.

Or possibly he was, he thought. Across the Grand Salon, he caught sight again of the elusive young beauty, possessor of those laughing dark blue eyes, which had haunted him for two weeks. Studying her now, he realized her looks depended more on dazzle and expression than on bone structure, a trait rarely recorded successfully by portraitists. Then, that very moment, her eyes laughed for the moustached man in the full dress wig standing next to her.

Stricken by acute jealousy, a condition not hitherto experienced by Damien, he glared at her companion, an imposing man of thirty or so who wore a black robe with an eight-pointed white cross stitched on its breast, signifying that he was a knight of the Maltese Order. That alone signified little—the Maltese Order abided by few principles pertaining to the godly; wealth and the acquisition of property were its major vows.

Damien knew the man slightly. He was Claude Fabreville, whose dry wit had gathered about him a following of bored courtiers, as well as the patronage of Monsieur, the Duc d'Orléans and brother of the king. Monsieur was a flamboyant quasi-transvestite.

Unobtrusively, Damien deserted his position near the *fauteuil*, the coveted armchair, and threaded his way toward the damsel. Though the dames of the court dressed in the bright colors of the peacock, she wore soft pink again, this time a dress of silk with Mechlin lace flouncing the sleeves and the low neckline.

Although she didn't look at him, he knew she was aware of him. Tall, with a warrior's build and blessed with the dark coloring of the people of Anjou, Damien had had no trouble attracting women who were tired of the court's prancing, painted dandies. Nor did he lack confidence.

Without even the courtesy of a bow, he said with the bluntness of a soldier, "Mademoiselle, you have been ever in my thoughts."

At last she turned those fabulous eyes on him, their blue darkened further by the thick fringe of lashes and the influence of a

black beauty mark placed beneath the corner of her left eye.
Neither a blonde nor a brunette, he noted; her piled hair beneath
the *fontange* was the shade of wet sand along the seashore. The
ends of her budlike mouth twitched with amusement but otherwise didn't concede any discomposure at his prosaic and abrupt
approach. "How so, monsieur?"

He forsook a courtier's flattery for the obvious. "You are unwed?"

Dimples appeared beneath the rather indistinctive cheekbones,
but before she could reply, her companion intervened. Looking
down his long, narrow nose, Fabreville asked languidly, "You
have intentions toward my cousin, monsieur?"

Somewhat relieved by the relationship, Damien replied, "Only
the most honorable—marriage." An absurd reply in a court where
decadence was the norm, but Damien was caught up in the throes
of first love. However, the second the statement left his tongue
he was appalled. It was the last thing in the world he had intended
to say, ever.

Still, at that very moment, the idea took seed. His aimless life,
which moved idly just ahead of him like his own shadow, suddenly had purpose.

"Ah, then I must disappoint you," the young woman said, her
eyes twinkling, "for I intend to be a *femme savante*."

"A waste of womanhood, Mademoiselle . . . ?"

Claude's nostrils flared, as if detecting an unpleasant odor, and
the ends of his waxed, dark moustache followed the line of his
disdainful smile as he said, "Monsieur of the Stables, the Marquis
de Marchesseau would consider your suit sheer folly. Come, my
dear."

Damien's swarthy face blanched. All that street life had taught
him about survival deserted him momentarily, especially the need
to remain at ease in a situation where anger robbed one of self-
control. His hand edged toward the haft of the broadsword at his
left side, but such an act was one of even greater folly. To engage
in a duel in the king's presence was to risk banishment from the
court, or possibly much, much more.

A mordant smile pleated the sides of his mouth as he watched
Claude draw the young woman away. Verily, he would have the
girl as his own.

So he began to lay siege to the young woman. He learned her
name, Hélène—and that her father was a wealthy silk merchant

of Blois. Of the *noblesse campagnarde*, the nobility of the country-side, her father was born high enough to climb higher and wealthy enough to purchase a title: Marquis de Marchesseau.

Comtes, marquises, and barons had originally been part of a graduated hierarchy, as in the English peerage, but all trace of differentiation had vanished by the time Louis Quatorze ascended the throne, and not one of those titles yielded precedence to another. Only ducs, descendants of the Twelve Peers of Char-lemagne, held higher rank. The titles were all territorial, attached to the land and not to the individual. When one of the titled estates was sold, the buyer acquired the title with the deed.

Since Marchesseau wished a prestigious marriage for his daugh-ter in order to further the family name and fortune, Claude, son of the marquis's younger brother, had volunteered to sponsor his cousin at court.

Damien forsook the king's billiards salon, the gaming tables, and the tennis courts to attend the Royal Opera or performances of Molière's comedies, where he observed his quarry from afar. Always she was attended by her cousin. Once Damien found her at an *appartement* given at the salon of *Les Divines*, two *femmes savantes* who wished to attract the gifted and the wits of the court.

Surrounded by would-be suitors, the object of his affections ignored him totally. She scintillated, and he eavesdropped in awe as she recklessly tossed names like Rembrandt, Rubens, and Ra-cine into the conversation. Uneducated, Damien felt uncomfort-able in the circle of *philosophes* who frequented the salon. He made no effort to approach her just yet. Often that evening he seemed occupied by whatever bejeweled lady claimed his momentary attention. Still, he was rewarded with an occasional covert flicker from Hélène's bright eyes.

This impasse was totally unknown to him. Usually, he simply took whatever and whomever he wanted. But Hélène was an intelligent young lady of quality, and he would be a man of patience, a warrior trained to win the ultimate battle.

One rainy Sunday, he literally bumped into her as he descended a twisting back staircase from his third-floor garret. Behind her hovered her maidservant, a young, peasant girl who was broad of shoulder and hip.

That part of Versailles was windowless, and for a moment

neither Hélène nor Damien recognized one another as they both stooped to retrieve a book she had dropped. Their hands closed over the book simultaneously, and Hélène's fingers jerked away. He rose and stared at the book's title for a long moment as he put the letters into words. Slowly, a grin broadened his mouth.

"*La Princesse de Cleves*," he said, not bothering to hide the triumph in his voice. "The novel all Europe is talking about. A romantic story, is it not, mademoiselle?"

She reclaimed the book from his large, battle-scarred hands. Sudden embarrassment suffused her face with a rosy hue. "So you can read," she managed to say.

"Barely," he acknowledged with a crooked smile. He kept talking to keep her there with him. Behind her, the maidservant eyed him coyly, but he heeded her not at all. "A comrade in arms— a Jesuit who forsook the tonsure for the helmet—taught me to write my name and read a little. But it comes hard for me." He wanted to reach out and touch her lips, fresh, soft, and unkissed. So different from the bored noblewomen who schemed to entice him into their beds. "But I am a quick learner, mademoiselle. Now, if you were willing to teach me . . ."

How could a young girl resist such determination in a suitor? There was something about him that proclaimed him an innocent, though court gossip whispered he was more than experienced in the art of seduction. That conundrum in itself was a challenge to her.

"If you will teach me to ride," she conceded with just a hint of feminine guile in her smile, "then I shall teach you to read." She gathered up her panniers, saying, "Now, if you will excuse me, monsieur."

As if the deities had blessed Damien's plan, the following day dawned fair and golden. Damien had a gentle palfrey for Hélène waiting at the Baths of Apollo. As grand equerry, he had his selection of mounts.

When the appointed hour came and went, he despaired. He stroked his restive Arabian gelding, silently berating himself as an oaf to take her careless words literally. Then he saw Hélène hurrying toward him along the *allée* of live oaks

"La!" She laughed when she reached his side. "I had to rid

myself of both my maidservant and my hawk-eyed cousin, a task, I assure you."

Was ever a woman so exciting, so alive, so *précieuse*? He delighted in watching her as she chattered about court gossip and Molière's play. "A boring one," she declared with mock solemnity, "titled *The Bores*."

They bypassed the Parc aux Cerfs, where Louis XIII once raised stags for his favorite sport of hunting and which acreage Louis XIV had now broken up into hotels and gardens for noblemen who had either no place of their own or for whom there was no room at the palace. Hélène sat the sidesaddle competently upon the little palfrey, and Damien began to suspect that her request for riding instructions had been a ruse—that pleased him greatly.

"I have heard you are from Anjou," she said, casting him a sidelong glance, "the home of hardheaded men."

He grinned. He was enjoying himself immensely. "I am told the Loire Valley produces the most beautiful girls in France."

"Do not flatter me, monsieur. Beautiful I am not. But . . . perhaps pretty."

"When the beauties of the court fade with age, you will still be lovely, mademoiselle."

She reined in her palfrey and stared at him wonderingly. "Why, I believe you're serious!"

"Never more so," he assured her gravely.

"You should have been a troubadour from Languedoc," she told him without any of the brittle, jesting tone she displayed in the salons.

He was amazed at himself; his earlier cynicism was no match at all for the purity of this first love. Two days later, he submitted himself to her tutoring. They found a stone bench beneath the chestnut trees that bordered the Allée de Bacchus in the Versailles gardens and removed from the noise of the constant construction work. Masons and other workmen, almost forty thousand of them, were everywhere. Only the year before had Versailles been completed sufficiently for Louis to move his court from the Louvre.

"Aristotle, Socrates, Plato," she said earnestly, "you must read these philosophers to understand the true nature of man."

He wasn't interested in the nature of man, only of woman, in particular, this very appealing woman. He was paralyzed by the power of his feeling for Hélène. It was as if he'd never developed his profound knowledge of women. The heat of the afternoon sun enhanced the scent of her skin, exciting him further. He had discovered early how important the true smell of a woman's skin was to the overall attraction she held for him, and the cloying perfumes the women of the court wore usually concealed this natural stimulant.

"Your cousin, mademoiselle. Your family entrusts him to find a suitable bridegroom for you?"

She eyed him surreptitiously, then trilled a little laugh that made him catch his breath. "If I ever marry, monsieur, it will be on a sudden impulse, as a man slits his own throat."

He studied her, intrigued. "Marriage terrifies you that much?"

"A wife is nothing but a chattel. I told you, monsieur, I shall be a *femme savante*. I shall have my own salon and hold small theatricals and balls. Only the most entertaining will be admitted. In truth, the only thing that terrifies me is being bored."

From that point in their relationship, Damien strove to be unfailingly entertaining. In the early hours of the morning, when most of the court still slept, he induced her to meet him in the billiards salon, where he taught her the rudiments of the game. Sheer paradise awaited him when she leaned over the table to make a shot and exposed the delectable V of her lace-bound breasts.

At a reception for a Spanish grandee, he boldly led her through the figures of a quadrille with the grace that came from his soldier's agility. Their shoulders touching beneath upraised hands, Hélène said, "My cousin does not approve of my dancing with you."

Damien flicked a careless glance at the slit-eyed knight and said, "I don't approve of his relationship with Monsieur."

Hélène gasped, laughed, then slid away into the next steps.

On another day, in a secluded grotto of the gardens, he played the troubadour to which she had compared him and sang to her: first, romantic odes of ancient heroes; then, at her pleas, the soldiers' songs, omitting the bawdier versions. In return, she read to him from Descartes and Locke and Scarron.

Sometimes her freethinking startled him. Once she exclaimed to him, "Have you ever noticed, Damien, that it is the male who is the peacock, who is encouraged to exhibit and accentuate his lines? Why we females don't even possess legs!"

At a time when it was common to encounter couples locked together in darkened alcoves of the palace, the noblewomen's skirts hitched up like country wenches, Damien's courtship of Hélène was curiously chaste. Even so, his insides were strung as tightly as lyre strings by her nearness and the need to capture her for his own, to couple with her until they became that mystical one that so far had eluded him in endlessly meaningless affairs.

Everything about her blared unawakened passion and sexuality: the full lower lip untempered by any ingénue smile, the almond-shaped eyes whose lashes could not disguise untapped sensuality, the breasts that heaved rapidly when he dared to brush them with his fingertips.

At times, he was certain he could make her his, could possess her and have done with it. But he wanted more. He wanted her as his wife and as the mother of his children. Bourgeois ideas, he knew, but he couldn't help himself. So he bided his time, hoping the king would keep his promise of a reward for Damien's performance on the battlefields of Flanders and confer on him a title that would recommend him to the Marquis de Marchesseau.

On lazy, sunny afternoons, he and Hélène strolled easily along the Grand Canal where *jets d'eau* flung two walls of water thirty-five feet high, or they wandered among the flowered *parterres* rolled out on both sides of the walkway like great Oriental rugs. "Did you know that the color of your eyes is the color of infinity," he said, tucking a blossom of lavender behind her ear, "and the color of your soul. Beautiful."

"You speak more like a courtier than a soldier," she teased lightly, but he heard the breathlessness in her voice.

Sometimes they visited the village where the hunters rendezvoused, and carters and wagoneers halted, their vehicles laden with beef from Normandy bound for Les Halles market in Paris. He would take her hand in his and feel a happiness he had never known.

"Your cousin?" he asked as they were riding one spring day along the outskirts of a *bosquet*, where the leafy shadows concealed them with prying eyes. "Does he object any more when you ride out with me?"

For a long moment, Hélène said nothing, and there was heard only the brittle crunch as the horses' hooves disturbed leftover winter leaves. Then she raised her eyes, a blinding blue. "He has been keeping my family informed of our meetings. My father has ordered my return when the court journeys to Fontainebleau this summer."

"I see," Damien said.

He dismounted and came around to her palfrey. Hélène watched him with an inquiring lift to her thick, straight brows, but he reached up and caught her under her arms, drawing her off her mount. Instead of releasing her, he held her against him. She barely reached his chest. His nostrils flared with the heady scent of her flesh, and through the material of her peach-colored riding habit, he could feel her heart pounding erratically.

"Marry me now," he demanded.

The deep blue of her eyes darkened perceptibly. Then she pulled gently away and turned from him for a moment to tug off her plumed hat, a masculine affair with a silk-lined apricot brim. He wanted to release her elaborate coiffure, to tangle his fingers in her ivory-brown hair. "You didn't answer me."

She twirled around to face him. "And what shall we live on, Damien? Do you win enough at the gaming tables to support us both?"

"If I leave His Majesty's service, I have a soldier's pension. To supplement it, I could find work as a mercenary in the Dutch or Austrian army. I could take you to the capitals of the civilized world, Hélène. You would never be bored."

"You *are* an innocent," she said. And then, more wearily, "Damien, I don't want to leave Paris. All my life I've dreamed of court life, of attending the—"

He caught her by her upper arms, pulling her against him and delighting in the feel of her soft woman's breasts pressed flat against the muscular plates of his chest. His lips nuzzled the tender white flesh of her neck, and he heard the soft little moan she made.

"Marry me," he repeated.

"My father would never countenance it," she said in a breathless murmur.

"Then we will wed without his consent," he growled, and, unable to contain his passion, captured her trembling lips, pressing them apart until she capitulated and granted his tongue entry. The shyly hesitant parry of her own tongue excited him beyond any polished erotic performance by his past bed partners.

When his mouth at last released hers, she drew away from him, her passion-flushed face weighted with sadness. "The king will never grant his permission. We can't fight the entire world, Damien."

"The king is not the entire world."

THE CHURCH OF ST. PIERRE AUX Boeufs disregarded all rules imposed on matrimonial candidates. The Gretna Green of Paris, its priest performed marriages without the publications of banns and without the consent of parents.

Wearing pink as usual, a pale rose velvet, Hélène du Plessis had never looked more radiant as she and Damien made their way by unlit coach back to Versailles that night. Dawn had not yet broken when, in his little attic room, he tenderly let down her hair and removed her layers of clothing to expose her delicate white flesh shadowed by tufts of soft, springy coils beneath her arms and at the enticing fork of her legs. With infinite gentleness, he strove to initiate the first virgin he had ever known into the rites of Venus.

Their heated passion staved off the chill of the room. After three days closeted away, with only Hélène's maidservant to bring them food, Damien knew Hélène was not his first love but would forever be his grand love. In possessing her, he was also possessed. Once the intensity of the pleasure ebbed into the relaxing afterglow of lovemaking, she enchanted and entertained him with animated stories of her childhood adventures and escapades, and songs that she had learned to play on the harpsichord—and with her own hesitant inquisitiveness. Never had a paid whore satisfied him as much as this woman, his wife.

"When I was nine, I fell in love with my cousin Claude and was desolate when he became a knight of the Maltese Order." Languidly, her forefinger tatted the wiry hair that whorled around one of Damien's rapidly hardening nipples. "Now I am glad he did, or I might never have spent such a pleasurable three days abed."

His voracious kiss silenced her laughing lips.

Their respite had to end, and Damien found himself summoned the following morning to the cabinet of His Majesty. From the warmth of their rumpled bed, Hélène clutched his hand. Fear glazed her eyes, and her bottom lip was white with the imprint of her teeth. "I knew this would happen. He will be furious that we have wed without his permission. Please, Damien, you must placate him, or it will mean banishment from court."

With her pale brown nipples peaking through the twin ocher veils of her hair, it was difficult for Damien to be overly anxious about the royal summons. At that moment, he wanted nothing more than to join her in the warm bed that was so redolent of their lovemaking.

"And would banishment be so bad, *ma mignonne*, my pretty?" he joked. "I am weary of the constant round of court *fêtes, divertissements*, and *plaisirs*. I feel like I am cooped up in a perpetual house party."

For what seemed an eternity, Damien paced the *oeil-de-boeuf*, the antechamber to the king's cabinet. The melancholy eyes in a portrait of a prominent Florentine woman, Mona Lisa del Giocondo, seemed to follow him, and he turned his back on the portrait. At last he was admitted into the presence of *le roi soleil*.

Though physically plain and below medium height, with the purple veins of a dissolute life cobwebbing his skin, the Sun King still managed to reduce the court's most gifted speakers to tongue-tied muteness. An indomitable egoist, he could thoroughly intimidate with his Bourbon characteristics: the harsh gaze and hooked nose. A receding chin, caused by the removal of his teeth, made him appear no less fierce. Especially when he was irate, as he was at that moment. Beneath hooded lids, his dark eyes flashed.

Damien's plumed hat swept the carpet with his bow, but when he fixed his eyes on *Le Grand Louis*, he did not quail. Although his sovereign had domesticated France's nobility into a framework of servility, Damien was a man of basic philosophy. Between the whorehouses and the army, he had learned that all men are the same, with only the pomp of clothing to elevate their status. Louis's skinny legs, his thinning hair hidden by enormous wigs, his rotund girth could be risible—if anyone dared such a reaction.

"Your Majesty?" Damien said.

Louis snapped his fingers, and from behind a tapestry that partitioned his cabinet from a private apartment emerged his painted and powdered brother, the Duc d'Orléans, and the black-robed knight, Claude Fabreville, who inclined his head, his smile thin and mocking.

"My brother and his . . . companion," Louis said, "inform me that you have contracted a marriage."

Damien never took his eyes off Claude. Other than tattling, what was the knight's part in this—and why? "That I have, Your Majesty. With the knight's cousin."

"And without my sanction," the king said. He raised his gold-knobbed cane and tapped it on the parquet floor before Damien. "Last year, my Turkish ambassador was foolish enough to marry a native of that backward country. And one not of the *noblesse* at that. A woman below his birth and rank. Do you know what happened?"

"You had the ambassador recalled, I believe," Damien said. He refused to cringe, but the feeling of independence that gives a man his identity was being threatened, and he didn't know what he could do about it. He had felt he was his own man, but now he couldn't simply disappear to lose himself as a mercenary in the service of some foreign army. Love and Hélène had complicated his life—and at the same time enriched it.

"And had him banished from court, Monsieur," the king's brother, purred.

Damien bowed. "I am yours to command, sire." For him, the punishment would almost be a reward.

"I find your attitude commendable," the king said. "But I am not finished. You are to retire to Blois, your wife's family estate, where you will engage in the work of the silk industry until I feel inclined to change my mind."

Damien said nothing, could say nothing. To be forced into a

trade, when he was a born soldier, would be the unmaking of him, he was sure.

Hélène waited for him in his garret, her hands twisting together. "What happened, Damien?"

He caught her small hands between his. Her flesh was cold, and he chafed her hands while he talked. "Your cousin is working mischief, *ma mignonne*. We have been banished to your family estate until Louis's anger passes. Only a matter of months, I am sure."

The old quarter of Blois, a picturesque medieval city high above the Loire, had to be approached by steep flights of stone steps. Above it, on a crest, the magnificent Marchesseau château dominated the entire valley. Its grounds were said to be as vast as Paris. The splendidly decorated palace was known all over the province simply as Maison Bellecour. Rich Gobelin tapestries, as well as expensive blue wallpaper, kept out the drafts. The woodwork shined like mirror glass, the porcelain doorknobs gleamed against the carved oak doors, and the Carrara marble was polished enough to satisfy a Medici.

More than one nobleman with a duchy title in Louis XIV's court coveted the enormous Maison Bellecour and would willingly have married off a son to the provincial marquis's only child. But it was on Damien that such fortune fell.

From the château, Damien could watch the Loire flowing past on its way to the Bay of Biscay and the world of far-flung countries. Rare, though, were the restless nights when he stole to the deep-set casement window and viewed from there the moon-streaked black currents with an indefinable yearning.

Most nights, he found refuge in the arms of Hélène from the staleness of his days. After his vagabond, baseborn life, his lively, aristocratic, young wife was a gift of new life to him, too good to be true. Sometimes he feared the gods might recant of their generosity, and he worked twice as hard to keep peace both at the château and at the silk factories.

The peace was a strained one. Gaston de Marchesseau, a big, blustering man, strove to contain his contempt for the uneducated soldier who was now his son-in-law as he introduced him to the workings of the factories; his wife Claudette, frail but without

Hélène's handsomeness, did not get along well with her daughter. Where Hélène sparkled, her rustic mother wore a look of disenchantment with the world. Claudette was a dry, duty-bound woman. As for Damien, she refused to acknowledge his presence, never addressing him directly.

Hélène suffered as well, though it was not so obvious until cousin Claude journeyed down from Fontainebleau to pay the Marchesseau family a visit. Over supper, she avidly questioned the knight about court happenings, laughing with a delight that was rarely heard those days when he would recount with his sly wit the passions and politics at court.

For the occasion, a fine Dutch linen cloth draped the table. A *surtout*, an exquisite piece of goldsmith's art, dominated the table with its accommodation of salt, pepper, spices, and ivory toothpicks. Utensils with white, bone handles had been laid.

"You will agree, will you not," Claude asked of her, "that Racine's plays all have the theme that reason is powerless to resist the swirl of passion?"

Did he intimate that his cousin had lost her power of reason in *la belle passion* for a common soldier? Damien, silent, chewed tender *petit pois* and listened with barely suppressed irritation. He was sorely tempted to destroy the effete handsomeness of the knight.

"Ah, but his heroes are men of passion," she said, laying aside her spoon in her enthusiasm for the discussion. "I prefer Corneille's men of honor, where there is a sense of society as an ordered world."

Her father presided from his high-backed leather chair, eating steadily, oblivious to the discussion between his nephew and daughter. Her mother's mouth was set petulantly, her food barely touched. Hélène belonged to a world her provincial mother could never understand. In that, her mother and Damien were nearly alike.

Jealousy of Claude simmered in Damien, for witty conversation did not come easily to him and became twisted in his mouth. He was no match for Claude's eloquence. Still, instinct told him his wife's cousin could offer no competition in the bedroom. There the love between husband and wife banished the outside threat of reality. After Claude left, Damien returned to the silk factories with a sigh of relief.

That fall brought no message of reprieve from the king; what it did bring was the confirmation of Hélène's pregnancy. With the birth of a son, Philippe, Damien was at last able to put behind him his yearnings for the military life. When he saw children, most of whom were younger than seven, working at the silk factories' warp webs and frames and looms, he was thankful that Philippe would not have to live that kind of life, nor the life he himself had led.

He loved watching Hélène nurse their son, and would sit in the privacy of their bedroom, gaping upon the madonnalike scene. Once Hélène said to him, "You never talk of your mother."

"I told you, she died when I was young. I've been a soldier all my life."

"But you never said how she died," she persisted. "You tell me nothing of your childhood, where you lived in Anjou, what your father did."

His fingers played with a vibrant swath of ivory-colored hair, twining it behind her shell-like ear. He carefully kept all bitterness from his voice. The past was behind him. "My mother was a prostitute. I don't know who my father was, don't even know if du Plessis is my real name. My mother died of the disease of Venus when I was fifteen."

Somehow, the events of his life he never meant to tell slid past his tongue. "Her death freed me from my role as a thief. At fifteen, I sought out the life of a soldier, which at least promised daily food in my belly. A priest-turned-soldier is the closest I have to a family."

He didn't add that until he fell in love with her, he had trusted no one, made no friends. All his life, he had been a loner—and had been desperately lonely. Now he had her; now he had a son; now he had his own family.

"I was sent to the wars in the Netherlands," he continued in a casual tone, "where I was fortunate enough to distinguish myself with the Normandy Regiment."

"And since then, *mon petit*, your father's rise through the ranks has been meteoric," she said with a tender smile to the babe suckling at her breast. "Straight up to the captain of the Guard in the Black Musketeers, then grand equerry to the king. You see, I tried to find out all I could about the relentless young man who pursued me."

The infant united both father and grandfather in a common interest, and life eased for Damien at Maison Bellecour. When his towheaded son began to crawl, both Gaston and Damien toasted the occasion. Damien's mother-in-law carefully removed herself from their presence as the two men grew pleasantly intoxicated.

He spent longer days at the factories, taking over some of Gaston's more laborious tasks. His efforts at reforming the labor conditions for the children brought a mild but plaintive scoff from Hélène. "You want to change the world, Damien; I want to live in it."

Not too long afterward, Claude paid the château another visit. Unable to abide the viper-tongued knight, Damien escaped to the château's forest to hunt, returning at sunset. Claude had already retired to the room provided for him, and Damien, putting away his short-barreled arquebus, sought out Hélène. He found her in their bedroom packing clothing into a trunk. She looked up at him where he stood frozen in the doorway and, unable to meet his accusing gaze, returned to folding her clothes.

"You're leaving," he said.

"Yes."

"Why?" Agony rasped his voice.

At last she straightened, her expression locking with his. In the wavering candlelight, her eyes glistened. "Damien . . ." she began in a faint voice, then, more strongly, "Damien, I'm dying by degrees here. Can't you see it? I miss the excitement of court life, the intrigues, the witty chatter of the salons."

"The king—"

"He has given me permission to return, if I so desire."

Her long, lovely fingers fidgeted with a chemise, and he knew there was more. "And I?"

The garment knotted beneath her fingers. Her voice was barely a whisper. "You have been refused."

"You would leave me?"

At the stark look of incredulity on his lean face, she dropped the chemise and flung herself at him, burying her face against his chest where the quilted jerkin was unlaced. Her tears dampened the wiry hair matted there. "I don't know . . . I didn't know . . . that loving could be so horribly difficult." She drew a deep breath and continued shakily, "I feel so torn, like two different women . . . and I feel so guilty . . . but I don't know what to do. I feel like the blood is slowly being sucked from my veins by leeches. The château is so deadly quiet, so dark, so empty . . . so boring!"

He stroked her hair, staring at nothing over her head. "You were born here, Hélène, you grew up here. It just takes time to get used to the life here again after court life."

She drew back her head and looked at him. "Oh, Damien, I've always hated it here! When I saw myself in the cheval glass, I knew I was destined to be more than wife and mother in a provincial little town! When I was a child and Claude would tell his tales of the royal court, I knew with absolute certainty I would one day be a part of it."

He set her from him. "And Philippe," he blurted coldly. "You would leave him, too?"

"I'm taking him with me."

"Is that any place for a child?" he demanded, trying to rein in his runaway anger. "Have you learned yet what happens to the boys who are raised there? They become playthings for those jaded fops!" he said brutally, his voice rising in a mixture of fear and rage.

"I know, I know. Don't you think I love our son and want the best for him? Claude has found a nurse in Chion to look after him. The village is close enough for me to visit often. Every day if I want. Oh, Damien, please don't look at me like that!"

"You will not give away our son to be raised by a stranger. He is mine also. And he is your parents' grandchild. I will raise him here at Blois."

She turned from him, burying her face in her hands, and he knew there was more that she had not told him. "What else are you holding back?" he growled, jerking her around to face him.

Tears streamed down her cheeks. "You are being sent out with the Carignan-Salières regiment to protect the frontier of New France."

CHAPTER

New France　3　*May 1700*

THE FORT OF VILLE MARIE DE
Montréal, a rude little settlement, perched on the west bank of
the St. Pierre River just beyond the formidable St. Lawrence
Rapids. The incredible growth of the fur trade due to the demand
for beaver hats had resulted in a corresponding growth in population that had made it impossible to build within the fort walls.
So Sieur Damien du Plessis had constructed a well-palisaded
frame of two stories out where the rue St. Joseph ended. Once
a muddy pasture, now the area was abustle with the trading post
and warehouses of du Plessis and his partner.

His house, though larger than others on the oval-shaped island
of Montreal, resembled them in that it had a steep-pitched roof
and was whitewashed. The industrious white of the houses was
relieved by doorways painted in bright colors. Where other doors
were red or blue or even purple, Damien had had his painted
yellow—denoting a traitor or a cuckolded husband.

No one dared to ask the taciturn fur merchant what the color
stood for. But he had brought no wife with him, nor had he taken
a wife from among the women of the straggling colony, as had
his fellow Carignan-Salières soldiers, veterans of the Turkish wars
who had settled New France like Roman legionnaires.

Not that the settlement's women weren't attracted to the man.

At forty-three, while other males his age slouched about with protruding bellies, he carried himself with the severe carriage of the soldier he had once been. He preserved the lean, muscled tone of his body by daily, arduous physical labor, despite the fact he was veritable ruler of a small fiefdom. His dark brown hair was peppered with silver, but his moustache, as well as other hirsute areas of his body, as quite a few women could verify, was still pure brown.

If he wasn't, therefore, a deceived husband, the alternative of traitor remained. However the colonists had already ruled out that possibility. Du Plessis had served the colony well, first as a valiant officer of the Carignan-Salières and later as a fur merchant, who, two years before, had been appointed governor of the colony by Frontenac, the governor of New France. Du Plessis now carried the title of baron.

Baron. The title and the wealth he had worked hard to acquire meant little to him; the two things that mattered most were both a great distance away. His wife and his son. For them, he had worked like an ant and made something of his life.

From the open shutters of the windows on the second floor of his house, he could view the wharves below Montreal's sun-drenched slopes. The river ice was just beginning to break up, his cherry trees were swelling with buds, and the elder bushes were barely beginning to show their leaves. His grant had a frontage of ninety arpents and double that in depth. He had managed to purchase the immense grant with his yearly soldier's pension of a mere two thousand livres because it was located on a dangerous neck of land through which Iroquois warriors passed on their way to and from the Richelieu River. No one else had wanted it.

With Montreal becoming a great trading center, and since its rapids couldn't be bypassed by canoes bringing the winter pelts down to market, his mercantile business had profited into a swiftly mounting fortune, enough for him to build the best home for leagues around. Fort and château all in one, his house was one of the most important seigneuries of New France. The main bedroom, furnished with imported French furniture, stood empty, waiting. . . .

He turned away from the small window toward his bed. On the goose-down mattress lay the woman who had dedicated her life to serving the Ursuline nuns. *Mère Marie*. The middle-aged woman regularly wore a habit of her own design, an unrelieved gray, rather than that of the Ursulines since she was not officially of that order. At that moment, Mother Marie wore nothing. Her body was gaunt, lacking the fashionable dimples of the times, because she gave away everything she received at the Hôtel-Dieu, where she served the ill and needy.

Damien found her face a wonderful oval, remarkable for its harmony of line: an aquiline nose, a clearly defined and always smiling mouth, limpid eyes veiled by long, thick lashes. As he moved toward her, she opened herself to the monolith proclaiming his desire. For the past several years, she had assuaged his insatiable sexual appetite, and he felt a curious sentimentality for the woman. He bent over her, his mouth beginning the erotic love play on breasts that had never known the mouth of an infant.

Later, as he held himself within her, waiting for a renewal of his seed, his thoughts turned with anticipation to the morrow. . . .

Seated in the prow of the forty-foot birchbark canoe, Damien pushed away from the Montreal wharves. Behind him, thirty-two men paddled four more of his gaily painted canoes, all packed with supplies. The muscles of his arms and shoulders flexed as he flung his red-bladed paddle from side to side. It felt good to be battling with nature again. *Par Dieu*, it felt good just to be leaving Montreal!

True, the life of New France's seigneurial class and better-established merchants was similar to the opulence of the leisure classes in France. Shipments from France were no longer made up of sheer necessities.

Yet with the opulence came French governmental restrictions, a royal assertion of authority that had been missing when Damien had first arrived fifteen years earlier.

The lucrative fur trade was enticing men from their farms and from their duty to raise large families, the realistic activities that ensured a conquest of the new land. Habitants were now forbidden to move into town on pain of being fined fifty livres and having all goods and chattels confiscated.

It was also illegal for townspeople to rent houses or rooms to tenants from the country. A farmer could not own more than two horses and a foal because cattle and sheep were more important. No one could trade in foreign goods. Anything purchased abroad, except from France, was seized and publicly burned.

Only books of a devout nature were permitted, and public profanity incurred punishment that could bring about the cutting out of one's tongue. Rouge was immoral and forbidden to be sold to colonists, but somehow the wily females of Isle Royale found their own sources.

Le Grand Louis had ordered bakers to make dark brown bread, though no one wanted it, because the king believed the bread to be doubly nutritious. Damien knew from experience that Louis never ate anything but white bread. But bake brown bread the bakers must.

Worst of all, no one could return to France without royal leave, and the king rarely gave such permission. To what would he have returned, anyway? Damien asked himself. He rationalized, not for the first time, that the monotony of domesticity would suffocate him.

He allowed himself the satisfaction of a magnificent string of profanities, which made him feel almost cheerful, then he devoted all his attention to paddling.

The Summer Rendezvous was one of the few pleasures he allowed himself, though the annual one-thousand-mile journey was a rigorous one. The extreme physical exertion it required made him too tired to think, and for several months each year, he was completely free of bitterness.

The rhythmic singing and shouting of his *voyageurs* halted as they neared the first of many rapids. With quiet, cold concentration, Damien applied himself to the task of running the dangerous white water. The other canoes followed single file. As the guide of the canoe brigade, he plunged his craft into the foaming torrents. Icy water sprayed the paddlers. The canoe lurched and reared and plummeted like a wild horse through the tumultuous water.

In each boat, the middle men paddled furiously in order to hold a steady course, and the bowman and steersman in the stern flung their long paddles from side to side, shoving the craft away from menacing rocks and aiming it through the narrow chutes.

Clear of the rapids, the men broke into song again, this time the
bawdy *Rossignolet Sauvage*. Each song, whether sacred or profane,
ended with a piercing Indian yell.

That night, as the rest would be, was spent on the water with
the canoes lashed together. During the next six weeks, Damien
and his *voyageurs* traveled up the Ottawa River, down the French
River into the *Mer Douce*, or Freshwater Sea, which the English
called Georgian Bay. From there they traveled up the north channel of Lake Huron, then portaged across Sault Ste. Marie into
Lake Superior.

On its shore each summer, Damien met with his parner at the
village of Grand Portage. The old man would have spent the
winter trading for furs and, come May, traveled south to Grand
Portage with packs of pelts. They conferred and celebrated for a
month, then exchanged cargoes and returned to their bases before
the watery highways froze solid again.

As the birchbark flotillas entered Lake Superior, the paddling
stopped momentarily so that the Montrealers could exchange their
homespuns for blue jackets, red-tasseled caps, and gaudy sashes.

Other canoe brigades, also headed for Grand Portage, dotted
the lake. The rival *voyageurs* of Quebec were distinct in their red
coats, as opposed to the blue ones from Montreal.

Damien kept on his long-skirted blue coat with its turned-up
cuffs and immense side pockets. His one concession to adornment
was the scarlet worsted scarf tied about the coat's waist. Ten
years before, he had put away his soldier's heavy armor, soiled
doublet, highly polished breastplate, and casque with its frayed
white plume to become a member of the mercantile class. Now
he would dress no other way.

The post of Grand Portage spread out in a natural amphitheater
of rocky hills surrounded by a palisade fifteen feet high, reinforced
with bastions and a heavy gate. As the canoes neared shore, the
men's excitement became tangible. A week-long celebration of
drink and cards and orgies was just ahead.

Inside the stockade were a dozen buildings: the Great Trading
Hall, where both dining and business meetings took place, was
surrounded by living quarters, shops, warehouses, and a stone
powder magazine. One of the shops was the *cantine salope*, a har-
lots' tavern, and it was there the *voyageurs* headed to blow their

pay on liquor and on the large local complement of Indian and half-breed girls. Later, Damien would have to haul his men out of the jail, which the men called *pot au buerre*, butter tub.

On shore, Damien's destination was neither the *cantine salope* nor the butter tub but a log cabin that served as his living quarters while he was at Grand Portage. Smoke whorling from the clay chimney told him his old comrade in arms cum-partner, Jean-Baptiste Brissac, was waiting.

When Damien threw open the door, he found his partner kneeling before the hearth helping himself to stew from the great black kettle. The little man in stained buckskins had received the abbé's tonsure when he was nine and, after entering a Jesuit novitiate at seventeen, had renounced the calling at twenty-five. He was the only soul in the New World who knew everything about Damien, the only man Damien trusted. The two flung themselves at each other for a great bear hug.

"*Par Dieu*, if you don't get scrawnier every time I see you," Damien said, and stepped back to look at the lean ascetic. His partner's frailness of physique had never been a handicap, for Damien had realized long before that men who lacked robust health often survived the strains and privations of the wilds better than those of rugged frame and greater strength.

"*Sacre bleu*, if you don't look more like Lucifer every day!" Jean-Baptiste exclaimed, pounding the taller, bigger man's shoulders. "It's that wicked moustache. You must give up your wild life, *mon ami*, and settled down and marry."

"I am already married," Damien said drily, stepping back.

"Ah,yes," Jean-Baptiste murmured, tugging at his straggly grizzled beard with embarrassment. "So I forget. Then let us talk of other things. Come sit at the table while I pour us a tumbler of nectar, the best rotgut in Grand Portage. I have good news— six hundred of the most luxurious beaver skins ever taken out of the northwest country. And not just beaver. We've marten, fisher, lynx, fox, and mink! The plews are already at the warehouse waiting to be loaded."

Damien sat back, loosened his coat, and studied his venerable friend, who continued to chatter on. The little man had a nose that was too long for his narrow face, but something benign shone in gray eyes that sloped from the weight of deep wrinkles. "A

rich lode this time, Damien! With Paris—all Europe—raging over
furred *balles* and busks and puffs . . . Why, Damien, you'll be
wealthier than you ever dreamed!"

"Jean-Baptiste."

His partner halted his outpouring. *"Oui?"*

Damien plunked his tankard down, the raw whiskey tasting
like brackish swampwater, and leaned forward. "You've never
been so voluble. What's wrong?"

The intelligent gray eyes ricocheted from Damien's piercing
dark brown ones.

"Well?" Damien insisted.

The other rose and went to the rear of the cabin where a ladder
led to the loft. "Rema," he called out. "Nicolas."

Damien sprang to his feet as a thick-bodied Indian woman in
soiled deerskins and leggings slowly descended the ladder, eyes
averted. Behind her came a boy of nine or so.

Damien's eyes flashed; his jaw clenched. "How dare you bring
them here!"

Jean-Baptiste stepped quickly between his friend and the others. "Damien! He is your son, and it's time you stopped denying
him the right to know his father."

Damien didn't move. His voice was low and terse. "My son is
in France."

Jean-Baptiste's crest of salted hair jutted forward.

"When are you going to acknowledge the truth—that Hélène
is nothing but a courtesan, the Duc de Chartres's harlot last time
we heard; that your son by her knows nothing about you; that
you will never see them again?"

Damien stormed toward the door, and Jean-Baptiste cried out,
"Wait! *Alors, mon cher ami*, at least talk with the boy! You owe
him that much. Or are you a coward after all?"

Damien spun, his teeth bared in a snarl. "All right, I will talk
with the boy. Then you will return him and Rema to the Chipewyan village. Immediately. Tomorrow."

Satisfied for the moment, Jean-Baptiste nodded and stepped
aside. Damien, arms akimbo, glared down at the *métis*, the half-
breed. The boy was thin, but above his prominent ribs lay a firm
sheet of pectoral muscle. His dirty, shoulder-length hair was blue-
black like his mother's, as were his eyes. In fact, Damien found
little to indicate the boy was half-white—let alone his. Except,

perhaps, for his height, Damien's height. The youth appeared tall for a nine-year-old Indian child. In his bony face, the eyes already seemed old and almost wizened.

In his mind, Damien counted the number of times he had seen the boy. Four—five, maybe, the last time three years before. But always either at the Chipewyan camp or at Jean-Baptiste's lodge, both over five hundred miles to the northwest. Those times with the boy and Rema had been, for the most part, the early years, when he had gone native; when he and Jean-Baptiste were trying to put together their string of fur depots to start their profitable Fur Company of Canada, or *Kanata* as the Indians called the country the French had dubbed New France.

"Come here, boy."

"His name is Nicolas," Jean-Baptiste reminded him. "Nicolas du Plessis. I myself named him for Saint Nicolas."

"I know that," Damien snapped, hunkering on one knee so that he could better observe the boy. "Come here, Nicolas."

The youngster's opaque eyes flickered. The Indian woman, her cinnamon-colored face inscrutable, nudged her son's shoulder, and the boy stepped forward. Damien frowned. The twisted foot was little better. He studied the boy as the boy's black eyes studied him. The face held little of conventional beauty, all relentless angles that should have been softened by childhood. And the head seemed too large for the body.

"Where is France's center of government?" Damien asked.

Nicolas glanced at Jean-Baptiste. Receiving an encouraging nod, he replied, "Versailles, for the present."

The boy's melodious voice was disarming. "The center of government for New France?" Damien said.

"Quebec."

Damien glanced at his partner's smug face, then rapped, "Who wrote the *Principles of Philosophy*?"

"Descartes."

Damien straightened to his feet. "You have done well, Jean-Baptiste. Better than you did by me, I believe."

"It was the long, uninterrupted winters. Your son is even quicker than you, Damien. He has a keen mind. By the time I finish with him, he will have an education worthy of the Jesuit College at La Flèche."

"For all the good it will do the little savage. Come, matters of business await us at the Trading Hall."

Rema's softly spoken Indian name for him stopped Damien in midstride. He turned to look at her. Ten years and a pregnancy had altered her once lithe figure into near plumpness. The beautiful bone structure of her face was obscured by thickening jowls, her skin coarsened by harsh weather and campfire smoke and poor diet. Her braids shone with bear grease. Well, at least she still had all her teeth, he noted, reminding himself of the persistent ache in one of his own back teeth.

She padded over to him and hesitantly touched his sleeve. Jean-Baptiste, seeing the look that passed between them, said, "The boy and I'll wait for you at the Trading Hall."

Suspended about Rema's neck was a brass trading coin bearing the likeness of Louis XIV on one side and on the reverse a beaver to denote its value of one pelt. The coin was worn as an ornament until it was redeemed at the company store for goods. He had given it to her on his last trip into Athabascan country three years before.

Seeing his interest, she touched the coin with dirt-encrusted fingers and smiled fetchingly.

He didn't return her smile. The sooty odor of her clothing, combined with the rancid bear grease on her hair, repelled Damien slightly, but those liquid black eyes called up the earlier times, the lust she had inspired in him—and everything else she had been to him. She had made those long, dark, northern winters livable when the gut-wrenching want of Hélène had deadened him to everything.

Rema had cooked, mended, and tanned leather and fashioned it into clothing and moccasins for him. She had dressed the game he shot and woven leather thongs into a supporting network for his snowshoes; had gathered firewood, berries, and wild rice—and had kept his bed warm. All for a very small purchase price. For a few blankets, her father, who had been of no particular rank, had sold him his twelve-year-old daughter.

Damien laid his hand gently on her cheek. "Yes, Rema," he answered her unspoken question. He began to disrobe before her toil-worn hands stopped him and lovingly took over the task. Watching her, he felt a great sadness for her—and for himself. For the whole damn world.

· · ·

All business in the Great Trading Hall was done on credit. Indians, on entering with their harvest of pelts, were disarmed and treated to a bit of tobacco and a few drams of Blackfoot rum. Any more than that and the Indians drank themselves into debauchery.

This year, more Indians than ever seemed to have journeyed to Grand Portage for the Summer Rendezvous: long-haired Miamis, uncouth Mascoutins, wild Kickapoos, gross and licentious Algonquins, and shaven-skulled Hurons. Most were dirty, practically naked, and outwardly sullen.

After the pipe had been passed about for some time, they would relate whatever news they possessed with great deliberation, relaxing their usual reticence in proportion to the quantity of rum they had drunk.

Among them moved French competitors for their trade. Jean-Baptiste squatted amidst a group of the more friendly Hurons. The boy Nicolas, hunkered next to Jean-Baptiste, his bird-bright eyes intent on the robust negotiations—a gun for fourteen beaver skins or plews; a blanket for six plews; two plews for an ax, shawl, or beaver trap.

Damien joined the group, and Jean-Baptiste looked up, his rheumy gray eyes shadowed. "What is it?" Damien asked.

"Our friends here"—the old man gestured toward the bickering Indians—"talk of a great uprising among the Longhouse Iroquois after the corn harvest. The Mohawks are stirring up trouble."

Damien's thick brows drew together in a frown. Of the Five Nations, the Mohawks were the most belligerent and relentless. Their cruelty to captives was notorious. They were divided into three families: the Bear, the Wolf, and the Tortoise. The Bear was the most savage, and it was this clan whose trail often passed through Montreal and Damien's seigneury.

"Then I shall cut short the month-long festivities and arrive back before late August."

"Your *voyageurs* won't like it."

Damien shrugged. "We'll need the extra time to improve Montreal's defenses. They'll go back."

The older man's voice lowered. "Damien, if we're to stay partners—"

Damien's brows arched. *"If?"*

"Yes, if. If we're to stay partners, I ask you to grant me this one boon. Your son, Nicolas, here—"

Damien straightened to his feet and looked down at the old man with barely controlled annoyance. "I have told you, *mon vieux:* My son is in France."

Persistent, Jean-Baptiste rose also. Looking like a bantam rooster who had participated in one too many cockfights, he said, "Nicolas must return with you. He has become like a grandson to me, and I want him to have a chance at something better than the degeneration of our noble savages here, sitting in a continual drunken stupor before some smoky campfire. You do owe me this favor, *mon vieux!*"

After a long time, tense moment, Damien looked down at the impassive boy sitting cross-legged at Jean-Baptiste's feet. The boy's twisted ankle was hidden from sight. With a grimace, he looked back at his partner. "I know you too well, old friend, and I know what you are plotting. It'll never work. I'll never acknowledge him as mine. He must understand that."

Within the week, the du Plessis canoes, heavily laden with stacks of castor, or beaver, plews, pushed off from the shores of Grand Portage. Jean-Baptiste stood on the bank, his gnarled hand raised in farewell to Damien and the Indian youth tucked in behind him. Damien saw the sadness that tugged at the wrinkles in the old man's face and cursed mankind. If he kept up this cursing, he told himself ruefully, he would soon be tongueless, should good King Louis's minions have their way.

CHAPTER

Montreal,
New France

4

August 1700

W<small>HEN</small> D<small>AMIEN</small> <small>ARRIVED</small> <small>HOME</small>,
his first task as governor was to strengthen the town's defenses.
He widened the moat and heightened the palisades. Two new
bastions were added. The boom of cannon at dawn and sundown
gave warning that vigilance was being maintained. He appointed
a crew of men to cut wood from the forests for the winter's
provisions and ordered the women to see that their larders were
well stocked.

In his spare time, he worked on the fortifications of his own
seigneury, adding a gallery for patrol along the insides of the
palisades and doubling the number of loopholes. He set Nicolas
to work alongside him and his hired men. The boy worked stolidly
but efficiently, his face as inscrutable as his mother's. Occasionally, Damien made conversation, but only because he could see
it piqued the boy to have to answer. A momentary guilt at baiting
the boy would assail him at times, but he would shrug it off and
reapply himself to the task of the moment. If he flagellated himself
for every mistake in his life, he told himself, he would be a mass
of scar tissue.

With the news of the planned Indian uprisings, the townspeople
became nervous and jumpy. Each tree trunk rising in the water
became a Mohawk warrior. Each bulrush, a hostile tomahawk.

Three times that fall the Iroquois, muskets in hand, had intercepted the mail boat, but the expected attack did not come.

Through that fall and winter, Damien and Nicolas barely tolerated one another's presence. Damien rarely socialized, so when Nicolas awoke one morning to find Mother Marie in the château, he was unable to conceal completely his confusion and consternation at the religious visitor.

The fire had burned out in the inadequate braziers and Damien was rebuilding it when Nicolas entered the room. Mother Marie rose to her feet, saying softly, "Good morning. I have been wanting to meet you, Nicolas."

The boy slid a quick glance at Damien but stubbornly said nothing. The nun continued, unperturbed. "At the hospital—the Hôtel-Dieu—besides making the beds, I bandage the patients' sores and care for them, and they have talked of Montreal's newest arrival. I suppose it is much like your drums—word travels fast."

Listening to her talk, Damien half noted that she and Nicolas both had musical voices. Pleasant. From the corner of his eye, he watched her cross to the boy, her worn gray habit rustling on the puncheon floor. The boy tensed at her approach. From the folds of her habit, she withdrew a small dog-eared book.

"I also visit the ships in harbor and tend the ill members of the crew. One of them, a learned Huguenot, gave me this—a copy of Racine's *Andromaque*." The boy made no effort to take the proffered book. "Damien has told me you can read, and I had hoped you would enjoy it. I'll leave the book on the mantel for you, if you care to look through it."

The book remained on the mantel for over a week, but Damien suspected the boy had indeed leafed through it and restored it to its exact position. When the nun next visited Damien, the boy managed without prompting to exchange a few civil words with her. So it went through the winter.

"Damien?"

"Mmmm?"

Marie nuzzled her cheek against his thick mat of chest hair. "A woman was submerged on the dunking stool yesterday. Barbe Boulogne. You remember her, the pretty, little blonde with twin boys."

Damien stroked Marie's unbound hair. Streaks of white had

invaded the brown. He stared into the darkness, trying to picture Barbe Boulogne's face. But, of course, the only image he ever saw was that of Hélène. How do you stop loving someone, even when you know the person is not worth it?

Barbe Boulogne . . . He remembered several years ago when she and her husband had arrived in New France from Alençon. She had been wretchedly lonely and miserable in the frontier colony. And he was always lonely, would always be so. They had found momentary solace in one another's arms, a passing affair.

"For infidelity?" he asked lazily.

"Yes. I don't know if she'll survive. When she was brought to the *hôtel*, her body was frozen through, poor thing, and she wasn't breathing at first. I can't stay long. I need to get back to her."

Damien's thumb tilted Marie's oval chin upward so that he could see her face better, but in the darkness only her eyes, deep and pure, were clearly visible. "You rarely talk of your patients— their problems and personal lives. Did you bring up this woman for any particular reason?"

She kissed his beard-stubbled chin and, with a small sigh, returned her head to its nesting place on his broad chest. "It seems to me that the wife's status under French law is pretty much that of a prisoner."

"Is that why you never married?"

"I'm not talking about myself."

His voice was filled with lazy amusement. "Then just what are we talking about?"

Her fingers twined in the hair that snaked its way downward past his navel. "Doesn't it seem a little bit unfair that infidelity on a husband's part is overlooked as understandable? Or, *ciel*, that a husband may beat his wife as long as he doesn't use a stick thicker than his wrist?"

Beneath her stroking fingers, he was feeling the renewal of passion. "Is all this leading somewhere, Marie?" he asked, his lips beginning a forage of their own along her widow's peak.

"Only that not all people are meant for marriage—and you must love them for what they are."

Something in her voice . . . His lips paused. "And . . . ?"

She lay very still. "And you must love your Hélène for what she was—a spirited, intelligent, lovely young woman, not for what you wanted her to be. She would have withered as your—or as anyone's—wife."

He rolled away from her and sat up. In the darkness, his voice was like a soft lash. "What do you know of my wife? I've never told anyone here."

"You call her name often in your sleep. *Ciel,* Damien, you might have crossed an ocean, but still word travels. A love story like yours, do you think it wouldn't have spread? All these years, most of Montreal has known. They call you the Marquis of Mystery—behind your back, of course. No one has the courage to ask you outright about your past, but a man as handsome as you, as silent as you, well, soon enough questions began to be asked."

"If you've known all this time," he asked resentfully, "why are you just now bringing her up?"

She reached out and touched his shoulder. Her voice was laced with compassion. "One of the king's sailors—he brought the news. Hélène du Plessis—she died three months ago."

His sharply indrawn breath sliced through the room's silence. Outside, sleet pinged against the shutters, and in the distance, muted sleigh bells tinkled. Then, within the room could be heard dry little gasps. Beneath Marie's hand his shoulder shuddered violently.

"How?" he asked after a long time.

"The disease of Venus."

Damien sunk into a stupor during which time he didn't shave or change his clothing for days. He was even less conscientious about his duties as Montreal's governor and as the château's seigneur.

Thus it was, when the Mohawks finally launched their attack at dawn one bitterly cold morning, that the château was taken by surprise. Nicolas tried to rouse Damien from bed and then, not succeeding, drenched him with the spirits of wine reserved for the washing of face and hands.

Damien leveled himself upright and blinked, bleary-eyed. "What is it?"

"We must leave," the boy told him pointedly, calmly. He pushed open the shutter and pointed to the fires that lit up the night—as if to say, "See for yourself."

The lane running crookedly between the rows of houses just

between Damien's stockade and the town was filled with shadowy wraiths setting fire to the homes. Damien knew that the lucky inhabitants would be those who died in their beds or were butchered in the first onslaught.

"The Mohawks," Nicolas said flatly. "They have already scaled your walls."

"No! *Par Dieu*, we will fight!"

The soldier instinct in him responded to the screeching bloodlust war cry, "*Cassee kouee!*" rising from below. He drew the great broadsword from its scabbard, where it hung over a chair. In the corner stood a little used bell-mouth blunderbuss. He handed it to the watchful boy. "Can you handle this?"

After a moment, the boy's large head nodded.

Of course he could; Jean-Baptiste would have taught him. For all Damien knew, the child would turn it on him instead; the boy was, after all, half-Indian.

From the landing, Damien surveyed the pandemonium below. A dozen, maybe fifteen warriors, their faces smeared with ceremonial paint, were wrecking the furniture, which Damien had imported at a dear price, with vicious whacks of their tomahawks. One brave had found Damien's *bonnet rouge* and was prancing about with the warm woolen head covering clamped over his closely shaven skull. Another had the *chaussettes* of wool used to cover the legs wrapped about his upper arm like bracelets.

In the same moment, several of the warriors sighted Damien and Nicolas. At once, Damien stormed down the stairwell. He swung his broadsword about him like an avenging angel. The two savages directly below him went down. Rapidly widening red gashes bisected their chests and necks. Where they fell, others leaped over their bodies to take their places. The assault continued, with Damien forced to retreat step by step.

"Fire the blunderbuss, damn you!" he called over his shoulder to the boy.

An explosion cracked Damien's skull, and he crumpled backward on the steps.

It was a constant amazement to Damien that the Indian savages could trudge through silent, snowbound forests in seminakedness, oblivious to the cold that froze the toes and noses of the captives. Of all the tribes, the Mohawks were noted for their endurance.

He tried to keep up with the group of seven braves who had taken him prisoner. To stumble and be unable to rise meant instant death. What was so galling was the boy. Nicolas had little problem keeping up with the captors; of course, Damien rationalized, the boy hadn't taken the whack of a tomahawk on his head as he had.

On the heels of that thought followed another. Had the blunderbuss's pin misfired—or had the boy simply chosen the side of the victors?

Damien knew he wouldn't find out the answer soon, anyway, since speech was forbidden by his captors. Two or three times, the braves halted the trek as their path crossed that of other war parties returning with their pitiful captives to their villages along the Finger Lakes. During those times, he and the boy were allowed to squat. At one halt, he spotted Barbe Boulogne's battered husband among the captives before one of the warriors shoved him face down into the snow.

After a while, Damien lost track of time. The dense forest concealed even the grayest of sunlight; too, he became disoriented as low branches slapped him time after time. The effort of placing one foot ahead of another was all that his thoughts could hold on to—that and the crunch of his slow footsteps on the snow.

At last, their destination was reached. The Indian village consisted of two hundred lodges behind triple palisades thirty feet high. Pandemonium ruled within. The war kettle had been brought out and was simmering like a cauldron of wizardry in the center court. Mohawk braves from all quarters had been coming in for days. There had to be five hundred or more. Those who had arrived earlier were feasting and drinking and singing war songs. The squaws screamed and jeered, and the children joined in. Innumerable dogs, unlike the barkless canines of Montreal, snapped at Damien's heels. Behind him, Nicolas savagely kicked one of the scurvy mongrels, and it went yelping off.

The Indian at Damien's side laughed broadly, then jammed his club between Damien's shoulder blades, thrusting him toward the nearest lodge, an oblong shelter of rough-hewn boards bent into an arch. Inside, smoke from the center fire lay in a heavy cloud over the malodorous room. Damien blinked at the fumes stinging his eyes. It was no wonder the Indians had so many eye problems.

A toothless and quarrelsome squaw took over duty as guard and with bravado shoved and kicked her two captives toward one of the platforms that lined each side. After she disappeared through the murky haze, Damien collapsed on the platform, too tired to care about what would happen next.

Only minutes later, a shrill scream rent the air, and he jerked upright. He looked at Nicolas. The boy's eyes were expressionless. But they both knew.

After a while, Damien discovered that the platform had lice. He sat up again and tried to study their surroundings. He was still alive, so hope was still alive. In the drafty, upper reaches of the lodge, unshelled corn hung on long lines looped from section to section, along with family clothing and skins—cured and uncured. Hunger got the better of him, and he rose from the platform.

"No," Nicolas said.

"Why not?" he asked irritably. "We'll need all our strength."

"The corn will only make you sick. Wait. They will feed us. They want to keep us alive."

"For the stake," Damien grumbled. He began to pace before the platform. The smoke was thicker when he stood, and tears burned his eyes. He sat back down again. There had to be a way out of this mess.

The haggard old squaw returned, bearing a wooden bowl of cornmeal mush and meat as dried and withered as she was. She shoved them at Damien. Then she turned on Nicolas and prodded him from the platform toward the door.

Damien shot to his feet. "Where are you taking him?" he demanded, but the haze of smoke enveloped them and then he was alone.

Whatever hunger possessed him evaporated as more tortured screams reached him. He set the bowl aside and crossed toward the doorway. A rapid survey of the scene showed several stakes piled high with faggots. He saw no victims, for which he whispered a fervent prayer of thanks, but the nauseatingly sweet odor of burnt flesh reached him. Barbe Boulogne's husband? Or Nicolas? The thought made him ill.

Festive warriors danced or sat about talking and drinking. How did they endure the bone-chilling cold? Even in the doorway, the winter wind seeped through his clothing, seeming paradoxically to burn his exposed skin.

Where was Nicolas?

Should he try to escape now? If he waited, he might grow too weak; still, there was the hope his captors might eventually drink themselves into insensibility. He chose that possibility as the best option for a successful escape and returned to the platform. The mush was a thick ball in his throat, but he forced it down.

When night came, and the shouting and laughing grew louder, he deemed it time to make his bid for freedom. His guard, the squaw, was lax in her duty and had not returned to check on him since she had brought the bowl of mush and strip of meat. He felt a surge of hope.

He slipped outside, his body flattened against the side of the lodge, and began to ease his way around the far corner. Any hope of escape was shattered when the old squaw loomed up before him. Her toothless mouth gaped in an excited cackle. He would have strangled her on the spot, but he was suddenly grappled from behind. A furious snarl ripped from his throat. He exerted all of his strength, willing his muscles into preterhuman resistance. This would be his only chance, his last chance, to flee.

The ill luck that had greeted him on the day of his birth in a prison was still shadowing him. Two warriors wrestled with him, and he might still have gained his freedom, such was his determination, but the hoary squaw struck him with a savage blow of her club in the soft area just below his ribs. He collapsed, gasping, cursing at his helplessness.

He was dragged into the center court, his boots making parallel tracks over snow already pitted with moccasined footprints. Within a matter of minutes, he found himself bound to one of the stakes. Dazed, he watched other squaws rush to pile fresh faggots around him.

God grant that the end would come quickly.

He lifted his head, Anjou arrogance blazing in his eyes. He would give the savages no satisfaction of eliciting screams from him. With a little sickness in his heart, when he thought he could feel no further emotion, he saw Nicolas with a group of drunken warriors. The boy was laughing.

When several minutes passed and the torch was still not put to the faggots, he looked around, curious at the delay. Again hope welled within him. Perhaps his captors were reconsidering.

Then he understood when he saw the ancient squaw advancing

on him. He was to undergo slow torture before dying at the stake, something worse than merely tearing off the nails, leaving the hands bloodied stubs.

She toted a leather skin filled with splinters of fat pine. He had heard of that particular grisly torture. His flesh was to be punctured with those splinters, like a porcupine with quills. The splinters would then be set on fire. He would be turned into a living torch. Men so executed lived long after the splinters had burned into their skins.

Something in his brain screamed and screamed. He shoved the scream back before it burst from his lungs. Tears he was unable to check poured down his cheeks. A soldier's shame washed over him at his weakness, even as he felt the cosmos give way at his sphincter. Through the blur of tears he saw Nicolas raise an iron tomahawk, saw it spinning, blade over shaft, endlessly spinning toward him. His last thought was that with Hélène's death, the twilight of his life had become night.

PART

2

CHAPTER

The dirty little street, rue Quincampoix, had become Europe's finance center. In nearby Place Vendôme, tents and wooden shanties had sprung up as traders and gamblers poured in from all over Europe to get rich quick. Fortunes were sometimes made in a few hours by bankers and hotel waiters alike, by duchesses and prostitutes. All because of a Scotsman, John Law.

Philippe du Plessis, Marquis de Marchesseau, had first noticed the Scottish banker's placards posted on the wall of the Café Parisienne the year before. Shares were offered by Law's French Compagnie des Indes Occidentales for real estate in Louisiane, the land of Louis. The placards depicted Louisiana as a land of tropical beauty, of milk and honey, with gold and silver mines, equaling the dream cities of the Arabian Nights. In this land of palm trees and blue, moonlit nights, Frenchmen were said to live like kings, surrounded by beautiful, Nubian slave women of great beauty. Why, the very servants gossiped about the magic of Louisiana.

On his uncle's advice, Philippe purchased a thousand shares from the Company of the Indies and then hurried in the light, two-wheeled calèche back to Hôtel de Gesvres, bought by himself just prior to his marriage. A cold, marble building with none of the warm charm of Maison Bellecour, it had the attraction of being near the Palais Royal, and it was centered among Paris's places of amusement. Here, he and his young wife resided when the Blois silk factories did not demand his presence, which, *grâce à Dieu*, was not too often.

When he arrived at Gesvres, Natalie was already at her toilette. She turned from the gilt-edged mirror, relief and love brightening her eyes, the color of which was an uncommon silver-green matrix. But then nothing about Natalie was common. Not even her chin, which was blunted by an intriguing cleft, an irregularity without which mere beauty was vapid.

"Philippe! I was beginning to worry."

"I must hurry and change, dearest. You know the duc—how he detests late arrivals."

He had little respect for the degenerate regent who was even accused of entertaining an incestuous relationship with his own daughter. Still, there were court appearances to be kept up.

Philippe crossed to his wife and kissed her shoulder, over which lay an artfully arranged ringlet of hair, the pale blond shade of a summer child's. Even after four years of marriage, he was still infatuated with his child bride. At sixteen, she had carried off his three-and-thirty-year-old bachelor's heart because . . . Well, he still couldn't put his finger on it.

Educated at the convent at Poissy, she was the daughter of the Maréchal de Camp de Villeroi. Louis XIV had seen to it that the daughter of the late field marshal of the French army received the best until she came of age. She had been taught to sing and recite plays by heart by the famed Jeliotte of the Comédie-Française. Through interminable lessons of elocution, the old master of drama had developed her husky voice into an unforgettable smoky contralto that charmed all near enough to hear.

Her cool beauty attracted attention in a court where beauty was mandatory. Only Philippe knew that her aloofness was a façade. Having been raised in the provinces, she had abeen unprepared for the unrestraint and sophistication of court. When dealing with the unfamiliar or when uncertain, she became increasingly cool and distant. She was clever by half, an attribute of which he sometimes despaired, but how could he fail to be enchanted by her?

Natalie tilted her head to one side, allowing his lips access to the depression created by her collarbone.

"Philippe," she breathed.

"*Qui, chérie?*"

"I am with child."

Her voice was so low, lower than usual, that at first he thought he had not understood her. One look into the clear depths of her eyes convinced him otherwise. His fingers tightened on her shoulders, pearly and bare. "*Corbleu!*" he gasped, then broke out in delighted laughter. "When?"

Though twenty, with more than three years spent at the most licentious court in Europe, a blush managed to deepen her adroit application of rouge. "I think August."

He drew her upright from the cushioned stool and held her against him. "I can't believe my good fortune, Natalie! I have always known I was born beneath a lucky star."

She tilted her head, eyeing him beguilingly from beneath the heavy fringe of lashes. "Must we go tonight, Philippe?"

He chuckled. "*Oui!* How else shall I so rapidly spread the good news? My uncle must be the first to know!"

A double line of coaches, all loaded with guests, turned the broad rue de Richelieu leading to the Palais Royal into a river of light. Outside the home of the regent of France, the roof was covered with candles and the marble fountains flowed with wine.

The masked ball was by invitation only, yet, if the usual number were issued, a woman could depend on her dress being torn by the crush. At the last ball, several people had actually died of heat or cold or fatigue or asphyxiation—or at least so went the gossip of Paris.

Arm in arm, Philippe and Natalie entered the main ballroom. Outside it might be winter, but inside spring had blossomed. The walls of pink marble and trellis work were filled with vine leaves, bunches of grapes, and flowers. Real palm trees, trunks garlanded with roses, flanked buffets draped with pink velvet fringed in gold. Everywhere one looked there were pictures and statues of the royal family.

Upon their entrance, those closest to the couple turned to stare. The new arrivals might be wearing demimasks, but they were immediately recognized as the Golden Couple. Only a dolt would not have heard of the enviable pair.

Both were blessed with that white-gold shade of hair that powder could never duplicate. Philippe accepted his beautifully chiseled features and ivory skin with complacency. He had long been Paris's—no, France's—most eligible bachelor until his marriage. That night Natalie thought he was particularly handsome in a coat of pale blue satin damasked within the bounds of good taste. Behind the matching demimask, his brown eyes caressed her with warm passion.

She counted herself more than merely fortunate to have married him. He was literally her paladin. Originally one of the Twelve Peers of Charlemagne's court, a paladin had come to represent a heroic champion, a knight—and Philippe had been her knight since the afternoon he had ridden up to the Poissy Convent with his entourage of aristocratic ladies and their partners, noblemen of the court.

She had been gathering apples that had dropped from the branches outside the convent walls with Sister Béatrice. It had been impossible not to stare at the handsome Philippe, nor to be unaware of the tittering and sneers of the court ladies. Indignation had simmered in her. Why should she shrink? Was not her father of the *noblesse campagnarde*? Was she not a Mortemart on her mother's side, and who, after all, were the Bourbons when compared with the Mortemarts?

Her head had come up imperiously, her back had straightened, and in that moment the apples had gone tumbling from her apron. As she scrambled to regather the apples, the ridiculing laughter of the visitors had shamed her. Heat had flushed her face. Then, suddenly, she had glanced up to see Philippe, sitting on his heels before her—helping her to collect the scattered apples!

From that moment, she was hopelessly in love. When he courted and married her in a whirlwind of a few weeks, she felt she was truly the most blessed of women. All of Paris was charmed by the Golden Couple. Well, not quite all. Among the court were the usual ill-wishers of a couple who seemed blessed with everything: good looks, health, wealth, and love.

For appearance's sake, however, the outnumbered foes put on their best faces and mingled with the friends of the couple in greeting. Natalie counted the duc's eldest and favorite daughter, the Duchesse de Berry, among her friends. When the poor woman had lost her husband five years earlier, she had simply added to her lovers—and her weight.

Philippe tugged Natalie away from conversation with the duchesse to search out his uncle, who was in actuality his mother's cousin. Since Philippe's grandfather had died before Philippe turned thirteen, the intimidating knight had acted briefly as executor for the Marchesseau estates. Even after Philippe reached his majority, he still leaned on his uncle for advice.

The man was not difficult for Natalie to spot despite the crush of masked guests. Claude Fabreville continued to wear the black robes of the knights of Malta. A well-curled wig covered his close-cropped hair, which was now thin and gray as was his waxed moustache. She pitied his frumpish wife, whom he had married for her modest fortune. He openly acknowledged the deed, having needed the king's dispensation to marry. For years, he had neglected his wife, leaving her to wilt at her family's country estate.

Perhaps there was something in the smothered rumor that he had once been an "intimate" friend of the late Monsieur.

Still, he was the only relative Philippe had left and, as attorney general, had procured tax rebates and other privileges for the Marchesseau silk industry. "Uncle," Philippe said, "I have the best of news for you."

"You took my advice?" Claude asked. "You purchased the Compagnie des Indes stock?"

Natalie slanted her husband a worried glance. He hadn't told her of the purchase, perhaps because he believed her ignorant in matters of finance.

"*Oui*, but that is not my good news," Philippe said, his arm encircling her waist tenderly as if already protective of her new condition. "We are finally to be blessed with a child!"

When there was no immediate response from his kin, Philippe covered the awkward silence. "Now that I'm to be a father, I thought I'd do something really worthwhile—perhaps purchase a seat in Parlement to pass on to my son."

At that Natalie had to smile. "You are so certain it is a son?" she asked in a lowered voice.

"Let me offer my congratulations," Claude said at last. "Now, if you'll excuse me, the duc is desirous of my attendance."

Once the old knight was gone, she asked, "How many shares of the Compagnie des Indes did you buy?"

He shrugged his shoulders. "A thousand. But the return will be ten times that much."

With the paper value of the shares more than eighty times the total value of all the gold and silver known to be in France's Banque Royale, it seemed to Natalie that the outcome of such a venture should be obvious. Still, she told herself, they could easily afford to lose the money. Before his death, Philippe's grandfather had increased the family's silk fortune through wise investments, and upon the death of Philippe's father, Philippe had inherited the Canadian fur company, almost doubling the Marchesseau fortune.

Philippe caught her chin and tilted it upward. "Come, you must not worry, *chérie*," he said, searching her face, his eyes tender.

How could she be annoyed when he looked at her like that? After the first blush of romance had worn off, she found to her surprise that she still loved her gentle and tender husband. He possessed the absorption in the moment without the tiresome prudence that always has to be looking ahead. She was constantly caught up in his spurts of joyous enthusiasm, his contentment with life.

"Will you dance with me now, my love, before your horde of admirers descends on us?" he asked, teasing her out of her pensive mood.

He led her out to join the gavotte that was forming. For a while, she enjoyed herself in the lively dance, was even able to ignore the lascivious leers of the male guests and the visually thrown daggers of *les femmes débauchés*. By midnight, the two sexes would be pairing off in search of the nearest unoccupied rooms—some even uncaring if the room was already inhabited.

The Palais Royal—indeed, all of Paris—was a virtual Sodom and Gomorrah. Natalie would not have been surprised had lightning struck and the entire city sent up in fiery smoke. The city of Paris had more mistresses than wives, and the Prince Regent, the Duc d'Orléans, was the Prince of Libertines.

Born bored, and accustomed to debauchery, the fat, myopic duc d'Orléans, nearing forty-seven, worked conscientiously enough during the day, but night meant retirement to more diverting tasks. When the doors of his rose-silk-upholstered private apartment were closed, he was no longer a regent, not even if Paris were on fire.

That did not mean that one ever underestimated the duc. The great-grandson of Louis XIV was not quite eleven, and until the good-looking boy reached his legal majority, the duc ruled France as regent. He was highly intelligent and very subtle.

However, he was seduced more by pleasure than by power. He consorted with ladies of quality and ladies of the street. His intimates or companions he called his *roués*, men ordinarily broken on the *roue*, or wheel, for their blasphemous behavior. He was more an onlooker than a participant as life leaked away, and night after night repeated itself. Nothing was sacred, especially love.

Now he was annoyed at being drawn away from the gaming tables, but the shrewd old man who awaited him in the rear cabinet was usually a worthwhile diversion. The old knight had procured for him quite a few of the most delectable teenage dancers of the opera. The duc's late father, Monsieur, had had a hand in giving the reins of attorney general to Fabreville. As such, Fabreville had the power to cut off parliamentary investigations of a financial nature that the duc might find embarrassing.

In the *arrière-cabinet*, the regent retired to write his instructions to his secret agents abroad or to study their reports. Here, his private diplomacy was carried out without anyone else's knowledge. Fabreville waited beside a gilded, thin-legged, rolltop writing desk. The old knight laid a paper on the desk where a candle was kept burning for the sealing of documents with wax.

"Your grace, I find I must preserve the honor of the Marchesseau name. Unfortunately, I have discovered that my late cousin's son, Philippe du Plessis, is guilty of fraud involving black-market wheat. A *lettre de cachet* will be necessary."

With only a passing glance at the paper, the duc dipped the quill in the inkwell. "You are a cunning one, Claude."

Watching the regent affix his name, Fabreville's mouth slitted into a sneering smile. A husband might obtain a *lettre de cachet*, or sealed letter, to imprison a suspected wife; a father, to prevent the marriage of a daughter to someone beneath her station; or, in this case, a concerned relative, to prevent the succession of an estate to an as yet unborn child. The accused would never be tried; the accuser, if he could prevail upon the monarch, secured the right of administration of whatever property was involved.

Fabreville had hoped that France's largest estate would naturally pass to him, and his son Robert, since for years Hélène's son had seemed bent on leading the gay life of a bachelor. When Philippe finally took a wife, Fabreville was relieved to find that the woman apparently was barren. Such was not the case, after all.

He scanned the letter with satisfaction. The order was a simple one:

> On behalf of the king: the Marquis de Marchesseau, Philippe du Plessis, and his wife, Natalie, are ordered to take themselves to the Bastille and the Salpêtrière, respectively, His Grace forbidding the said husband and wife to depart until further orders on his part, under pain of disobedience.
>
> Signed this the 13th day of February 1720, the Duc d'Orléans, Regent.

Natalie was with her wardrobe mistress, Emilie, when Philippe rushed into the *petit appartement*. His face was waxen; his lips taut. "The Royal Musketeers," he said, shutting the door behind him. "They are waiting below with a *lettre de cachet* for us both."

The wardrobe mistress put her hands to her mouth in a smothered scream. Natalie blanched. The large folio containing fabric swatches of her gowns dropped from her suddenly inert fingers.

Philippe caught her clammy hands in his and said, "You must escape while I delay them!"

She shivered uncontrollably but said in a raw whisper, "No, I'm staying with you."

He shook her shoulders with fearful impatience. "Listen, Natalie. With you free, there is the hope of discovering our accuser and clearing my name."

When she opened her mouth to argue, he pressed, "For the love of God, Natalie, consider our child!"

Reluctantly, she nodded in compliance, too stunned to disagree.

Quickly, he laid plans for the loyal Emilie to don one of Natalie's cloaks and to descend on his arm to meet the waiting guards. The ruse would be discovered all too soon, within minutes, but with luck Natalie would have a chance to get away.

Her husband had to pull himself from her grasp. "Philippe!"

she cried when he turned to leave. Her lips quivered, and tears brimmed unchecked over her lids. For too long a moment, she stood in the suddenly empty room, trying to find the strength to will herself to move. Her body seemed to have grown too heavy for her legs. The child! She grabbed another cloak from the immense armoire, any cloak—it was an ermine and velvet one— and hurried through the servants' corridor.

Fearing that the coach's crest of arms might attract unwanted notice, she took a *chaise à porteurs*. As the porters carried her through the crowded rue de Sevres, she was assailed by the ghastly recollection of a man rumored to have been imprisoned under a *lettre de cachet* by Louis XIV for forty years until the man's death— his identity concealed behind an iron mask. Could that really happen?

With grief choking her breath, she urged the porters faster toward the Hôtel de Soubise, the residence of Claude Fabreville. Surely, he, if anyone, would have the power to have the regent revoke the letter!

The old knight received her in his *petit cabinet* with the calmness she lacked. She babbled out her story, ending it with, "You must help Philippe!"

He removed her hands from where they clutched his robe, distorting the eight-point cross. "I will do everything that I can, Natalie. I will go at once to the duc and petition him for clemency. In the meantime, you must rest and conserve your strength. All this excitement cannot be good for the child you carry."

Feeling some measure of relief, Natalie obediently accepted the warmed wine brought by a servant. She paced the room, little noticing the art collected with discrimination: Poussin, Titian, Raphael, Veronese, del Sarto. Her steps slowed, her lids blinked away the sudden weariness. Then, with sudden suspicion, she flung the stemmed glass from her. It shattered in one corner of the marbled floor. The realization that she had been drugged came too late, and her body sagged, then collapsed onto the Aubusson carpet.

CHAPTER

LA SALPÊTRIÈRE WAS A VAST, gray-brick enclosure on the Seine that had first been a saltpeter-powder magazine. Louis XIV had converted it into a home for beggars, the aged, and mentally afflicted men and women. Soon a prison for incorrigible and undisciplined women and girls was added.

Now it was a prison for women criminals only, as well as for the debauched and the insane. Seven thousand women were crowded inside it, two thousand of whom were prostitutes. Natalie found herself confined to the better section known simply as the Prison, reserved for those women interned by royal order.

Those first few days, she sat listlessly in her ten-foot-square, cell-like room, part of the outer western wall of the dungeon. When she stirred herself, it was to curse Claude Fabreville quietly with a venom of which she had not suspected she was capable.

At least, she consoled herself, Philippe was still alive and not far away in the Bastille. She told herself that she could be worse off. The governor of La Salpêtrière was a portly old gentleman, who, for a slight commission, permitted the prisoners certain comforts of home.

With the jewels she had been wearing when she was incarcerated, she was able to have her own books, furniture, and linen in a private cell. However, the windows were mere apertures, and within days she became obsessed with the need for light, particularly sunlight. Come sunset, a smidgin of wintry, bleak light slid rapidly down the wall and soon vanished.

No provision had been provided for heating, and she suffered greatly from the cold. So she did not trade her velvet and ermine cloak for superfluous items. She often wondered how many times she had worn the luxurious cloak and taken its warm ermine trimming for granted.

Warmth and sunlight, those things she would never again take for granted. When she and the other seventy-eight women interned by royal order went for their afternoon exercise in the bare courtyard once a day, she would toss back the cloak's hood and turn her face up toward the gray, winter sunlight.

Closing her eyes, she would pretend that she was at Maison Bellecour, walking through the maze of the boxed gardens or among its classic statues . . . feeling the cool breeze off the Loire that played with the loose tendrils of her hair . . . trailing her fingers in one of the mirror ponds . . . wandering through the orangerie, smelling the sweet, sultry scent of cape jasmine, her favorite flower.

"The sun is bad for your skin, *ma petite*."

Natalie's eyes snapped open. She recognized the woman from her first year at court. Madame Madeleine Remoneaux had been sent to La Salpêtrière by royal letter after the duc had tired of her. The middle-aged woman had a natural redhead's sallow complexion. She now resorted to henna to cover the gray strands that had invaded her hair.

"On the contrary, I shall shrivel and die without the sunlight," Natalie replied, politely but sadly. She really didn't want to establish any relationships. It would be an acknowledgment of a permanency there at La Salpêtrière.

By the second month, loneliness drove her to talk to the others, most of whom were courtesans like Madeleine Remoneaux, though a few unfortunate daughters, sisters, and wives also occupied the private cells. Natalie sought out Madeleine more often than the others, for the woman seemed the least bitter about her circumstances.

"I try to look at the worst that could happen," Natalie said one evening. The two were having dinner together in Madeleine's cell, which was elegantly swathed with heavy red drapes to keep out the insidious cold drafts. "I judge I'll be imprisoned here two years at the most. By that time, Louis will turn thirteen and come into his majority, and the duc's reign as regent will end. Surely then the *lettre de cachet* will be revoked." She sighed and rubbed her slender hands together for warmth. "But that seems like a long time."

She noticed the middle-aged woman, who continued to paint her face each morning, lower her lids, seeming to concentrate on chewing the cold *salmis*.

"What is it?" Natalie asked her.

The courtesan shrugged her shoulders and took a sip of the sparkling wine. "The time will pass quickly enough—with the comforts of home to sustain you."

Natalie laid down her fork. Her appetite had dwindled such that she had to force herself to eat for the sake of the unborn child. "If I'm careful, I think I can stretch the money I've received for my jewelry."

"Expenditures here can eat up the money rapidly, *ma petite*. More rapidly than you realize."

"How have you managed after four years in this—this place?" Natalie looked about her. Despair choked at her throat. "Four years!" she whispered. "*Ma foi!*"

Madame Remoneaux's eyes twinkled, and she smiled. Her teeth were terrible. "I write pornography."

"What?"

"*Oui*. When I realized that I might be here for many years—and that the little money I had wouldn't keep me in the style to which I was accustomed, I bought pen and ink and paper. I sell my stories to a press in Amsterdam."

A smile wormed its way onto Natalie's tightly pressed lips, then she laughed merrily. "If I could, I would, but I fear my imagination is sadly lacking."

"Ah," the older woman said, "you've only had one man?"

Natalie blushed. "*Oui*."

The woman looked pointedly in the direction of Natalie's mid-section, which was gently straining the limits of the satin-covered buttons. "You are *enceinte*?"

Natalie nodded.

The woman set down her wine glass. "Do you know what happens to the *bébés* born at La Salpêtrière?"

The tone in the courtesan's voice, the pity . . . Natalie couldn't force herself to ask. The *chocolat à triple à vanille* she had just consumed suddenly weighed heavily in her stomach. Eyes wide with dread, she simply waited for the revelation.

"The child is taken from you and reared in the portion of the prison reserved for indigents—the Great Prison."

A mother's protective instinct came to life in Natalie with a mighty force. She was an awakened feline, ready to defend her cub. She sprang to her feet. "Then I will go with my child."

Madeleine shook her head, her orange-red curls quivering with the movement, and looked up at the bow-taut woman. "You do not know what you are saying. The Great Prison is a living nightmare. The habitual women criminals are also kept there: prostitutes infected with disease, poisoners, thieves, counterfeiters, the insane. You would be one against many. Your child— should it survive infancy—will become a plaything for the more depraved."

Slowly, Natalie sank into her chair. For the first time since her arrest, she buried her face in her hands and truly cried, great, heaving sobs that wracked her body. "Dear God, dear God, what am I to do?"

Madeleine rose and, coming to the younger woman's side, knelt and put her arm about Natalie's shoulder. "I have no words of comfort—except that life is better than death. Always. You must try to fortify yourself to withstand whatever happens."

Natalie gritted her teeth. The chocolate dessert threatened to thrust its way up past her esophagus. "I will find a way before I let them take Philippe's child from me. This baby is all we have left of each other."

As the weeks passed and Natalie's condition became more obvious, no solution to her predicament presented itself. The apparent laxity of surveillance in that part of the prison was an illusion. Should she make her way past the heavy patrols to the large courtyard, where the females held under royal order were permitted to exercise, there were still the portcullis, which was always guarded, and the moat to negotiate.

Her imagination, which she had told Madeleine was quite lacking, now exerted itself incessantly by day and night. Nightmares left dark shadows beneath her eyes. She would awaken in the morning with her pillow wet and not remember weeping. Madeleine told her that she sometimes cried Philippe's name in the throes of her dreams.

She longed for him terribly. In the four years of their marriage, they had not spent one night apart. She had to console herself with the knowledge that at least he was incarcerated in the best of prisons. Most of the inmates in the Bastille, imprisoned for debt or some amorous intrigue, had their own cooks and valets, received visitors, and even gave banquets.

Winter crept along at its interminable pace. Sometimes Madeleine read a problem passage from her writing, but Natalie was always too embarrassed by the lurid descriptions to offer suggestions.

Her waistline expanded more quickly, so she had to let out her clothing. "If you insist on having this child," Madeleine declared one afternoon as they walked in the courtyard, "I shall act as your midwife. Why, I was witness to the Dauphin's birth in the queen's oval chamber. There didn't look that much work to the task. The royal bed was covered in crimson for the birth, but when the queen went into labor, she was moved to the smaller bed. All the while, more than two hundred members of the court waited in the antechamber, trying to watch from the doorway. With the windows closed, it was so hot that I thought the queen would faint."

Natalie really didn't want to hear the details, but Madeleine blithely continued on. "Then, when her time came, she was seated in a chair. The midwife squatted before her on a stool. Imagine, *ma petite*, after the Dauphin was born, the midwife drank some wine and spewed it into the infant's mouth!"

The story should have been diverting, but Natalie was reminded of her own plight. Rather than bring the child into a world of horror, she was at the point of asking Madeleine to smother it at birth. Yet, she couldn't quite take that final step. Something would happen, surely.

It did . . . in the form of Hervé Bertin.

La Salpêtrière's governor had decided to relieve the austerity of the courtyard, and apparently his own grim life there, by adding a fountain. Men from La Force Prison were marched in to construct the fountain, the building of which was overseen by a dandified little man whom Natalie took to be the fountain's designer.

The guards prodded their pikes at the laboring men as if they were beasts of burden. Maybe they were, but they entered and left La Salpêtrière regularly, something she could not do.

Hervé Bertin stood out from the other male prisoners. Though only of average height, he was robust, with a barrellike torso; in comparison, the others were pale and skeletal. The women inmates talked about him, and the male prisoners from LaForce as well, with excitement. Most of the women had been too long without a man, and they flirted openly with the men, casually walking in groups as close to the working site as the guards would allow.

Natalie, too, watched, but for a different reason. She noted the way the blond man's massive muscles rippled beneath the too tight tunic as his pick dug away the dirt for the pipes or the way they bunched into knots when he unloaded the heavy carved stones from the wagon onto his behemoth shoulders.

It was more than just his uncommon strength that intrigued her. The blond Atlas swaggered with confidence. Time and fear had not yet stooped his shoulders or demoralized his spirit. If anyone, he could succeed in helping her to escape.

But how?

During the allotted hours of exercise, she observed everything: the routine of the guards, the movements of the male prisoners. Even if she could disguise herself as one, she would never get pass the portcullis, for she knew the men were counted each day before they were marched from the courtyard.

As the fountain began to take shape, stone by stone, she knew her chances for escape were dwindling. Maybe two—possibly three more days before the fountain would be completed.

The following afternoon, when Hervé Bertin approached the wagon once again to heft another stone, she noted the tool chest. Almost the size of a coffin.

"Madeleine," she said that evening, "I'm going to try to escape the day after tomorrow. Will you help me?"

"No."

Natalie laid aside the threaded needle she plied through a seam she was letting out. "I had thought we were friends."

Madeleine continued to write without looking up from her manuscript. "We are. That's why I won't help you."

Natalie yanked the quill from Madeleine's grip. "Look at me! I will not let my child come into a world of depravity. But rather than kill it, I would as soon kill myself. Do you understand? I will commit suicide first." She picked up the sewing scissors and rubbed her fingertip across their points. "It would be easy enough."

"Suicide or escape?" Madeleine asked.

"You will help then?" she said with a hopeful little smile.

Madeleine sighed. "Natalie, if your escape fails, you will find yourself interned, this time in La Salpêtrière's Great Prison. *Canaille*—the scum of the underworld—inhabit it. Better you commit suicide than find yourself there."

"The escape will not fail. I have thought it out." She proceeded to tell Madeleine her plan, incomplete as it was and dependent too much upon luck.

The next day, she put the plan into effect. When the hour came for exercise, she placed herself as close as possible to the wagon. When the man called Hervé next approached, she swayed, then collapsed in a feigned faint. At once he was kneeling over her. She slitted her eyes. Up close she saw that his heavy brows slanted down at the other corners like a bloodhound's. The hazel eyes were perplexed but intelligent enough. Yes, she could trust him.

She had perhaps five or six seconds before the others arrived. "I will be hidden inside the toolbox tomorrow when the wagon leaves La Salpêtrière," she whispered quickly. "If you help me escape, I will see to it that you are amply rewarded."

Then two guards were pulling him from her, and Madeleine was pushing her way through the crowd of women. "It's the child she's carrying," her friend explained. "Help me get her to her room."

"Well?" Madeleine asked when the two of them were alone. "Will he help you?"

"I don't know. He didn't have time to answer."

"*Nom de Dieu!*" Madeleine smacked her forehead with the heel of her hand. "I must be crazy to do this."

The next day, Natalie watched Hervé, hoping to see some sign of acknowledgment from him, but nothing passed over his bloodhoundlike face. Now that the time had come, she was frightened out of her wits. Had Madeleine asked her who ruled France at that moment, she wouldn't have known the answer.

Madeleine did ask, "Have you changed your mind?"

What choice did she have, really? She shook her head, but the negative reply was merely the shaping of her lips. No sound would come forth.

"All right." Madeleine sighed. "God go with you, *ma petite.*"

Natalie hugged the courtesan; it would be the last time she would see Madeleine.

The older woman sniffed, dabbed her eyes with a lace handkerchief she produced from her ample bosom, then spun around and delivered a mighty slap to the woman nearest her—a comtesse who put on airs and whom Madeleine had never liked, anyway.

"What—?" The heavily powdered woman staggered back, her hand pressing against her scarlet cheek.

"Slut!" Madeleine taunted as the other curious women crowded around.

The comtesse gasped, outraged. Her hand snaked out and yanked a handful of Madeleine's red curls. The fight was on. It was the first excitement any of the women had experienced since Madeleine's last book of pornography had been smuggled in, and they leaped into the melee like seasoned gladiators. The male prisoners, along with some of the guards, gathered to laugh and shout and cheer the women on.

During the fracas, Natalie slipped off and casually made her way to the back of the wagon. When the captain of the guards stepped in to break up the fight, she hauled herself up, somewhat clumsily, onto the wagon bed. With pounding heart, she swiftly wedged her body into the cramped tool chest.

For what seemed like hours, she lay squeezed on her side within the narrow box. The air was stuffy, and her fingers and toes grew cold from lack of movement. But what bothered her most was, as usual, the lack of light. She had the irrepressible urge to throw open the chest lid. Instead, she concentrated on taking shallow, little breaths and imagining herself back at Maison Bellecour.

Occasional muffled instructions reached her. What would happen when work on the fountain halted for the day and the axes, picks, chisels, and mallets were piled into the tool chest?

At last she detected the sounds of the prisoners gathering for the march back to La Force Prison. This would be the moment that would decide whether she got past La Salpêtrière's gates, the first of many obstacles.

When she heard the thuds of the implements being tossed onto the wagon bed, her breath congealed. The tool chest's lid creaked open, and a shaft of sunlight blinded her; then, beneath sloping brows, Hervé's spangled hazel eyes coalesced within her vision.

Anyone watching merely saw the barrel-chested man replace the implements in the chest with an inordinate amount of attention and then shut the lid.

Buried beneath the weight of tools, Natalie let out a long, pent-up breath. The rest of the escape was up to him now.

CHAPTER

7

THE SUNLIGHT THAT NATALIE
craved rarely penetrated the dense Forêt de St. Germain; for that
matter, neither did the king's grenadiers.

Self-conscious, she sat with her feet tucked under her skirts on
the far side of the crackling fire. The cold of the spring night
seeped through the fragmented stone walls and partially thatched
roof of the abandoned gamekeeper's hut. She would have drawn
closer to the flames but for the ravaged faces of the four motley
brigands sitting cross-legged on the other side. Gnawing loudly
on chunks of ham and morsels of bread, they slid occasional leers
of curiosity her way.

She shrank back farther against the crumbling wall and willed
herself to pick at the hard, dark bread and ash-encrusted ham.
For the sake of Philippe's child, she had to eat. She still found it
difficult to believe that she was free. For hours, it seemed, she
had lain crammed in the box beneath the heavy tools. With every
bounce of the wagon, particles of dirt had sifted over her face.
At times, she had felt that if she didn't get out of the chest—
now, immediately!—if she didn't stretch her cramped limbs, she
would begin to scream and never stop.

She had forced herself to think of other things: of her father,
his jolly eyes set in his battle-scarred face, recounting intriguing

tales of foreign lands; of Judith, her beloved governess, singing lullabys mixed with delicious stories of trolls and gargoyles; of Poissy's abbess reprimanding her for substituting the convent's goat milk for the holy water; and, as always, of Maison Bellecour. Memories of it held the most comfort, for it was the secluded months she had spent there with her beloved Philippe that she cherished the most.

Then the jouncing of the wagon halted. She tensed. Muffled conversation was followed by thumps, a yelp, and silence. Once again, the tool chest lid was lifted. One by one, the tools atop her was removed. Twilight filtered in, then portions of a face, the blond Atlas. Blood trickled from a battered nose, but the bloodhound's drooping eyes twinkled. Behind him, peered the cadaverous faces of the prisoners.

"Where are we?" she asked.

"In the quarry." He had a gravelly voice.

"The guards?"

A grin split the lantern jaw, revealing irregular teeth. "Their heads are cracked like eggshells."

She struggled to sit up; her hair fell about her face and shoulders in golden snarls powdered with dirt. "I . . . we must hide . . . Claude Fabreville . . ."

She had fainted then, and, when she came to, the wagon had been wobbling along through the dark. This time her rescuer had thoughtfully left the lid cracked open.

Where was he now? Would he return? Or had he deserted her, leaving her with these brigands of the forest? She stole a look at her dinner companions, who had grudgingly given her food in his absence: all nondescript faces of every age, with bleary eyes, shaggy beards, and ragged clothes in common.

She looked down at the dirt-stained cape she wore, ermine-trimmed and lined with the finest silk, Marchesseau silk. It would buy the food the brigands had no doubt stolen earlier that day a thousand times over. What if they turned on her? An uneasiness rippled through her. Yet, studying the four again, they all looked rather pathetic. Tired, hungry, sad, angry—but not violent.

A faint noise outside warned her of someone's approach. She looked up to see her rescuer stoop to enter the hut. Quickly, she came to her feet. "Where . . . ?"

"I got rid of the wagon and covered its tracks," he answered, grinning, obviously delighted with his successful prank. He crossed to one of the men and took the ham hock from his hands. The man surrendered his food without protest and turned to dig about inside a burlap sack to remove a hunk of cheese.

"I am Hervé Bertin," he said, settling his great hulk near her. "Who are you?"

She inched away. "Natalie." She offered no more. "I want to thank you for what you did. I will see—"

"Oh, no. Not just Natalie." He grinned again, looking for all the world like a child at a favorite game. "It must be Comtesse Natalie something-or-other. Or Marquise Natalie. Or Duchesse Natalie. You are a pretty lady. Your skin is milk-white; your hands—" He picked one up in his big paw, which was crusted with quarry dust. "You've never scrubbed clothes or scoured pans. And you were in that part of the prison kept for the nobility."

His lips pronounced the last word in a sullen tone. His fingers, almost as big as sausages, fingered her cape's ermine trimming, now torn along the hem and no longer white. "You know the attorney general?"

She stiffened. The other four brigands stopped eating, alert with interest. She glanced from one hardened face to the next and then back to the pleasant Nordic features of her rescuer. He, too, eyed her with interest, but of a different sort. Her fingers clutched the frogs of the cloak; her mind raced. Tell the truth, and she might find herself held for ransom. She knew now that Claude Fabreville would pay a great deal to rid himself of the future Marchesseau heir.

"I was his mistress; he evoked a *lettre de cachet* against me when he tired of me. He wants nothing more to do with me."

Hervé grunted. He sank his strong teeth into the meat and tore off a chunk. "You spoke the swine's name with fear," he said, his mouth full.

"You mistake disgust for fear."

He tossed aside the picked-clean ham bone and tore off a hunk of bread. "You mentioned an ample reward."

She shrugged the cloak from her shoulders, and fingers of chilling cold wreathed about her. "The cloak is worth several thousand livres."

He shook his head slowly. "Not secondhand." Petulance pouted his mouth. "I didn't risk my life for a handful of livres."

"You escaped also," she pointed out, trying to deal logically with the overgrown boy.

"I had already planned to escape with the finishing of the fountain." His heavy brows furrowed into one disgruntled line over the swollen nose as he plodded through the problem. "Taking you with me made the escape more dangerous. You slowed me down. The king's grenadiers mightn't bother to scour the forest for just a brigand, but they would for a prisoner by royal order."

Suddenly, the other four brigands didn't look too pleased at her presence either. Inspired by desperation, she blurted, "The convent! The Poissy Convent, where I was educated. Some of my belongings are still there, a few clothes, but also some items of value that would make it worth your while to take me there! A gold-inlaid jewelry box, a pearl-encrusted comb. And other baubles I meant to send for one day. Best of all, the sisters will take me off your hands; they will grant me refuge."

One of the brigands, who was missing an earlobe, she noted now, wiped his mouth with the back of his arm and said, "It might be a good idea, Hervé."

Mollified, Hervé's face brightened. He slapped his palms on his thighs. "We'll leave at dawn."

For the first time since she and Philippe had been served with the *lettre de cachet*, she felt real hope. The other brigands curled up where they were, amidst the crumbs of their meals, to sleep. She had never slept without a bed, not even in prison. Besides, she was too wary of the others to let herself sleep and too exhausted to stay awake. She glanced at Hervé. He was still young, full of life—and ready to spend that life's seed on the nearest available female, if she was any judge, by the hungry look he cast her way as he crawled on all fours toward her.

They were both about the same age. He seemed an impulsive young man. She knew that if she could reason with him, she could sidetrack him. "Hervé," she tried to say calmly, coolly, "I need your help, for you are the strongest of us all."

He halted in front of her, squatting back on his heels. "I have helped you enough already. It's time you help me." At least he had made no move to touch her.

"I will. When we get to the convent. But I am weak, I am with child." The blush warmed her face, but she hurried on. "Surely you must have had a little brother or sister. Do you remember when they were babies how you had to be very careful with them? I must be very careful with the baby growing within me."

His big face softened. "I wouldn't hurt you." He looked down at his massive hands. "I used to steal fish from the seigneur's stream—for little Paul, my youngest brother." He looked up at her, and she wilted a little at the misery in his eyes. "Until the seigneur caught me. That stream belonged to God," he added truculently. "Not to the seigneur."

"What happened?" she whispered.

He shrugged his shoulders. "We—my mother and my brothers—were put into the debtors' prison. I alone have stayed alive," he finished simply. "After five years, I was released."

"How did you come to be in La Force?"

"Salt smuggling."

Her eyes widened. "You should have stayed with stealing fish." Salt smuggling was a serious crime. Salt was taxed at twelve times its value, and those smugglers caught were usually condemned to a lifetime of hard labor.

"You can't steal enough fish to put clothes on your back," he said bitterly.

Perhaps she was foolishly trusting. Claude Fabreville's success at treachery would confirm her foolishness. Nevertheless, she pulled the big brigand into her arms and rocked him against her breast as she would her own baby. When she awoke later, it was she who was cradled in Hervé's arms. She lay there, eyes closed, pretending that it was Philippe who held her, that their complacent world still existed. Tears slipped from between her lids and she angrily wiped at them.

When Hervé stirred, she scooted away. Above her, the faint light peeked through the patches of roof. She sat up and tried to make herself presentable, combing the shreds of straw and leaves from her tangled hair. Some part of vanity was still intact.

With daylight, she and Hervé left the shelter of the hut and the camaraderie of the four brigands. They kept to the edges of the forest, skirting the villages, and made for the Poissy Convent to the south. Natalie was not used to walking. One of her silver heels broke. The raw spring wind stung her face. By midafternoon, she would have given her cloak in exchange for the aban-

doned wagon, but she had to agree with Hervé that to travel on
the road might draw unwanted attention.

He had explained that he was not worried as much about the
soldiers as he was about the thousands of unemployed who roamed
the countryside. Nearly a tenth of the rural population went
begging from farm to farm, asking for even a morsel of bread.
Natalie was somewhat conspicuous in her ermine cloak, tattered
and dirt-stained though it was.

By dusk, they came in sight of the cobblestoned village of Poissy
and its gray convent walls. Outside its great wooden doors, Hervé
paused and gave her a crooked grin that was surprisingly shy for
the cocky young man. "I'm almost sorry to end our journey so
soon."

Weary beyond words, she summoned a grateful smile. "You've
been very kind, and I won't forget you. Somehow, I will repay
you for . . ." Her words trailed off.

"I know," Hervé said softly, and, embarrassed by his unexpected display of sensitivity, turned to pull the convent's bell
rope. A moment later, the door creaked open to reveal not the
benevolent features of old Sister Béatrice but a row of implacable
faces of the Garde Royale—and the thoroughly pleased countenance of Claude Fabreville. He stuffed a pinch of snuff up one
nostril and said languidly, "I had thought you would seek out
the nearest familiar place."

"God! God!" Natalie lifted clenched fists that were shackled at
the wrists. Her muttering wasn't a prayer or a beseechment but
a curse that was lost in the babble of prison inmates.

At first she had prayed for strength, but she wasn't certain who
answered, God or Satan. She remembered thinking that nothing
could be worse than La Salpêtrière's section reserved for the
women interned by royal order. But life in the Great Prison,
which housed thousands of habitual women criminals, had become, as Madeleine had warned, a living nightmare after only
ten days.

Still, at the moment, even the discomforts of searching for an
occupied corner to sleep in, of scratching at the body lice until
her skin was raw, of picking through the bowl of watered rice to
remove the pebbles and worms, seemed infinitely preferable to
the horror that awaited her.

The women around her, mostly coarse-faced prostitutes, parted before the flank of guards. Here and there, a few of the braver women dared to hiss obscenities at the soldiers. The soldier in front, whose eyes had lost whatever compassion might have been found there years before, growled at Natalie, "Come along, you're next."

"Take your hands off me," she said coldly, haughtily. She drew away her emerald velvet skirts, now tattered, for the gown was the same one she had worn when first arrested. "I'm not a thief."

The guard chortled. "You're here doing charitable works, I suppose?"

"You must listen! I'm the Marquise de Marchesseau!"

He swept her a low, mocking bow. "Yes, and I'm his grace, the regent."

He, no doubt, thought her *tête de bois*, as mad as the stringy-haired, teenage girl who stood in a corner of the cavernous room the entire day, day after day, eyes vacant, picking or playing with herself in a distracted form of self-abuse.

He signaled to the soldiers, and they took Natalie by her arms and hauled her along the dark, slime-musty tunnel that led out to the moat surrounding La Salpêtrière. Even though it was dawn, the faint winter sunlight blistered her unaccustomed eyes. Before her was the cart that would take her and nineteen others accused as thieves to the Palais de Justice.

The cart rolled through filthy streets that were beginning to stir with life. Odd, she had never noticed how ugly and dirty Paris was.

The layout of Paris was that of a village that had overgrown its islet boundaries established three hundred years before Christ—narrow streets that surrounded houses of rich merchants and ennobled lawyers known as the *noblesse de robe*, very much despised by the *noblesse de épée* and *noblesse campagnarde*, the old feudal families such as the one from which Natalie professed to come.

The lame, blind, and maimed were already begging on the streets. Come nightfall, these miscreants would return to the Court of Miracles, a place out of reach of the authorities. There, they would shed their wooden legs and eye patches and other props, and indulge in nocturnal orgies. It was these nightly miraculous cures from infirmity that gave the court its name.

At the Palais de Justice, the women prisoners were herded into a courtyard dominated by a scaffold. Though it was early yet, a great crowd had assembled to watch the weekly spectacle. People filled every window space and stood on roofs. A tile, knocked loose, shattered on the cobblestones below, only a few feet from where Natalie stood, the first in line.

She pressed her lips over chattering teeth and steeled herself to behave with dignity, to endure what was to come in stoic silence. Although disaster after disaster had befallen her, she was still naively hopeful of some heavenly intervention.

The sight of the branding iron, spitting in the forge erected on the scaffold, sent fear rattling down her spine. Her throat felt raw from the screaming inside her trapped body. Her teeth were clenched so tightly her jaws ached. Despite the dawn's wet chill, sweat, rank with body odor, oozed through her pores.

When the guards took hold of her, cheers erupted from the atavistic spectators. All of her good intentions to comport herself with noble bravery vaporized in the cold morning air along with the breath that carried her silent screams.

She struggled between her captors, kicking and clawing as they mounted, stair by stair. Thrust onto the scaffold, she could feel the heat from the forge. Only that morning, in the bone-chill of La Salpêtrière, she would have sold her wooden shoes to feel the warmth of a fire again. Now she cringed away from the fierce heat. She didn't see the avid expressions of those nearest, only the red-hot sizzle of the branding iron moving inexorably toward her.

At last her voice exerted itself. She threw back her head and screamed, the agonizing wail of a beast in torment. She writhed between the two soldiers. In her struggles, her breast was bared instead of her shoulder, and the fleur-de-lis burned into her flesh. The branding iron's hiss left a putrid stench of smoking flesh. Her pain-stunned body reacted. Her nails gouged flesh from her palms. Her eyes rolled upward. Her womb heaved in sudden, violent contractions. Finally, her brain willed her into merciful unconsciousness.

In desperation, the Scotsman John Law sent his hirelings into France's gaols and hospitals and bagnios in search of involuntary settlers to populate the torpid French colonies administered by his Compagnie des Indes—the Antilles, Louisiana, and other French lands beyond the sea. In addition, it was an easy way for France to rid herself of undesirables.

Sometimes, even innocent or respectable persons were kidnapped. A purse of gold slipped into a hand, a whisper in an ear went a great way to get rid of a competitor in the realm of either love or business.

Law's ruffian, quasimilitary police came to scour the dregs of La Salpêtrière early in June. They came in search of prospective brides for the many bachelors in the vast Louisiana wilderness. The female felons they indiscriminately picked were to be provided with a chest of clothing and linens as a dowry so that they might marry with all possible dispatch. Of these assembled *filles à la cassette,* or casket girls, few were favored with either youth or beauty.

Natalie's beauty was virtually unrecognizable beneath the prison filth, and at twenty-one she felt her youth was gone, robbed from her by Claude Fabreville. The unshed tears for the baby she had miscarried had turned to venom. She watched the police move among the *filles de joie,* thieves, orphans, and murderesses, singling out one here and there for a casket girl.

She came to her decision easily. She faced the rest of her life confined to La Salpêtrière's Great Prison, for who, other than Fabreville, knew of her incarceration? Should Philippe be released from the Bastille, he would learn only that she had escaped from that section reserved for prisoners by *lettres de cachet.* When she did not return to him with the passage of time, he could only come to believe that she had died in the process of escape.

Her one hope—for herself, for Philippe—was to insinuate herself within the circle of selected casket girls. In a matter of months, the Duc d'Orléans would no longer be regent; upon Louis XV's ascendancy to the throne, she could return to France and Philippe.

Surely for a period of a few months or so she could evade the expected marriage. She could support herself by giving Italian or English lessons. The Company of the Indies posters told of a settlement that almost equaled Paris. *La petite Paris* it was called, though the official name was Nouvelle Orléans. Her lips twisted mordantly at the name given in honor of the Duc d'Orléans. She hoped that was the extent of similarity between the man and the settlement.

. . .

The send-off of the bride convoy from Paris was quite festive. Thirty tumbrels, escorted by archers, bore the three hundred and fifty-three gaily waving women sentenced to transport to French Louisiana. Eighty-seven of the women were from La Salpêtrière. Some of them, like Natalie, bore the red brand of the fleur-de-lis.

The *émigrés* were accompanied by a *curé* and two Ursuline nuns. The church had provided a yellow ribbon bow for the coiffure of each virtuous maiden, as it chastely designated the female *émigrées*. Who was to contradict the church's choice of description?

Behind the carts walked half that number of male deportees, who wore cockades of the same yellow shade in their hats. Most of this contingent, grouped by pairs in chains, comprised the riffraff recruited from all of the *dépôts* of the capital, but some, mainly yokels and simpletons, had been seized off the streets. Among them also straggled the lame and the blind.

In crossing Paris, the wenches sang as though without care and hailed passersby, inviting them to come along on the voyage *aux isles*, meaning Louisiana. Natalie stood in the rear, her face lifted to the bright, blinding spring sunlight. For this alone, she would have become a casket girl. She was leaving her beloved Paris and her beloved Philippe; yet she was free, free to return when it was once again safe.

Outside Paris, the female *émigrées* were deprived of their transportation and forced to proceed afoot, along with the male deportees. Bound for the port of La Rochelle, they were herded like cattle along the roads of France. At night they were locked up in barns, and when shelter could not be found, they were forced to lie down in ditches, while guards stood over them with pikes or bows and arrows.

That first night Natalie lay down to sleep, but sleep would not come. The ground was hard and damp, and the nights cold, not so different from La Salpêtrière really. She lay there and planned. Planning was good; it eased the hate.

Those three months in the infamous Great Prison had become an ordeal of constant struggle to hold herself together as a person under conditions that were totally subhuman. She hadn't hardened like the others yet, and found such simple things as lack of privacy when attending to the body's natural functions during the march excruciatingly embarrassing.

Along the way, additional deportees, mostly kidnapped children or waylaid servant girls, were added from foul-smelling collection centers that were crawling with vermin. During the journey, two men escaped into nearby fields. Not Natalie. She wanted to go farther than Fabreville's long arm of power could reach.

She was still susceptible to the misery of others and ended the second day of travel by comforting a tearful, delicate-featured girl of no more than twelve years, who had two thick braids hanging down her back. A shopkeeper's wife had taken covert revenge on the pretty, dark-haired maidservant and arranged for her kidnapping.

"I don't—don't want to marry." Jeanne-Antoinette sobbed.

Natalie replaited one of the girl's braids. "Of course you don't. And you won't have to, I'm certain." Surely the church would refuse to perform such a marriage?

At the end of the third week, the *émigrés* straggled lamely into La Rochelle. Crowds turned out along the shabby streets of the sordid port to watch the arrival of the deportees. At the waterfront stood two towers, the Tour de la Chaîne and the Tour St. Nicolas, between which was suspended a heavy chain when the port was closed. Here, the five hundred or so prisoners were separated and consigned to one of the three ships that made up the bridal convoy. Natalie was assigned to the *Baleine* and managed to keep Jeanne-Antoinette at her side.

To her joy, she discovered that Hervé was among those waiting on the rotting wharf to board the *Baleine*. She had often wondered what had become of her mighty rescuer. When she called his name, he stared at her without recognition. Why would he recognize her, she thought sadly. Instead of elegant clothes, she wore rags and wooden shoes. Her shining hair of pale gold was matted, and straggled from the soiled yellow ribbon in dark, dirty lanks about her shoulders. Not even rouge adorned her dust-smeared face.

"It's Natalie," she said, her dimpled chin tilted arrogantly.

Despite his manacled wrists, his large hands encircled her waist and lifted her into the air. He grinned whimsically. "Natalie, *la comtesse!*"

"*La marquise,*" she corrected, catching his broad shoulders for balance.

Those about the two snickered with contempt at the airs the young woman put on. He set her down, his gaze slipping to her midsection. "The babe?"

"Stillborn."

"That swine Fabreville—he was the one who had us arrested?"

She nodded, her hatred so keen that words were impossible.

A soldier prodded Hervé with the butt of his musket and ordered him back in line. "At least," the brigand called over his shoulder, "the swine will never find you in Louisiana."

The *Baleine* was a three-master with a lateen mizzen. Before Natalie was herded below to the orlop deck, she surreptitiously pulled the yellow bow from her hair and leaned over the side. The soiled ribbon fluttered briefly between her fingers before twirling into the foamy, gray sea.

CHAPTER

Montreal,
New France   *June 1722*

For years in New France, the French government had discouraged free enterprise by individual trappers in favor of its Company of the Indies. If the tendency to roam couldn't be eradicated, it could at least be controlled. A compromise measure was reached regarding those bold vagabonds of the woods and waterways known as *coureurs des bois*.

If they wanted to hunt and trap, they were required to purchase permits. Naturally these *congés* were hard to come by. The permits were obtained by friends of high-placed officers in the colony and then resold secretly to the highest bidder. In the early years, those caught trapping without permits had been whipped and branded the first time, then set to the galleys for life the second time. The latest French practice was to impoverish the successful trappers with fines in order to support the excesses of the French court.

Nicolas Brissac was one of these renegade *coureur des bois*; but then, being a half-breed, he was a renegade to begin with. He merely turned to doing business with the English, smuggling his pelts out of the country in the false bottoms specially made in the hulls of their ships by enterprising captains.

With the arrival of spring, he was coming out of the frozen wilderness with twice as many furs as his canoe could carry. The day before, he had cached the surplus of superb dark pelts to await his return.

Three half-naked, top-knotted Chipewyan warriors traveled to Montreal with him. Between the four of them, they carried the canoe and its supplies in short relays across the rugged twelve miles of Methye Portage, which separated Hudson Bay and the Arctic watershed.

The watershed was an immense wilderness few white men had seen. It contained the greatest fur bonanza on the continent, an incalculable quantity of beaver, marten, mink—and the prized ermine, which, though brown in color in the summer, changed to yellowish white in winter. Only in areas of extreme cold did the ermine's fur turn pure white, areas such as that where Nicolas had wintered, north of the treeline where a mighty river snaked into the remote Arctic Ocean.

First with Jean-Baptiste Brissac, from whom he had taken his surname, and then later on his own, he had explored and mapped the labyrinthine waterways, rugged mountains, bleak tundra of the Artic north, and the innumerable twisting streams that crossed desolate portages.

He remembered his first view of the immense, fur-bearing region, of standing beside the little Jesuit turned soldier on a cliff towering seven hundred feet above the Clearwater River and looking out with awe over dense evergreen forests that stretched as far as the eye could see.

After his father's death—after he had performed the *coup de mort*—he had sought out Jean-Baptiste and returned to that vast wilderness to harvest pelts. They had been accompanied only by a few members of the Inuit, or Eskimo, bands.

Peaceful scenes of polar bears rambling across the frozen wastelands and glistening towers of floating ice that looked like the French castles Jean-Baptiste described had not diluted the bitterness inside the boy-man. The bitterness took its toll of him, and his body grew thinner by the day.

In the midst of a raging winter storm, the worried old Jesuit had hustled him back to Montreal, back to Mother Marie's keeping, by means of a sled drawn by native dogs with belled harnesses that had rung incessantly in his ears.

Between the old man and the nun, they nursed him back to health. Against his stubborn will, they gently prepared him over the next five years for life in an Anglo-controlled society. With their deaths, scarcely a year apart, he had returned to his mother's tribe, the Chipewyans. But he discovered that he was no longer one of them, nor was he French.

Where did he belong?

For teachers, he had had two nonconformists—a priest turned soldier and a passionate nun. Each time he returned to Montreal, he missed his mentors and their abiding love more than he could bear to acknowledge.

Now he was returning to Montreal at one of its most picturesque times, the Fur Fair, an event carried over from medieval days. In all European countries, the cities and towns set aside two weeks when merchants from all parts brought their goods with them and set up booths wherever they could find space. Dancers, jugglers, magicians, and mummers followed in the wake of the merchants and entertained in the streets for the largesse of pennies.

The Montreal fair was conducted on the same principle. Indians, painted and feathered, came down the Ottawa in one huge flotilla, sometimes as many as four or five hundred canoes at once. On the outskirts of town, they pitched their tepees and set up their kettles, with much shouting and singing and quarreling. All who witnessed the spectacle agreed that it was at once exciting and slightly terrifying.

In the meantime, Montreal took on a gala air. Merchants from all parts of New France brought their goods to barter and occupied temporary booths.

Nicolas strolled through the rout and rabble, the commanding height of his leonine head visible above the others. At his side trotted Loupe, a fierce, furred running dog of the Eskimos that was part timber wolf.

About him streamed Indians, inebriated with the white man's firewater, brandishing tomahawks and screeching their wildest woodland notes. Some of the *coureurs des bois* were no less exhibitionist, stripping off their clothes and parading half naked through the town.

The *coureurs des bois* were easy to distinguish from the French habitants. For one, their colorful and gaudy homespuns betrayed them. Another sign was the birchbark cases containing a knife for eating that some wore around their necks. Also, there were the *pièces*, or sacks, slung on the small of their backs along with the beltlike leather tumpline that looped their foreheads.

The woodsmen's most obvious giveaway, however, was their lack of facial hair. The Indians with whom they traded found the curly hair of the French grotesque and their beards and moustaches nothing short of loathsome. Indeed, they were surprised at the roughness of European skins, their own being soft and delicate as a result of the constant application of oil and grease.

The *coureurs des bois* had gained a reputation for courage and élan, a reputation as a gay, devil-may-care lot lacking in fear. These wood runners were a wild lot with paddle in hand, pack at their feet, and a song on their lips. They were inured to waterways, where the bateau and pirogue were the sole means of transportation, and the trackless forests where the northern lights danced like marionettes. Known for their capacity to adapt themselves to any environment, they were true sons of the wilderness.

Nicolas strode among them, one of them, yet apart from them. His twisted ankle had eventually straightened, and for the most part he had lost the tongue-tied feeling he had so often experienced in the presence of his father and other white men.

Without even so much as a glance, he bypassed the large storehouses of the successful Fur Company of Canada, du Plessis holdings. At the door of the two-story Café Le Roi, he commanded Loupe to wait and entered the crowded tavern to search out his erstwhile partner.

He found François de Gautier in a narrow little room above. The usually elegant man was sprawled ignominiously beneath the apothecary's dark-haired daughter, whose naked buttocks wriggled and bounced above him. Sensing another presence, François sent the girl sprawling and sprang upright. "What the—? A pox upon you, Nicolas! Are you so uncivilized a savage that you can't even knock?"

An amused grin passed over Nicolas's face. The girl grabbed up her clothing before her, flashing him an apprehensive glance as she scooted past him for the door.

François burst into raucous laughter. "The wenches flee at the sight of your handsome face, Nicolas." He reached for the brandy bottle on the floor beside the bed. "If the *donzelles* would only stop and listen, your voice would seduce them on the spot."

"And I thought it was my prowess between the sheets that lured them like the Lorelei."

"*Mais, oui!*" François swilled a drink and shook his head. "You know, after three years, I'm still amazed by you. A fierce *coureur des bois* quoting Locke and Cicero, learned at both ancient and modern languages—why, you even outshine me at mathematics and engineering."

Nicolas peeled away from the door and crossed to a ladder-backed chair. Turning it around to straddle it backward, he said quietly, "If you would forget the wine and the women . . ."

With elaborate affectation, François preened his luxurious, reddish brown moustache. "It's the women who cannot forget me. After all, a handsome lord—"

"A lord without a castle," Nicolas said, smiling at his friend's boasting, though what François said about women was true. The dashing nobleman was a true son of Gascony, the natives of which were prone to be very sure of themselves and not above gasconade, the vainglorious talk named after them.

"Acch! Must you remind me? You are looking at a gentleman caught in a pigsty of a village." François took another swig and tossed the empty bottle toward where his discarded clothing lay heaped. The bottle joined a collection of two others. He could drink any man under the table and still keep his head. "You're two days late."

Nicolas shrugged indifferently and said, "I don't like this latest idea of yours."

François sat at the edge of the bed, his hands braced on his knees, his heavy genitals dangling. "But you will parlay with this New Englander, Nicolas?"

He stood and swung away from the chair. "*Oui*. But I warn you I have no interest in a permanent venture with the English. Invite them into Canada, and they will be no less a despot than your own government."

"France is your government, too, I might remind you." François rose and began to dress. The silk stockings he rolled up over hair-matted legs were of the best quality, though slightly threadbare.

"No, François," Nicolas said flatly. "I belong to no nation. I will not be subjugated."

. . .

The parlay was to be held deep in the woods beyond the immense pasture, La Commune, where the *coureurs des bois* engaged in a rugged Indian game played with long sticks curved at the end to contain a webbing of catgut. The object of the contest was to keep possession of a ball. The French had coined the name of *La Crosse* for it.

François and Nicolas, with Loupe at his heels, moved among the people who had turned out to watch the woodsmen demonstrate their speed and agility. New France's air was so clear and healthy that the men attained great strength. Few children died in the cradle as they did in the mother country. The men born in the colony were of a new race: French-Canadians. They grew straight and tall and strong, with broader shoulders and arms hard from unceasing swing of ax and dipping of paddle. Even their voices had changed, the soft accent of the French provinces giving place to deeper, clearer notes that carried a musical ring over long stretches of water and through dense forests.

However robust and courageous the *coureurs des bois* might be, it was upon the rakish François de Gautier that the young women of Montreal cast languishing, coquettish glances. Though only of medium height, and with his curly brown hair receding slightly in a U shape above each temple, he possessed an inordinate amount of good looks that created an enticing *diablerie* of expression.

He appeared dashing in a coat of rich gray levantine cloth that matched the fine gray leather of his buckled shoes. Tucked under his arm, he carried a tapboard hat with the brim turned up to show off the scarlet silk lining, more than likely Marchesseau silk.

Regardless of François's circumstances, he would not permit himself to dress and act less than the gentleman he had been born. He had only to look around and see the French-born who, through careless habits, had let themselves degenerate into scum such as those found in sordid seaports like Marseilles.

His father had been chancellor to the minister of the marine, the Comte de Pontchartrain. The family wealth did not cover the youngest son's lust for life's pleasures, so François was put into the navy to seek his own fortunes. Like Nicolas, he did not enjoy being subject to the orders or whims of a superior.

Perhaps that was why he was drawn to the erudite half-breed, whom he had met in Acadia, which the English, who now controlled the French province, called New Scotland. Having surrendered his captain's commission, François had just arrived on a ship out of Le Havre and was looking around at Nova Scotia's pathetic little fort of Port Royal. The prospects of acquiring a fortune there looked nil.

Then his attention had been caught by Nicolas Brissac. How could it not have been? He was taller than the rest, savage-looking with a swarthy face. He was dressed like an Indian, his powerful torso bared to the waist, from which dangled a tomahawk, and he was tanned as brown as a walnut. A leather tumpline looped about his forehead held back the black, shoulder-length hair. As he walked along the wharf, he was trailed by a sled dog equally as fierce-looking.

A gabby barmaid at the local tavern had told François that the man was a half-breed engaged in the extremely lucrative business of fur trapping. At that, the ears of the enterprising François de Gautier had perked up. Why not? he had asked himself. Why not go into the fur business on his own?

Of course he had realized there was a major drawback. The best furs were deep in French territory, the northwest territory— and only a native of New France, a true *coureur des bois*, could make such a venture successful.

Most certainly, François had no knowledge of the woods or of trapping. What he did have was contacts with English sea captains willing to risk smuggling the French furs.

However, finding a partner was a little more difficult. First, those self-reliant men born and bred in Canada had little liking for the French-born. Second, many of the *coureurs des bois* were wild and dissolute and threw their profits away in drunken carousing in the towns. Drinking was fine, but throwing away profits—*mais non!*

By coincidence, the formidable Nicolas Brissac was exactly the kind of partner he was seeking. First, the man set himself apart from the Canadien Clique. Second, discreet inquiry revealed the man did not drink anything stronger than table wine. Thus armed, François had approached him and offered his services in exchange for twenty-five percent of the profits.

Brissac had refused. François had offered him a larger percentage. The half-breed had refused him again. François had been close to despair. A fortune lay at his fingertips, if he could but convince the fur trapper.

Surprisingly, it was François's engaging personality that finally
elicited a laconic agreement from Brissac. Faced with what appeared to be an end to the negotiations, François had desultorily
talked of other things while he drank.

He had been amazed when the *coureur des bois*, who was about
the same age as he, had responded with a knowledgeable debate
on the theory of the nobility of the savage. Brissac had quietly
argued against the position with astounding eloquency. François,
holding his own on behalf of the Indians he knew so little about,
had declared that primitive man was nobler and more sensitive
than the highly civilized products of European society.

"How can you proclaim the Indian a savage," François had
asked, out of patience, "when you yourself are an Indian and
educated better than most Europeans?"

Beneath the high, prominent cheekbones, a dry smile had curved
Nicolas's lean lips. "*Mon ami*, you do not know of the savagery
I am capable of."

From there the conversation had covered the arts, politics,
religion. By that time, François was no longer astonished to find
that Nicolas Brissac could conjugate Latin and Greek verbs and
had translated Cicero and Horace before he was fifteen.

Somehow, the partnership had been reached without François
being quite certain of the terms. He *was* certain that, as partners,
they would complement one another. His own temperament was
mercurial, his enthusiasm boundless; Nicolas was more contained, dispassionate, and without the need to succeed that so
plagued himself, the need to establish his own seigneury like the
one he had surrendered to his older brother.

François arranged for the rendezvous with the New England
sea captain to take place at the dilapidated sawmill of a drunken
half-breed, old Vincente. The sawmill's shack perched wobbily
on the bank of St. Martin's Brook and looked as if it might slide
into the rushing water at any minute.

Long, curling, fragrant-smelling pine shavings scented the
clearing before the shack. Nicolas halted midway across the clearing. "What is it?" François asked.

Nicolas, his gaze swinging in an arc about them, stroked the
fur that bristled along Loupe's neck. "Vincente has had recent
visitors," he said at last.

"A war party?" François trusted Nicolas's instinct. The *coureur des bois* wrought havoc around the Iroquois villages, and they feared him. A certain story was told around Montreal and Trois Rivières that, in hopes of his capture, the old women of the Long House gathered faggots to burn Nicolas Brissac at the stake.

Nicolas shook his head. "No. The tracks are made by wooden shoes, not moccasins."

François's hand eased away from the Italian stiletto tucked beneath his coat. "Perhaps some of the New England contacts."

Once again, Nicolas shook his head. Just then the shack door creaked open, but it wasn't old Vincente who stepped into view but a squat, tonsured priest wearing the brown, hooded cassock of the Récollect order.

François's heart sank. It was the provincial of the powerful Society of Jesus, Pierre Tournaire. The Jesuits, through their control of the Indian neophytes, were said to be attempting to assert a monopoly on the fur trade. No one could prove it, but their papal ensign was as common a sight in Canada as the fleur-de-lis. Their influence reached not only to France but to Rome as well.

François feigned congeniality. "Reverend father, you are far from your mission. Seeking a convert in old Vincente, are you?"

The father fingered the three knots on his belt cord that symbolized his three vows of chastity, poverty, and obedience. In the sweat-beaded face, his eyes were brilliant. A sad smile of resignation found its way to his small mouth. "Alas, no, my son. I am here to point out traitors to France."

He made the sign of the cross in the air, and with that three crimson-coated soldiers spilled out of the shack doorway. The bell mouths of three muskets were trained on Nicolas and François.

"I happen to know you are in league with the English captain," the priest continued with a self-satisfied smile. "Your furs have been impounded, Nicolas Brissac, and I'm afraid I must ask the two of you to accompany the soldiers."

François shivered. In an instant, his mind's eye saw images of a metal boot tightened by screws and a rack that was turned until the victim's joints were pulled asunder.

In that same instant, Nicolas's tomahawk hurtled across the intervening space. With a soft thud, it caught one of the soldiers between the eyes. Even before the guard on the right could pull the trigger, the sled dog launched an attack that knocked the guard on his back. Snarling, it went for the throat. At the man's shriek, the third soldier abruptly swung around and fired.

It was the last thing he ever did. Nicolas flattened him from behind. The soldier tried to rise from his stomach, but Nicolas straddled him. With his left hand at the back of the man's head and the other one at the base of his throat, Nicolas gave one quick, brutal twist to the neck, backward, upward, and sideways. In the suddenly silent forest, the crack of the cervical column was audible.

The priest, realizing Heaven wasn't on his side this time, was already sprinting for the woods as fast as his weight would permit. François took off after him and easily closed the gap. With a leap, he hurled himself at the priest's fleeing back. The rotund man was knocked to his knees and tried to scramble away. François slashed out and caught Tournaire's white cord sash. The priest went down on all fours. He was panting or sobbing, François wasn't sure.

"All right, Tournaire," he snapped, "you better say your beads, because then I'm going to strangle you with them."

The priest reared up with a strength that surprised him. His pudgy hands clutched a piece of wood he had found on the forest floor. Before François could block the blow, the priest clubbed him across the temple. The blow only stunned him momentarily, but by then the priest was off and running again and would gain the pasture and help first.

Half-dazed, François made his way back to the sawmill and Nicolas. "The bastard Tournaire got away," he said, breathing heavily. He leaned over, bracing his hands on his knees while he got his second wind. His gaze passed over the grisly sight of the soldier whose windpipe had been ripped from his throat, then moved on to Nicolas. Silent, the half-breed sat back on his haunches, stroking the blood-matted fur of the lifeless sled dog.

"*Foutre!*" François spat. "An entire year's work—gone. The best furs ever taken. All because of that frigging Jesuit! Now I don't dare show my handsome face around here again."

Nicolas lifted the bark spread with melted resin from the fire and crossed to Vincente's commandeered canoe. "You might try testing your prowess on the Eskimo maidens. The Jesuits' influence doesn't stretch that far north, *mon ami*."

François grunted. "The Arctic is too far north. My one trip with you quickly convinced me. To live there, a man has to have blood like brandy, a body of brass, and eyes of glass."

"Then I suppose our partnership must end here." Nicolas laid the stripped birch bark over the hole in the canoe's hull and ran his fingers along the patch's edges, sealing its fringes with the melted resin. "What will you do now?"

He blinked at the smoke that twisted upward from the fire. "I don't know. I'm thirty-three and still have my fortune to make. I do know I don't want to go back to France."

"And you can't stay here."

François's head snapped up, his face brightening. His eyes flashed with the first enthusiasm he had felt in months. "Nicolas, listen to me! Why not go south instead of north? They say that some of the richest fur-bearing country is in the Illinois territory, still untapped. Just waiting for us."

Nicolas looked over his shoulder at him but said nothing.

"What is there to hold you here?" he pressed. "No family, no business, no ties."

"All right," Nicolas replied at length. "You may have something there. But I propose we expand our venture if we're to make this fortune of yours."

He canted his head and lifted his brows quizzically. "You have a suggestion?"

"Yes. Trading with both the French and the Spanish—and the Indians. In No Man's Land."

François thought for a minute. He knew as much as the next man about the area called No Man's Land, which wasn't that much—only what was gleaned from occasional travelers coming up from the lower reaches of the Mississippi.

No Man's Land was a strip of neutral territory extending several miles on either side of the Arroyo Hondo, which was accepted as the boundary between the French outpost of Louisiana, Natchitoches, and the Spanish one of Texas, Los Adais, which was the capital of Texas.

"*Pourquoi pas?*" he said, grinning at Nicolas. "We have nothing else better to do."

. . .

One glimpse, three months later, at the remote French outpost and he was ready to recant his agreement. Poste de la St. Jean Baptiste des Natchitoches, the oldest town in the vast region claimed by French Louisiana, was little more than a palisade of logs erected along the wooded banks of the Rivière Rouge and fringed by a scattering of cabins in the surrounding hills. The fort contained barracks, chapel, powderhouse, kitchen, outdoor oven, and guardhouse.

This was in contrast to San Miguel Arcángel de Linares de Los Adais, which was fifteen miles away and consisted solely of a Spanish mission and presidio.

That August, he and Nicolas constructed a rudimentary log cabin. Shirtless and sweating in a merciless sun, he cursed eloquently and constantly. When the ax handle broke in his hands, he complained, "I could've earned more money and fewer blisters in the navy."

Nicolas continued to swing the ax, the muscles rippling beneath the cinnamon-colored skin. "But think of the pack trains that will pass between here and San Antonio. Your pack trains, *mon ami.*"

François was tired and sore—and pent-up with the need to bury himself in a woman. He had gone too long without one. The few women he had met at the fort were all married. Not that that would have halted him, but he would not sneak about; on the other hand, he didn't want to have to battle an enraged husband.

"And just where do I acquire 'my' pack trains, do tell?" he asked, feeling out of sorts.

The ringing of the ax stopped, and Nicolas wiped his brow with the back of his arm. "You acquire your pack trains by selling the wild horses we are going to capture."

"You're talking about riding into Comanche territory. I think I'd rather face the Jesuit torture racks."

Nicolas shrugged his shoulders. His white teeth, good teeth, lightened the dark face. "I get along well with the savages."

"Then you go for the horses." François chunked the heavy ax head at the ground. "I'm going for a woman."

Nicolas grunted. "So you've heard about the bride ships?"

The Mississippi River was "all ears," and gossip invariably traveled from its mouth northward a thousand miles. This time the word went out that young women out of orphanages were coming from France and that bachelors on the scene when they arrived would either have prime choice or draw lots to have the first pick.

"I heard. And I'm ready for a wife."

"You're ready for bedding whatever you can get. And that's about what you're going to get, a grab-bag selection of virgins who are whores—and the pox."

François could feel his temper rising with the heat off the baked earth. "I won't live like you, Nicolas. Like a savage."

The black eyes slitted. "Are you certain you know how to live like a gentleman?"

François had taken just about enough that afternoon. He lashed out with his right fist. Too late, he saw Nicolas sidestep and drive his knuckles forward and upward, just below his ribs. He gasped, the breath *whoosh*ed from his lungs, and he fell onto his knees.

His eyes widened as another, different pain shot through all his nerve endings. There was no air in him left with which to scream. "The ax head . . ." It was a raw, agonized whisper.

CHAPTER 9

Colony of Louisiana   September 1722

BLESSED SUNLIGHT FELL ON Natalie's face when she emerged from the *Baleine*'s hold along with the rest of the human flotsam or "brides." For a moment, she shadowed her eyes from the piercing glare with her forearm.

The previous season, the *Baleine* had brought a cargo of blacks from the Guinea coast. The brig reeked of urine and sweat and death and fear. Not all of the *filles de joie* had survived the trip. The food was moldy and sometimes rotten, the water, stale and usually impure.

Natalie, the only one among the eighty-eight casket girls who could read, saw the contemptuous notations scrawled next to the girls' names on the shipping list: "Perfect Pig," "Confirmed Debauchee," "Knife Wielder," and, next to her name, "Delusions of Grandeur." Of the three hundred and twenty-five *émigrés*, sixteen from the ages of seventeen to thirty-eight were branded on their shoulders with the infamous fleur-de-lis, marking them as the most dangerous, the most jaded of the bunch. Natalie's brand, imprinted between her breasts, remained hidden, but she carried its true imprint on her spirit as well.

With Jeanne-Antoinette clutching her hand, she staggered across the deck to the railing. The sunspots that danced before her eyes faded, and the shoreline of the New World took shape. Ship

Island was the closet the bride convoy could moor to Fort Biloxi, ten nautical miles away. The marshy isle was a desolate place with a few withered trees and sand that reflected blindingly the torturously brilliant, tropical sunlight, but it did have two fresh-water ponds where the *Baleine* and the other two vessels could refill their casks.

Landing conditions were chaotic. The cargo and humans were transferred to swaying and leaky barges. Natalie made sure that Jeanne-Antoinette stayed with her as they were herded onto a lorry with large wheels that was pushed out across the sand into the water. Ahead of them, a cart was upset and the women floundered waist-deep in water, shouting and screaming like harpies.

Her fingers dug into the lorry's wooden side. She shut her lids against the broiling sunlight and whispered an Ave Maria. Sweat streamed down the sides of her rib cage and along her inner thighs. Nowhere . . . Not one place for shade, no vine-strewn stone walls like that in Maison Bellecour's cool gardens, no pastel shades of flowering arches of entwined wisteria.

No food, no water, no escape—and there was the blistering sun.

There were times, such as when she lost the baby, that she wished she had died with it. If it were not for Philippe, if it were not for the one hope of being reunited with him one day . . . She opened her eyes, lifted her chin, and willed her expression into unruffled acceptance of what was to happen.

At her side, Jeanne-Antoinette fought back quiet, little sobs. "Hush, my sweet," Natalie told the girl. "Soon we'll reach shore and some kind of shelter, I'm certain."

"*Ma mère, mon père.*" The girl wiped at the tears that glistened on her olive cheeks. The dark braids about her round, little face were matted with filth. Natalie knew her hair was straggly with dirt also. She didn't care anymore. "They will wonder what happened to me." The girl hiccoughed. "I want to go back, to go home!"

"You will one day." A lie, most likely, but what else could she say?

On her other side, Solange, a coarse, dishwater-blond whore, jeered, "I suppose the comtesse will write to the king and set this misunderstanding aright." She peered around Natalie and said to

Jeanne-Antoinette, "Well, you'll never leave the place. You're condemned here for life, do you understand? For life. And if you think differently, you're as daft as this one is, putting on airs and behaving like royalty, will you believe!"

Jeanne-Antoinette buried her head in her hands and began to weep again. Natalie stared the whore down until the young woman tossed her brassy blond head and looked away.

Soon the mainland came into view, a long, undulating, towering line of deep green. Trees! Shade! Other carts were already unloading their share of immigrants, and she searched among the cluster of confused, lost souls for Hervé's solid physique.

A line of archers were holding back a score or more of anxious men, a spindly looking lot. Of course, Natalie thought scornfully, prospective bridegrooms. A grizzle-haired gentleman who seemed to be in charge was overseeing the landing, sending some of the women to join one group, directing others to another.

The wheels of the cart crunched against dry sand, and its human contents spilled onto the shore. Dazed, Natalie followed the women ahead of her. Amazement and despair were written on their faces. Some stared stupidly at their surroundings. Others laughed or cried hysterically.

Natalie and Jeanne-Antoinette joined the other women from their cart to cluster beneath the merciful shade of moss-covered live oaks whose branches hung down like the sides of a green, leafy tent. Jeanne-Antoinette dropped to her knees, crouching next to Natalie.

Presently, the man Natalie had noticed earlier approached them and introduced himself as the governor of the province, Sieur de Bienville. Like his soldiers, he was dressed in a blue woolen uniform, but his was spangled with gold braid. With a sardonic twist to his lips, he welcomed them to the "paradise" and then began reading a list of names in a stentorian voice:

"Françoise Boisrenaud, Jeanne-Catherine Travernier, Marguerite Duanet, Louise Dufresne . . ." He called perhaps twenty more names, then pronounced their destination: "the outpost of Pascagoula.

The women were separated and led away, and the process was repeated, this time the destination being a place called Yazoo. The next group of names, numbering only three, were appointed to the French wilderness post of Arkansas; then Black River received four casket girls. Natalie held her breath, hoping. The chances appeared good that she and Jeanne-Antoinette would be together. Several more girls were apportioned to the villages of Cannes Brulées and Fort Mobile, named for the local Mauvila Indians. Then Jeanne-Antoinette's name was called first of the next grouping but not Natalie's. The girl was to be sent to Fort Rosalie, wherever that was.

Jeanne-Antoinette clung to Natalie's skirts. "Noooo!" she cried when two of Bienville's soldiers, uniformed in sweat-stained, ragged jackets with missing pewter buttons, came to pry her away.

Natalie inserted herself between Jeanne-Antoinette and one of the guards. "Wait!" she pleaded. "Let me have just a minute with the girl. Can't you see she is nothing but a child?"

She turned to Jeanne-Antoinette and cupped the girl's distraught face between her palms. "Listen, my sweet, it will be all right. You must believe me. I will do something. Trust me."

Then the soldiers tore Jeanne-Antoinette away from her. Concern for the child had kept thoughts for her own welfare at bay. Now her teeth dug into her bottom lip as the process of separation was begun again. At last the name she had given, that of her hairdresser Angelique la Croix, was called. She was to be sent to Nouvelle Orléans.

Relief swept over her. This was the new capital of the Louisiana territory, which extended thousands of miles northward. Surely in this city known as *la petite Paris* there would be enough educated citizens desirous of learning Italian that she could support herself. Perhaps she could even earn enough to send for Jeanne-Antoinette—if the child was fortunate enough to escape a forced marriage.

Natalie shuddered at the horror. Once more she searched the crowd of immigrants for Hervé. This time she was rewarded by the sight of his blond curls. Without thinking, she started toward him, only to have a squat sergeant, burned as dark as a Moor, grab her by the arm. She slipped from his grasp and thrust her way through the milling women toward the group of chained convicts. Behind her, the sergeant shouted in gutter French liberally streaked with imprecations. Her steps quickened.

She reached the brigand just ahead of the furious soldier and gasped, "Hervé, please, you must protect the child Jeanne-Antoinette! She is bound for a placed called Fort Rosalie."

His heavy brows wrinkled over the droll eyes that looked down at her with a puzzled expression, and she knew he was trying to recall the girl. Only now, looking at the brigand, did she realize that he had lost quite a bit of weight on the trip. His face was bruised, his upper lip swollen.

Bon Dieu, what had she hoped to accomplish when he was in chains, even more of a prisoner than she and Jeanne-Antoinette? She wasn't thinking logically anymore. She put her hand to her head, but her hand was jerked away and a fist cuffed her temple just hard enough to make her ears ring.

"Slut!" the sergeant said. "Disobey again, and you'll find yourself strapped to the whipping horse in New Orleans."

She had never been spoken to like that. Without thinking, she raised her hand to slap the insolent man, but in a flash Hervé stepped between the soldier and her. The brigand's chains clanked as his right arm drew back, his hand clenched in a fist meant for the soldier. The chains permitted no further movement.

"Not so fast, my big, tethered animal," the swarthy sergeant sneered, "because we won't wait for New Orleans. You can face the cat-o'-nine-tails here and now."

Natalie spun away to return to the women so that Hervé wouldn't know she had witnessed the look of futility and hopelessness and utter degradation that passed over his face.

With her portable trunk, the *cassette* that contained two dresses, two petticoats, six headdresses, and a few sundries, she set out with the other *émigrées* apportioned to this new Paris, New Orleans. The journey was something that she would remember as long as she lived.

The soldiers and their retinue of twenty-three brides threaded their way across terrain as soft as pudding. It was difficult to tell where the land and water met. The very air seemed soaked with water.

Natalie, who for once had looked forward to dusk and cessation of sunlight, found that the mosquitoes made even the act of breathing difficult. They clung like a black veil before her exposed face. She slapped vainly at the bloodsucking pests and continuously cast apprehensive glances into the impenetrable reeds around her for the legendary sixteen-foot alligators and the snakes that were said to hang from the trees like vines. The rain-drenched forests were alive with thousands of sandpipers, parakeets, and other marsh birds of brilliant hues that protested indignantly at the disturbance made by the passage of the humans.

Natalie knew she was going to hate the muddy wilderness, the enervating or, humid, subtropical climate, and the boggy forests that hid the precious sunlight.

That first night the soldiers had to build a platform to sleep on, for water covered the low, marshy land on which they were camped. The swarthy sergeant kept a lusty eye on her during a frugal dinner of salted beef and hard, dark bread, alleviated only a bit by wine. A thundering chorus of frogs kept her awake until late into the night. Sleeping fitfully, she worried about Jeanne-Antoinette. Such a child, but what could she do to help her? What could she do to help herself? She seemed as much a prisoner here as she had been at La Salpêtrière.

By the following day, the sojourners reached a bayou, a corruption of the Choctaw *bayuk*. St. John Bayou was a four-mile-long, narrow ribbon of sluggish water that interlaced the surrounding steaming delta and served as a backdoor to New Orleans. From the bayou, they followed an ancient Indian trail known as Portage of the Lost until they were within sight of the province of Louisiana's new capital.

The last vestige of hope died in Natalie's breast when she laid eyes on the sodden hamlet of New Orleans. Hacked out of the cypress jungle, it fronted the crescent-shaped bend of an immensely wide river named *Michi Sepe* by the local Indians.

New Orleans was situated in the midst of a flat and swampy ground thickly wooded and covered with canebrake. Its perimeter was palisaded and moated, with forts at each corner. The rough little village consisted of a few hundred wretched bark and cypress-slabbed huts with palmetto roofs. The streets, laid out in a grid, were bordered by alleged ditches that drained to a moat and elevated *banquettes*, causing the city blocks to be given the French term of islets, which they literally were.

Indeed, the entire town was an islet created by the *Michi Sepe*, or Mississippi River; Lake Pontchartrain, named for the frivolous minister of the marine; and the surrounding swamps. There would be little room for suburban growth like the *faubourgs*, or false cities, of Paris.

Men crowded the mud-mired wooden sidewalks to watch the procession of casket girls. Some doffed their tricornered hats, some whistled and hooted, and others from far-off outposts merely stared, hungry for their first sight of a white woman in years. Natalie estimated that there had to be at least eight hundred eager bachelors in the township that week.

As the females were shuttled toward the parade ground, the Place d'Armes, her nose wrinkled at the stagnant stench of the refuse floating in the open ditches. The Place d'Armes faced the river, and on the opposite side of the muddy parade grounds, also facing the river, stood a rude log church with a presbytery on the left and a guardhouse and prison on the right.

The log church was to be their final destination that evening. The *demoiselles* of the demimonde were locked up here for the night under the watchful eyes of the two Ursuline nuns, supposedly to preserve their chastity. As usual, Natalie slept apart from other females, who openly ridiculed her lofty demeanor.

Their attitude bothered her very little. It was her immediate future that bothered her a lot. The next day would see the beginning of the courting process.

"I want a military officer for a husband," came a whispered declaration through the darkness. Solange's voice. "They make good wages and will have pensions."

Natalie snorted to herself, thinking of the ragged uniforms of the provincial soldiers.

"Ah, but I have my eye out for an officer of the *compagnie*," said another female voice. "Just imagine the amount of property their concessions will have."

Swamp property, fit only for miasma, mosquitoes, and alligators, Natalie thought, this time with a certain pity for the woman's hopeful dreams that were soon to be shattered. Could they not see that only the strongest of females would survive in the godforsaken wilderness?

The fortunate few would be those who made their way back to France and the bordellos. She would be one of those who returned to France—when the timing was right, when the Duc d'Orléans was regent no longer.

As for her own dreams that night, they were foolish ones of creeping vines growing through the open windows and curling about her neck to strangle her. How she hated that junglelike land!

Early the following afternoon, the twenty-three brides, led by

Sister Marguerite, promenaded through the city streets. They were dressed in their best, one of the two dresses provided in their *cassettes*. The dresses were not very gay as they were made of brown or gray lutestring. Over these the women wore their cardinal cloaks with the hoods folded back, of course, to expose their pulchritude, such as that might be.

Natalie preferred her own gown, tattered though it was, and her own cloak. They were all she had to remind her that she had once been a human and not an animal.

The feminine entourage walked along the rue de Quai, a tree-shaded walk that led along the riverbank to where a small embankment had been thrown up to hold back the Mississippi's floodwaters. Across the river on the other bank towered dark, dense forests that abounded, so the soldiers said, with leopards, bears, and panthers. But fear of the wild animals didn't prevent the inhabitants from sleeping outdoors most nights.

It was on the rue de Quai that the men of the colony gathered in the late afternoons and evenings to sit and talk of far-off France, as the bright tropical moon hung above the forest on the opposite shore.

That afternoon the men did not talk of France but of the various attributes of the casket girls who coyly sashayed close by so that the bachelors could appraise them and make a choice. The women had the privilege, of course, of refusing any candidate, and they did not hesitate to ask questions of the embarrassed swains who paused in front of them.

"How many acres do you have cleared?"

"How many rooms are there in your house?"

"Does it have wooden floors? How many windows? Does the hearth draw well?"

"Have you a proper bed and plenty of linens?"

"Have you a horse? How many cows, pigs, and sheep? How about chickens?"

"How much money have you saved?"

Soldiers were posted at street corners to break up the periodic quarrels that broke out among the men over the casket girls. Solange, whose narrow face possessed pretty but brittle features, flirted openly with the cretinous sergeant who had accosted Natalie on the beach.

Standing apart from the others, Natalie studied the local suitors. Within the palisaded walls was a motley crew of Frenchmen, a few Swiss and Germans, and a sorry lot of abandoned aristocrats. She found most of them undersized, emaciated, and scorbutic. The more robust Canadians, who had come with Bienville and his brother to build the capital, were in truth more stalwart and they stepped out with a vigorous stride that the tropics-enervated Frenchmen lacked, but these men from the cold north all appeared to be unkempt churls who sported wild beards.

With a mere look, she refused the men who dared to approach her. If worse came to worst, she would become a domestic.

Seldom, however, did the other women chance refusing a suitor. They had come out for husbands and did not want to be among those who were passed over by the shuffling, staring males. An unwanted casket girl would be a tragedy, a fate sadder than that of a confirmed spinster, for she had publicly proclaimed her willingness to be chosen.

Ironically, the more comely of the *demoiselles* were passed over in favor of the plumpest girls. The bachelors wanted healthy partners who could be depended on to do their share, or a little more, of the work. A bad complexion or a squint could be overlooked if the figure was buxom.

This selection process continued over several days, with the men and women attracted to one another pairing off and wandering as far away as possible from the strict surveillance of the Ursuline sisters. Each day's outing brought forth a lesser number of females as the chosen brides were married off by the Carmelite priest in the crude little log church.

During this time, Natalie had ample opportunity to study the colonial society, and concern mounted in her as she began to realize that there was no demand for linguists. Or domestics, for that matter; slaves, better suited to the climate, were imported from the sugar stronghold of Saint-Domingue or the West Indies to do both field and house work.

When at last she admitted to herself what her only option was, her concern turned to fear, which lay heavy as sin in her heart. A fraudulent marriage.

On her fifth day in New Orleans, she surveyed what remained of the suitors. With so many bachelors in the vast colony, she still had her pick, though the combination of riffraff from French prisons and crude Canadians made for a doubtful selection.

She narrowed her choice to one man, whom she had noticed watching her each afternoon. Like herself, he had remained apart from the others.

Curiously, she selected a man as different from Philippe in appearance and actions as New Orleans was from Paris. He was dressed in a worn deerskin shirt decorated with porcupine quills that had broken and fallen off and fringed leggings. His black hair was too shaggy, and his bronzed face—clean-shaven, she noted—was so harshly angled that even the most generous could not have said it was a handsome one. Formidable was all that came to mind. The dolt was obviously tongue-tied, for he managed no more than a few mumbled words when, the day before, she passed him by, bestowing a somewhat formal smile on him.

In spite of these formidable drawbacks, the man had a prepossessing air about him that had initially caught her eye. When she overheard a prospective groom tell his curious bride-to-be that the man was a Canadian half-breed who owned property far north of New Orleans, Natalie settled on her choice. Claude Fabreville, should he ever learn of her second escape, would never track her down to the hinterland that stretched beyond New Orleans.

That the man she selected was a half-breed bothered her not at all. His character was of more concern, though it was pointless to worry if he was a wife beater or was stingy—or what he would demand of her in the marriage bed. Philippe had been loving. At least she had known joy in that part of marriage. If this man was at least kind, it was all she could hope for.

But how was she to make him choose her in marriage over the remaining *filles à la cassette*?

CHAPTER

10

SILENTLY AND ELOQUENTLY, Nicolas cursed François and the man's injured leg. If he hadn't felt responsible in a way for François falling onto the ax head, he would never have allowed his friend to badger him into such an idiocy, this enterprise on behalf of Hymen.

Accustomed to the silence of great forests or the thunder of mighty rivers that flowed through them, he disliked the shrill cacophony of New Orleans and its fulsome odors. For five days, he had endured the town while he inventoried the casket girls. A poor selection it was. Most of the women had to paint and rouge to hide the ravages of time and vice on their faces. The few who did not behave like strumpets were a frumpish-looking lot.

And François expected him to find a virgin for a wife from among these women who were to build a new world?

Toward afternoon, he once more stationed himself beneath the spreading shade of a cypress that bordered the rue de Quai. Soon, the *filles à la cassette*, accompanied by their strict duennas, the Ursuline nuns, ventured forth. As was becoming a habit, he looked for one certain woman. A drab, left all eyes by the hardship of the voyage. Her skin was yellow, and her dingy hair was almost the same washed-out shade.

Nevertheless, she interested him over the others. She made no effort to attract a husband to herself. And she walked like a queen, trailing her bedraggled, cast-off velvets through the muddy streets.

However, she was frail, almost skeletal. Totally unsuitable for the Louisiana wilderness. Also, she was too old to be out of one of the public orphanages, whose charges were at least given a modicum of training for housewifery.

Still, there was something about her. The way she walked . . . Without ever looking down, she moved as if she expected the ground to be ready and waiting for her. The smudges of dirt didn't conceal the fine bone structure. Her haughty carriage, the arrogant tilt of chin with that intriguing cleft in it—everything proclaimed her to be familiar with the *haut monde*. Perhaps a lady-in-waiting.

He had dallied long enough; better to settle on another while there was still an adequate selection. The wench behind her smiled invitingly at him. Her teeth were bad, but at least she was not as frail. He was impatient to be on his way back to Natchitoches. He made up his mind that when the wench passed by, he would engage her in conversation.

The opportunity was cut off by a cocky soldier, his hide permanently burned by the intense sun. Nicolas had noticed him earlier at one of the sooty taverns that hunched along the rue de Bourbon. The smoke-hazed rumhole was frequented by the buccaneers out of Saint-Domingue, men contracted by Bienville to help hack a town out of the cypress jungle.

Not twenty feet from him, the man stepped before the drab, blocking her progress. "Still too good, eh, for the likes of Sergeant Jacques-Girard Laval, fifteen years in the marines."

She shrank away from him, but her chin tilted proudly. "You are a magpie of men, monsieur."

The soldier's eyes narrowed with speculation, his voice dropped to a low mumble as if talking to himself. "Mayhaps what I hear is right. A marquise is hidden among the recruited *filles à la cassette*."

"No!" she gasped. Recollecting herself, she whined servilely, "I am here to seek a husband like the rest of the women."

The soldier's grimy hand latched onto her wrist. "Who would have skinny baggage like yourself?"

"He will." Her gaze swept in Nicolas's direction, her large eyes imploring. "He has spoken for me."

The burly, dark-skinned soldier swerved toward Nicolas. "What have we here?" he jeered. "One of the Canadian woodsmen, no less. And a half-breed to boot! You are not overly particular, demoiselle."

At that, Nicolas stepped softly out of the shadows. The sergeant was brawnier than he but not quite as tall. It would be an even match. "You wish to settle the dispute over the damsel?"

Jacques-Girard spread his hands congenially. "As you see, I'm unarmed at the moment." He nodded at the two weapons visible above Nicolas's sash, a tomahawk and knife.

"That can be remedied," he told the soldier.

"The tomahawk then," Jacques-Girard growled. "I know of the *coureur des bois*'s skill with it and want it in my hand rather than in yours."

Without taking his gaze from the soldier's eyes, he removed first the knife, then the tomahawk, tossing it haft first to the other man. Jacques-Girard caught it easily and began sidestepping, circling warily around him. Nicolas did the same but crouched more, balanced on the balls of his feet.

Beyond the soldier, some of the casket girls had gathered, along with their suitors, a nun, and several other curious citizens, including the drab responsible for the fight.

Nicolas, knife in hand, returned his concentration to his opponent. The soldier feinted with the ax several times, trying to draw him into a foolish lunge. Nicolas wanted to end the fight soon, before any of the soldier's comrades came to join the fracas. He taunted the sergeant with a swift parry that only nicked the flesh of the shoulder with a thin, red line.

Enraged, the man lashed out with the ax in a broad arc. Nicolas heard the sharp gasp of the woman in question. At the same time, he nimbly backstepped. A mere distance of less than an inch separated his chest from the ax blade. Foolishly distracted by her, he had not tested the ground behind him. His heel caught on an exposed cedar root. He went tumbling. Someone screamed. Like a tree cat, he rolled to his feet. His knife lay at the foot of the cedar.

Jacques-Girard smirked. "Just try to go for it, you *fils de putain*."

Slowly, Nicolas backed toward the tree. The soldier grinned triumphantly and sent the ax spinning at him. He ducked. The blade cut into bark but didn't hold. With a soft, deadly thud, it tumbled onto the ground.

Jacques-Girard had just made a mistake that a skilled woodsman would never make: he gave up his weapon. Nicolas snatched up the hatchet and advanced inexorably on his opponent. The soldier's eyes rounded with alarm. His stricken gaze darted toward the knife. Nicolas kicked it beyond reach. With that, the soldier reconsidered the odds and dashed into the midst of the surrounding bystanders.

Some of the women tittered, but most of the onlookers quickly shuffled back, clearing a path for Nicolas. He halted before the drab. She smelled of bilge water and needed a bath. Her eyes flickered from his face, no doubt appalled by its fierce look, to the ax in his hand. When her gaze lifted to his once more, he was certain that she was disgusted by it all, which surprised him slightly. Who was she to be contemptuous of him?

To his own disgust, he found himself tongue-tied again; he, who could quote Aristotle with a mouthful of pebbles as articulately as Demosthenes. He said simply, "Your ladyship?"

Her eyes snapped at the mockery that had worked its way into the tone of his voice. Only then did he notice their color, the shade of a lagoon at moonrise.

She looked about her with that lofty set of her head, and the remaining bystanders sheeped away. After they were out of earshot, she glanced back at him, twisted her hands about each other, stared down at her worn shoes with their tasseled drawstrings, then looked back up at him. Her eyes held a wealth of anguish.

Pity prompted him to assist her in speaking, but his own words seemed to trip over his tongue. "Marriage? You wished to marry?"

Once again, without intending to, he sounded mocking. Her eyes flashed a hot green. "*Mais non*, my lord!" she said, her voice dripping with its own sarcasm. "I've only come to this barbarous backcountry because I was bored at court." She snapped her fingers imperiously. "*Oui*, I wish to marry!"

He was struck by her curiously husky voice. A cultured voice; it held a quality one didn't forget. When he didn't immediately reply, she drawled, "Well?" For all the insouciance in her voice, her eyes, too large for the small oval face, betrayed her anxiety.

"My partner," he fumbled, seeking the right words and cursing his sudden lack of fluency, "is seeking a wife. He's injured his leg—and is waiting at Natchitoches. Several days' journey away."

The way she watched him while he spoke . . . *Merde*, she must find him dull-witted! "I'm to select a wife for him . . . and marry by proxy," he finished up. He waited for a barrage of questions.

She frowned. "Several days' journey, you say. How many days? Is this 'Naqui—' Is this place difficult to reach?"

He blinked, trying to digest the essence of her questions. Not one about the man's name, his worth, his age, what he looked like. Not any interest in the potential husband at all. "Seven days. Perhaps eight. And, *oui*, it is very difficult to reach." Perhaps that would dissuade her.

"I will marry this man."

Her alacrity to marry incurred his suspicion. It was his turn to question. "Do you wear the fleur-de-lis on your shoulder?"

"*Mais non*," she said, indignation hoisting her chin another notch.

"Are you . . . a maiden, my ladyship?"

"Of course." So she could blush. "*Monsieur le Sauvage*," she added testily.

His lips twitched at her reference to his Indian heritage. And his white heritage? All the anger and bitterness and hurt came flooding back to him like the St. Lawrence after the spring melt. Somewhere in France, a male du Plessis, a Philippe du Plessis, held title to the Fur Company of Canada, to what Nicolas had rightfully earned for his own. That in itself was negligible. It was the right denied him to call himself a du Plessis that twisted inside his guts like a worm destroying an apple.

He studied the young woman's face, which was turned up to his disdainfully. She was no dormouse. The church's claim that the bride convoy contained only reputable young women was ludicrous. One had only to listen to the guttural French of the women to be certain of their previous environs. But this one, with her cultured voice, its smoky quality . . . Perhaps she was bagged with the other strumpets by mistake. He shrugged mentally. He was in haste to have done with his errand.

The next morning, the nuptials were performed with all dispatch at the little Church of St. Louis by the Carmelite priest, with one of the Ursuline nuns as a witness. The casket girl's face was pale as first Nicolas, then she, repeated the words that married her by proxy to François de Gautier. She looked as if she would cry at any moment. He supposed that all women felt like crying when they married.

If he were marrying, he knew he would certainly feel like crying. He was a true wanderer; he felt driven to move about. The same faces, the same things, day after day—for him, nothing could be deadlier.

She gave the *curé* her name, Angelique la Croix, in a low, almost inaudible voice.

When it came time to sign the register and he expected the woman called Angelique—Angelique de Gautier now—to make her signature with an *X*, he was surprised at the flourish with which she wielded the quill. Her hands, he noted, were slender and without calluses, but the nails were dirty and jagged.

He made no comment, merely lifted his brow. François had a surprise due him. His bride was certainly an enigma.

When his turn came, he scrawled first the name of François de Gautier and then his own, as proxy, using the surname of Brissac. This time, it was she who was surprised by his obvious education. her mouth opened, then she shut it and, like him, said nothing. She gave him a quick sidelong glance as sharp and penetrating as the point of a needle.

With her small dowry chest flung over his shoulder and her hurrying to keep up with his long strides, he set out for the palisade's rear gate, which led to Bayou St. John less than half a league away.

New Orleans was an island in a vast wilderness uninterrupted except for a scattered archipelago of modest plantations and hamlets. Somewhere canebrake was being burned to clear acreage for a concession. The burning cane crackled like rifle shot, and the young woman drew closer to him. His lips twisted wryly. François would repent of his impulsive desire to marry ere the month was out.

Nicolas found the canoe where he had cached it beneath a layer of tough, fibrous cane laid horizontal by the tropical typhoons that periodically blew in off the Gulf of Mexico. He pulled the canoe from its matted covering and pushed it off the bank into the bayou, where it rocked gently. Inside, along with blankets, his leather "possibles" bag, and a fine French pistol of large bore, was his rifle, swaddled in hide to protect it. He thrust the pistol through his sash.

He moved the rifle aside and held out his hand to François's bride, this time with mocking gallantry. "Your ladyship."

Automatically, she placed her small hand in his big one and, lifting her skirts, stepped aboard. How calmly she accepted his homage, his exaggerated attention, as if it were only her just due.

He shoved the canoe, which could almost float on dew, out into the sluggish water. With her sitting straight-backed in the prow as if it were a throne, he paddled along the shoreline, past the cattails that lined the bayou, the wisteria, and the sweet olive, whose delicate fragrance filled the air. Fortunately for the woman, the mosquitoes were few because of the wind, which quickened and sucked down between the forest-banked shores and encouraged the leafy tops into a susurration of gossip.

For much of the morning, she sat silently in the prow, for which he was thankful. As the remnants of civilization drifted behind, a look of relief eased the strain about her mouth.

They still had to cross lakes Pontchartrain and Maurepas before they could enter the Mississippi by way of the Amite and Iberville rivers, which meant finding a place to camp before twilight.

He picked a place to beach the canoe that offered high ground for a camp. She waited sedately in the prow for him to help her out, then made no effort to assist him in dragging the canoe ashore or packing the blankets and rifle up the bluff. She sat under a tall evergreen, her legs drawn up beneath her, while he procured bark and made her a shelter. His patience wore thin when he gathered the firewood and she watched from her dais of soft needles. She obviously wasn't going to do squaw work.

He dumped the load of firewood before her. "Do you think your ladyship could build a fire while I find us something to eat?"

She looked up at him, surprise at his disgruntled tone blanking her expression. "Of course, *Monsieur le Sauvage*," she said after a moment.

Ignoring her sarcasm, he proceeded to pile a small amount of the dry wood. Taking a small piece of cedar the size of his finger and a stick of mulberry, he put the two side by side between his hands and spun them together.

Soon a little fuzz spun out of the cedar and caught fire. The young woman, who was watching him intently, said, "Why, it's like making chocolate froth."

"I've never made chocolate froth," he said drily, and was surprised when she responded with a smile of amusement. Despite the accumulation of filth, she was very attractive. He wondered what she would look like cleaned up.

Such thinking was dangerous and he set himself to instructing her how to feed the fire so that he would have a hot bed of coals for cooking their supper.

Taking his fishnet of linden-bark fiber and lines equipped with hooks of fish bone with him, he started for the bayou. "Where are you going?" she asked anxiously.

He looked over his shoulder. She was a pathetic sight with her hair straggling down from the coronet of braids. He contained his impatience. "I hope to feed us. You will be safe enough here."

For more than twenty minutes, he fished in the bayou without receiving even a nibble. Behind him, the reeds shuffled. He pivoted to find her descending the slope. Thoroughly out of humor, he demanded, "I thought you were to tend the fire?"

She lifted her chin in the way that was beginning to grate on his nerves. "I did not care for all the smoke."

He managed to keep the irritation from his face. "In that case, we won't have enough coals for broiling the fish."

"The fish must be caught first" was her placid rejoinder. "Anyway, I already placed the wood on the fire."

"All of the wood?" he demanded more sharply than he intended.

She bristled at the implied rebuke. "Wasn't it for burning?"

"Yes, but only a small amount at a time."

"La! There is nothing but wood. All around us. One should not have to grumble over using too much."

Sacre bleu, but he was saddled with an irresponsible child-woman!

The tug at his line diverted his irritation momentarily. By the time he hauled in the catfish, he reconsidered explaining to her that the problem was not in sparing the wood but in the danger of a big fire and its resulting smoke attracting the notice of a foe. He could only hope she would learn from his example before they arrived at Natchitoches. She would have enough adjusting to do as it was.

She sat on a log and watched him clean the fish with a little grimace of distaste. After he broiled the fish, he served it on two clean pieces of bark. He passed one to her. "I hope you are not overly fastidious."

At his last choice of words, a look of perplexity etched a faint line above the bridge of her little nose. "You have been educated, monsieur."

He shrugged. "Somewhat."

She made an imperious little gesture for him to be seated. Mulling over that gesture and what it implied, he dropped cross-legged on the ground across the fire from her.

"Where?" she asked between daintily nibbled bites.

"A priest-turned-soldier by the name of Jean-Baptiste tutored me." He forestalled further questioning by retaliating, "Where were *you* educated?"

Immediately, her face closed over. "Here and there."

He set the bark plate aside. Bracing his forearms on his knees, he stared across at her and said, "I don't think you have told me the truth."

"I have not lied," she said grandly.

He knelt on one knee and ran a finger about a small footprint she had left in the soft earth. "Shall I expound on the effect that childbearing has upon the way a woman holds her legs when she walks—and the evidence left by her footprint?"

Her sharply indrawn breath was the only sound she made. He wondered what was going through her mind. Meanwhile, deep in the somber glades of the forest, the noisy chatter of squirrels could be heard.

"No," she said at last, quietly, thoughtfully. "I would prefer if you said nothing."

By remaining silent, by saying nothing to François of what he knew, he would be aligning himself with this woman. Yet it was not his place to accuse her of not being a virgin before François.

He rose and began to bank the fire, then passed her a blanket. It smelled, but no worse than she did. "If a storm should blow through," he told her, "the bark lean-to will keep you dry."

She watched him roll up in his blanket on the far side of the fire, then she did the same, stretching out beneath the bark shelter.

When he thought she was asleep, she surprised him by asking, "Who are you?"

With a sigh, he rolled over onto his back, hands behind his head. "Nicolas Brissac."

"I assumed that," she said with a hint of exasperation. "I didn't mean your name, but *who* are you?"

"Should I ask the same of you?"

She didn't respond, but he knew that it was too much to hope that she had fallen asleep.

"I am a fur trapper, a French-Canadian by birth."

"Ah, yes, a *coureur des bois*." He could hear the smile in her voice. "Those daring cavaliers of the bark canoe and bold vagabonds of the woods and waterways. You see, your reputation has spread even to France. Tell me about your fellow woodsmen."

He deemed the subject safe enough, and boring enough, to put her to sleep. "I am afraid we are a superstitious breed," he said quietly. "We believe the northern lights are marionettes that dance across the night skies. The magical aurora lights . . . they are something one never forgets. They whisper of the legend of the *loup-garou*, the hound of the skies that appears when death is near."

He paused, his thoughts drifting to other things, other people and events of his life, when he became aware that his intriguing tale had put his listener to sleep at once.

Dawn's sky was tinctured with a flamingo hue by the time he broke camp the next morning. As before, his charge sat silently in the canoe's prow. Sometimes, he pulled the pirogue ahead by hauling on the overhanging live oak and willow branches. By midafternoon, the scarcely moving Iberville River, which was more like a bayou, emptied them into the Mississippi.

François's bride sat absolutely still, her eyes large with excitement. She had looked upon the Father of Waters from the New Orleans levee, seeing the Mississippi only from a cross-section view. Looking upriver from a canoe was like gazing on an eternity of inexorable water. From that viewpoint it was a cumulative effect; the more one gazed, the more one realized the awesome power of that monster of rivers.

Nicolas passed her some smoked beef to still the hunger pains of midday and put his efforts into paddling upriver by skirting the edges of the mighty current, where the paddling was easier along the shoreline. Sweat ran in rivulets through the valleys created by his flexing muscles. Overhead, the sun burned cruelly, rapidly pinking the clear ivory pallor of the young woman's cheeks and nose.

Sometime later, they passed a high bank where a tall pole stood. "What is it?" she asked, pointing to the stick, which was painted red and adorned with fish and bear heads.

"*Baton Rouge*. It marks the boundary between the Bayogoula and Houma Indians, *ou les rouges*."

"Indians?" She peered up warily through the dense growth that lined the bluffs.

"They're friendly enough. They're allies of the French. We'll make camp with them tonight."

She didn't look too receptive to his plan, but he wasn't about to explain that with bands of Chickasaws reported wandering in the area, he felt it safer to seek out a friend or two. He would spare her the grisly story of the Chickasaws' recent raid on the *Côte des Allemands*, the German settlement twenty-five miles north of New Orleans. Only the week before, he had come upon a scalp of long blond hair posted to a tree as a warning against other immigrants.

They reached the Houma village just about dusk. Set along a fingerlet of the river, the village consisted only of two or three rows of simple cane huts thatched with cornhusks. There were no palisades to protect the village. When he entered it with the woman called Angelique trailing close behind, the Houmas came out to greet him. He could tell the woman was repelled by them— by their facial tattoos, their filth and odor. They bathed daily but were in the habit of standing directly in fire smoke at night to drive off the mosquitoes.

One of the older men greeted them with the customary "Ho." He was dressed in a calico shirt and breechcloth and wore a Spanish conquistador's tarnished breastplate, perhaps as a badge of distinction. Like the rest of the males, his hair was worn short. Nicolas understood only certain phrases and had to listen intently to the welcoming speech. At length, the man finished, and Nicolas responded with his thanks of a proffered hut for the night.

A comely maiden in a fringed tunic woven from grass stepped forward, smiling to show teeth that were painted black. Beside him, François's bride recoiled, her eyes wide, and she moved even closer to him, almost touching his buckskin sleeve.

That she trusted him with her safety was foolish on her part.

This was not a civilized village of France; he or some other back-woodsman could easily take her for the night and leave her for the Indians' pleasure the next morning. He didn't like this burden of responsibility that both François and she had placed on him.

They followed the Houma maiden to a hut that was nearest to the cornfield. The hut was bare except for the bed: four short posts planted in the ground with a reed frame covered with a deerskin.

His charge glanced at the bed, then at him. "We are expected to share this bed?" she asked in a tight, little voice that was as smoky as the room's cane torch, which burned to ward off the mosquitoes.

A *diablerie* came over him and he said, "Either this, your ladyship, or you share the bed of one of the Houma men. I told them you were my woman to spare you that."

He had expected her to swoon or to rail at him, but she said with feigned indifference, "Well, I suppose one *sauvage* is no different than another."

The frank humor in her eyes and the twitch of her lips implied no offense. For the first time, he noticed that her mouth was wide and untemperamental. Just when he thought he understood this woman, she showed him another dimension. He could turn about her question of him: Who was she?

He swept her a courtier's deep bow. "I thank you for the compliment, your ladyship."

At that moment, a crone of an Indian woman entered with food, *sagamite*, and he offered the bowl to the young woman. "Should I ask what it is?" she said, eyeing the cornmeal mush warily.

He sat on the ground, his back propped against the cane wall and said, "Nothing more than a porridge with beans and maybe a little bear fat or deer tallow for seasoning."

She sat also, arranging her skirts about her in a grand manner, and followed his lead in eating from the bowl with her fingers. He wolfed the porridge down, but she ate with dainty, little gestures. Still, he realized with a start, she was actually enjoying the novelty of the moment.

Without meaning to, he began telling her about an old Chi-pewyan who had scooped down what he thought was yellow porridge in one gulp. "It was mustard my father had brought with him from Montreal. Tears poured from the old Indian's eyes."

Her chuckle was rich and throaty, but a moment later she asked, "Your father was a Frenchman?"

"*Oui*," he replied shortly, and rose, putting an end to the conversation. "I am going to the stream to bathe. Do you wish to do so also?"

There was longing in her gaze, but she shook her head firmly. It made no sense. For someone so fastidious about everything else, why wouldn't she want to wash off the offensive dirt and smell? He shrugged and turned to go, but she called out, "Wait, please." She looked around the dimly lit hut uneasily and said, "I'll accompany you."

Outside, the last of the sunlight had faded, and the sky was a deep chocolate. Along the trail, he detected the scent of violets, warmed by the sun earlier that day. The cool glitter of the evening's first stars was caught in the acacia's feathery branches that bowed over the pooling stream. At the bank, the young woman turned around. Most certainly she had lain with men . . . yet she was embarrassed by the sight of a male's nudity?

He stripped down and plunged into the stream. The water was warm but refreshing. When he surfaced and shook his shaggy head, spraying droplets like a wet dog, her back was still to him. Whistling a trill of clear, liquid notes, he fell to scrubbing himself all over with sand from the stream bottom.

"Tell me about . . . my husband," she said, her voice a mumble.

"He is from the province of Gascony." He tried to think of what else a woman would want to know. "From a noble family. He had a commission with the navy and ended up in New France."

"Is he . . . a good man?"

Nicolas strode from the water and collected his buckskins for scrubbing in the stream. "He is honest enough, if that is what you mean." The rock he rubbed briskly over the britches accomplished little in the way of washing, but at least it got rid of the ticks.

She let out a little noise of exasperation. "I mean is he—would he— Oh, I don't know! I don't know why I came to this barbarous wilderness!"

He struggled into the wet buckskins so that they would dry

on his body and not shrink. "You came because you were seeking a husband, did you not?"

"Yes—yes, of course."

He didn't believe her. He wasn't sure what to believe yet. He wasn't even sure why he carried through with the farce of occupying the great hide bed with her a half hour later. He preferred the ground to the bed. Then why the need to taunt her with his nearness? Because she interested him as no other woman had done, except perhaps for Mother Marie. Hands clasped behind his head, he thought of his father's lover. The two women were entirely different. Mother Marie had been warm and loving; this woman was cool and distant. He smiled to himself, thinking of how she lay stiffly at the far side of the frame bed. François would have his hands full with this woman.

The journey resumed the next day. The air was sultry with a slowly gathering storm, and sweat poured from his frame. Whining mosquitoes circled him and the young woman, getting into their ears and noses. She sat in the prow and suffered silently.

Fatigued by the taxing labor of paddling against the powerful current, he made camp early that day high above the Mississippi, picking a site with a spring well back from the river, which would provide clear, fresh water. With the dusk, the mosquitoes became relentless. The woman barely touched the roasted clams, so busy was she swatting at the voracious black cloud.

Taking pity on her, he delved into his "possibles" bag, which held, among other things, an awl for stitching leather, a .50-caliber-bullet mold for lead balls, and a surgeon's folding lancet.

Despite her misery and preoccupation in combating the winged insects, she eyed him askance with a great deal of interest. When he hunkered before her with a gourd in one hand, she wrinkled her nose and asked cautiously, "What is it?"

"Bear grease, your ladyship." He smiled. "It will ward off the mosquitoes and block out the sun's rays."

"Uuhh!" she protested as he dabbed his fingers into the unguent and smeared a strip across her upturned nose. She shrank from his touch, but he caught her clefted chin in one hand and set about the task of covering her delicate features. Beneath his steady gaze, her lashes lowered, hiding whatever thoughts went on in that unusual mind.

He had known intimately several wives of officers stationed at Montreal, women with a modicum of education. They were bored women who had found him different and, therefore, intriguing. He understood this and understood them, perhaps better than they did themselves.

This woman, however, was more difficult to understand than a Huron war belt.

The following day, he made better progress against the current. He could tell the woman chafed under the application of the rank bear grease, for several times her fingers came up to touch her face, only to drop abruptly. At least she never complained at being cramped in the canoe for such long periods of time. For this he was grateful. He had enough of a problem scanning the shoreline for signs of unfriendly visitors: a dislodged stone, a piece of moss scuffed off a log, a mark left by a canoe in the mud. The Natchez nation, in whose territory they were now traveling, had lately been unreceptive to the French settlers around Fort Rosalie, named for the wife of Comte de Pontchartrain.

At midmorning, rain clouds scurried across the sky, and he was forced to stop in order to erect a shelter for the woman. He stood his musket upright in the canoe and instructed her to hold the stock in place while he draped blankets over it. The storm blew down the river, pelting his face with rain and making vision difficult for him. Yet he was determined to make Point Coupée and the Rivière Rouge that day and have done with the Mississippi.

From beneath her shelter, the woman flashed him a humorous glance that left him stunned. What manner of woman was this child-woman—educated, possessed of an aristocatic bearing, yet unchaste? A courtesan? Not likely, for she lacked the blatant seductive manner generally associated with such women.

The bushes along the shore were dripping wet. As there was no profit in landing, they ate their supper aboard, after which he resumed paddling through the night while she slept blissfully.

By the next day, they were far enough up the Rivière Rouge, and, exhausted, he broke camp well before dark. François's bride still sat like royalty, her back straight as a musket barrel, while he gathered firewood and erected a lean-to for her near a stream. However, when he went off to hunt, she deigned to assume the task of fire tender, going about it as if she were offering him a great boon. He grinned to himself. He suspected that, having had an opportunity to observe him at the task, she wouldn't make the mistake of burning all the wood at once this time.

He located a clearing deep in the forest and, for twenty minutes, sat absolutely motionless. Eventually, the squirrels mistook him for a stump and scampered about his feet. The tip of the knife blade between his fingers was released with an economy of movement. Foreseeing problems with his charge's delicate sensibilities, he skinned and gutted the squirrel on the spot. It dawned on him that his proprietorship was about to end and that the days of arranging for her comfort would soon be over.

When he returned to camp, she wasn't there. Instantly, his eyes searched the ground for signs. Her small footprints indicated that she had left the clearing alone. He followed the trail, which headed toward the stream. Too late, he realized her intent. After that layer of rancid bear grease, she had naturally wanted a bath.

For a long moment, he stood concealed in the mesh of grapevines and other undergrowth, watching the flash of white as she redressed, her back to him. He should have returned to camp; he should have had no interest in her. She was François's wife. But he had been surprised by the perfect symmetry of her body. Her soft, delicate shoulders tapered to the rib cage; below, the waist narrowed about the spine, then gradually flared into the rounded curves of the buttocks. Her hair had been freshly washed and, wet, shimmered like old gold. Her porcelain skin reflected the last leaf-filtered shafts of soft twilight before she drew the gown up over her shoulders.

Her cataclysmic beauty was irrefutable.

In the act of lacing up her bodice, she turned unexpectedly. In that paralyzing moment, she saw him—and he saw the shriveled, red brand of the fleur-de-lis burned between her soft breasts. The brand of the felon, the mark of the unredeemable criminal.

A deep flush washed over her. Seeing the shock in his eyes, she said, "Monsieur, let me explain."

"No explanation is necessary, your ladyship," he said abruptly, and turned from her.

CHAPTER

II

THE FLAT LAND GAVE WAY TO gradually heightening bluffs. Sharp, irregular hills twisted incessantly, giving the land the likeness of a great sheet of parchment that had been crumpled and then spread out loosely. The vast, highland forests of moss-covered oak peppered with pine and hickory had been cleared along the edges of the Bayou Amulee at its confluence with the red-silted river.

Here, on the Rivière Rouge, a paltry dozen log houses clustered within musket shot of the palisaded fort, named for the local Natchitoches Indians.

Natalie's glance took in the sparseness of the settlement that had been a bustling outpost even before Nouvelle Orléans was founded, and she despaired. How would she manage to endure even a year in such an isolated spot? The very air on the Red River was contaminated by the horrid effluvia of alligator urine and excrement.

She had never known such blasts of heat or such heavy rains that left the air only more steaming and hostile. Perspiration oozed from her pores morning and night. The mosquitoes left her flesh raw. With all the trees, there was no sunlight.

Then the dismal thought was chased away by the intrepid Nicolas Brissac, who helped her from the canoe with his exaggerated chivalry and a mocking "Your ladyship." His voice was a softly modulated baritone. She had expected—well, less cultivation.

Her chest in hand, she followed his broad back as he set out across the immense meadow bearing his rifle and blankets. His air of detached self-command had garnered her reluctant respect. Behind that formidable face, she instinctively sensed something fine and dignified. She liked his slow, attractive smile. During the journey, she had come to hope that he would become her ally, a friend she badly needed.

When he surprised her at her bath, she had thought to tell him the truth—to explain why the brand of a felon was burned between her breasts and why she was masquerading as a casket girl. But just how well did she really know the *coureur des bois*? Did she dare to take that chance when after a few words from him, she could find herself returned to Paris and Fabreville's hands?

Now the *coureur des bois* could only think of her as both a strumpet and a female felon. Would he tell his partner the truth about her? His partner—*bon Dieu*, the man was her husband! Could Philippe ever forgive her for his deception? Yes, she wanted to believe he would, that he would understand that need to survive, when one will do anything.

Every so often, she saw from the corner of her eye a woman come to stand in an open doorway, watching. Before one rustic cabin, two boys ceased rolling a cane hoop to run inside with the news of the female newcomer. Surely by the morrow the arrival of François's bride would be on the tongue tip of every inhabitant within fifty leagues.

François de Gautier. What was the man like? Nicolas Brissac had told her very little. What would his partner think of her? It was a little late to worry now. She was glad that she had bathed and neatly rebraided her hair. The sun had put a little color back into her cheeks. She wished she had donned the other dress in her trousseau. The one she wore was already stained with dirt and sweat, and its hem was tattered by the trail's undergrowth.

Still, with a little dignity and a great deal of effort, she would carry off this farce. Mentally, she vowed to make the best of a bad situation. She owed this unknown bridegroom at least that much.

As she followed Nicolas Brissac through fields spangled with

pansies and pink buttercups and phlox, leaving the sparse settlement behind, her bravado slunk away. What if this man François
. . . She had known only Philippe . . . How could she give herself
to another . . . Adultery . . . But what else could she have done?
She had sold herself.

She berated herself, rationalized to herself, then berated herself
again.

Her footsteps flagged, and Nicolas looked over his shoulder.
His glance took in her panicky expression. His own was inscrutable. "You have made your bed . . ." He left his condemnation
at that.

He started off again, cresting another wooded hill, and she had
to hurry to keep up. Now the *coureur des bois* followed an old trail
made by the buffalo on their winter migration from the plains of
Spanish Texas to the river bottoms of Louisiana.

With resolution, her legs strode quickly and accurately, like
shears, snipping off the distance between her and her purpose,
that of seeking a place of temporary refuge.

At the bank of a trickling stream, perfumed with the fragrances
of irises, orchids, and water lilies, he halted and pointed out that
place of refuge, her new home. In a field of tangled copses squatted
a solitary cabin framed with heavy cypress slabs. The high-pitched
roof was thatched with palmetto. Drawing closer, one could see
that the lime-washed house was chinked with a sort of adobe
mixture of mud that was reinforced with deer hair and Spanish
moss.

With a thudding heart, she followed the *coureur des bois* to the
heavy batten door. He pushed it open and called out, "François?"

"Enfin!" called an undoubtedly masculine voice.

Nicolas held the door open saying, "Your ladyship."

She preceded him inside and looked around. She was impressed
despite the rusticity. The pleasant smell of freshly chopped wood
still clung to the place. The walls were wainscoted, and beams
and rafters of cypress logs, marked by hatchet and adze, looked
sturdy enough to withstand the fiercest of storms. But sunlight
spilled through a window, sheathed by linen in lieu of glass panes,
to reveal what could have passed for a pigsty.

The room contained only a heavy trestle table flanked by two
benches and a simple cupboard. The tabletop was piled with

bones and scraps and earthen plates, begrimed with old food spots. Clothing and animal skins littered the puncheon floor, and a large fireplace overflowed with cold ashes. The fireplace backed the other room. With trepidation, she stared in that direction.

"Go on," Nicolas prodded quietly, "greet your husband."

With faltering steps, she walked through the adjoining doorway. His knee propped up, a man lay stretched out on one of two narrow beds. He raised himself on both elbows to stare at her, as she did at him, both assessing one another.

What he thought of her, she could only guess. She had not the artifice of *maquillage;* still, she knew that she had once been attractive to men. Now smudges of fatigue darkened the skin beneath her eyes. Her face was blistered, her flesh a mass of mosquito bites. She had lost so much weight, she was little more than bones. No, she certainly didn't look her best.

As for him, she was pleasantly surprised at the inventory: a rakish moustache above a mouth that she decided she definitely liked; lustrous, curly brown hair that was receding slightly at the temples; and brown eyes that looked like they could sparkle when not beset by uncertain curiosity. In addition, the man was fashionably dressed in nankeen britches and a soft, buff chambray shirt.

Nicolas's mockery was more pronounced than ever, along with his curt bow. "François, allow me to present your bride, her ladyship Angelique de Gautier."

The silence stretched out, and, waiting, she felt like a spring flower shriveling in an unseasonable cold spell. Then François broke the silence with a burst of hearty laughter. "You did it! *Par Dieu,* you did it, Nicolas!"

Then he turned his attention to her and said with a charming grin, "Mademoiselle, what a great pleasure."

He attempted to rise, and she held up a palm. "No, monsieur, it is not necessary." Lifting her frayed skirts, more from habit than to keep them off the mud-caked floor, she crossed to the bedstead and dropped a curtsy worthy of Versailles to her husband—her second husband, that was.

When she lifted her head, he was watching her with a startled expression. "Monsieur, please allow me to thank you for offering me your name and your home." She delivered her best recitation.

"I shall do my best to honor you and your home as long as . . ."

He stared at her, his finely delineated brows lifted, waiting. "Yes?"

" . . . as long as—as I'm permitted," she finished with a pretty little shrug.

"*Par Dieu!*" He slapped his knee, winced at the unexpected pain, then grinned again. "You'll be permitted to grace my home forever. Has the good abbé at New Orleans not said as much?" He paused, as if at a sudden loss for words, and ended by saying, "Please, be seated, mademoiselle."

Feeling ridiculously shy, she sat on the bed opposite him. Her back was regally straight, as the nuns of Poissy had always insisted, and her hands were clasped lightly, belying the tension that churned inside her. Her stomach actually felt ill.

Nicolas made to depart, but Francois forestalled him. "It's been hell these three weeks, *mon ami*, trying to get around with this wretched leg. Several times the commandant's wife sent a stew or some other dish over with her Moorish wench." His face colored, and he added quickly, "And our smoked meat kept me for a while. But the larder is empty now. We're out of food, candles— *Tiens*, but I'm glad you returned when you did!"

Silently, she blessed François for adroitly easing the strain of their first moments together by including Nicolas. Nicolas she was acquainted with, certainly, while François was still an unknown element. She and François needed time to adjust to the unusual situation. The presence of a third person smoothed the way while the two of them took stock of one another.

Obviously, Nicolas didn't agree. He set down her trunk and planted his hands high on his flanks. His slashing brows clashed in a line over his high-bridged nose. "It won't work, François."

Her heart knocked against her rib cage. She looked sharply at the *coureur des bois*. Was he going to tell François what he knew about her? If François rejected her, where would she go?

"What won't work?" François asked, a frown beginning to furrow his high forehead.

"The three of us living together. I'm going."

"No!" She and François echoed each other.

Knowing that it was *she* who was the uncertain element of the three, she deferred to François. He pushed himself upright, grimacing at the pain incurred, and said, "Winter is coming on, and there's no other place for you to stay. Besides, we're business partners, aren't we?" He indicated his leg. "I can't run a business on my own in this condition."

Nicolas drew a deep breath and let it out all at once in an exasperated grunt. "François, our business relationship does not extend to include our private lives. This—this situation can only—"

"Just stay through the winter. Come spring you can start your own place. I'll be well enough to help by then."

The half-breed flicked a glance at her, but she schooled her face to impassiveness. "All right." He sighed. "For the winter only."

With that, he excused himself, saying he meant to hunt before the light became too poor to get off a good shot. As there was no food in the house, François could no longer reasonably detain his partner.

After Nicolas's departure, François flashed a roguish grin that she found utterly appealing. "There is no point in skirting the issue, is there, mademoiselle? This is a highly uncomfortable situation, *n'est-ce pas?*"

"We know so little about one another," Natalie murmured, which was the wrong thing to say.

He manuevered himself onto one side and, resting on his forearm, said, "We shall just have to approach this in as civilized manner as possible. Please, tell me about yourself. What prompted you to become a *fille à la cassette?*"

Bon Dieu, but she was so tired already. Now months of having to watch her every word, of having to carry through with this charade, stretched before her.

What had prompted her, he asked? Pain, fear, death, an unborn child. What would he think of the last part of her confession? Hysteria bubbled in her throat. Unrepressible tears welled in her eyes.

He stretched out a slender, well-formed hand and said, "Don't try to talk now. I forgot that you have endured a long, difficult journey, that you have crossed an ocean in order to make a home for yourself."

She placed her hand in his, and, holding it gingerly, he said, "Perhaps it will help if you know a little about me. I was born the youngest of four sons. Since the family estate and title went

to my oldest brother, I was left the choice of either the monastery
or the military." He grinned devilishly. "Needless to say, I didn't
find the former an attractive option."

She dimpled at his jest, and he said, "Ah, that's better." The
upturned corners of his own mouth sobered. "Mademoiselle—
Angelique—I miss the home of my youth. I can never go back,
but I can establish my own home here. I can create my own
dynasty in this new world. It is important to me. Can you understand?"

"*Oui*," she replied uneasily.

François lay on his back, staring up into the darkness of the
rafters. His leg throbbed, but if he tried to shift his weight, he
feared he would awaken the young woman. Still fully dressed,
she slept soundly in the bed across from him.

Nicolas had done remarkably well in his choice of brides. François had expected very little in the way of beauty; in fact, he had
not been overly concerned with the looks of a prospective bride.
His active sexual appetite would have overcome such a minor
problem. He sincerely enjoyed women, but he had taken a wife
to make children with, not to love.

Yet a woman of uncommon beauty slept near him. She had a
low, smoky voice that he caught himself listening for. In addition,
she was intelligent and cultured, with a certain . . . what would
one call it . . . a *je ne sais quoi*.

The last puzzled him. He was not naive enough to think that
all the casket girls came from good families, as the church proclaimed. He had expected to take a wife from one of the girls of
destitute families or out of the orphanages, one who found the
alternative to the alms house appealing. Doubtless, there were
also prostitutes and criminals mixed in with the lot, as Nicolas
had warned. But a young woman of gentle breeding . . . He
couldn't quite fathom it.

Perhaps she was running away from a difficult situation at
home—a tyrannical father, a jealous sister, an arranged marriage
with some doddering widower.

He had not pressed her for her story. There was plenty of time
to learn. A lifetime.

He heard Nicolas rise from his pallet in the kitchen and quietly
leave the cabin. So, his partner couldn't sleep either. The man

needed his own wife. Of course, the *coureur des bois* would never be one to settle down. Like that timber wolf he had had, the half-breed in him would prowl in the dark of night in search of a female to ease his lust.

The sassy black wench of Commandant St. Denis flitted through François's thoughts. He groaned with the unrelieved need that quickened in his groin. This damnable leg would keep him from exercising his husbandly privilege for a while to come. His hand began the easing of his own lust.

CHAPTER

12

"**M**ERDE!" FRANÇOIS SWORE from the other room.

Natalie, kneeling before the hearth, tensed. During Nicolas's three-week absence to fetch a bride, the wound in François's shin had worsened considerably. Since her arrival, he had been running a low-grade fever. She felt helpless and, as was becoming a habit, had to rely on Nicolas.

She didn't think she could have made it through those first few days without the trapper's help around the house. She knew nothing about cooking or cleaning or making soap. With François abed, she depended entirely on Nicolas to instruct her. He did so, without making her feel imbecilic—a few quiet words here, a mere gesture or example there. Only by dint of washing and rubbing and scrubbing with the aid of lime had she been able to make the cabin clean. In the meantime, he continued to do most of the cooking.

With no candles or lamp oil that first night, he had ingeniously captured a few remaining fireflies in a bottle as a source of light. The next day, he had procured lamp oil from somewhere. Yes, she was lucky that François had convinced him to stay until spring.

Even now, Nicolas sat at the table, preparing a salve of beaver

oil and castoreum. She stirred the salt water in the kettle suspended over the fire. The warmth of the dancing flame flushed
her skin—or perhaps Nicolas was responsible for her heated flesh.

She was always conscious of his presence, of his contempt
veiled by the polite formality customary between strangers.

How long would he keep his counsel?

He rose from the bench and crossed to stand behind her. Civility demanded that she acknowledge him. She looked up over
her shoulder into the fierce countenance. "Is the salve ready?"

He held out the wooden bowl. Not for the first time she noted
his hands—a ferocious power in repose. "Between this and the
salt water, his pain should be eased and the swelling drawn out."

She made no move to take it. "You're not going to—you want
me to apply it?" she whispered.

Impatience flickered across his face and was gone just as quickly.
"He's your husband."

"He's your partner! If you hadn't left him alone, this might
not have happened."

He crouched on his haunches before her and stared her down.
Her eyes lowered. "Sooner or later," he said in that low, won-
drously musical voice, "you're going to have to assume *all* of your
wifely duties. You owe him that much."

Reluctantly, she accepted the bowl. Tending François would
require a certain intimacy that even after a week had not been
established between them. She was extremely grateful that his
injury prevented him from fulfilling the husband's role. Nicolas
was right, though. Eventually, when François was well again
. . . Of course she could make herself go through with it. She
would close her eyes and will herself to believe it was Philippe
who held her and made love to her.

Philippe, with the laughing eyes. Philippe, dear one, what kind
of torment are you enduring at this moment?

Her eyes misty, she turned from Nicolas's steady regard back
to the salt water that was beginning to simmer. "I'm quite aware
of my wifely obligations," she said briskly. "It's merely that François is not a small man, and I will need help in removing his
pants."

How matter-of-fact she sounded.

"I'm sure you've had some experience in that area, Madame de
Gautier."

She shot to her feet. Her hands trembled so that the offensive-smelling salve in the bowl she still held quivered like marmalade. In her eyes flashed the unquenchable spangle of green-silver. "Don't you dare to judge me!"

He rose, too, and braced his hand on the fireplace's stone wall, blocking her path. "Do you think the lie you're living is fair to François?" he asked in a low voice.

She lowered her lids against the contained force of the jet-black eyes. The *coureur des bois* was entirely too perceptive. "François wanted a wife to care for his home—and bear him children," she whispered. Her head raised, and she glared back at Nicolas. "The first I am attempting to learn. I've never done this sort of thing before."

"And the latter?" he asked lightly. "Don't tell me you've never done *that* sort of thing before. Your footprints give the lie to your words. You are no virgin, Madame de Gautier."

Her hands tightened about the bowl, and he said, "Uh-uh. Don't do it. Caring for François's wound is more important than salvaging your pride."

"François hasn't demanded the latter," she hissed, her conscience prickling her to justify herself, then blushed furiously at her bald admission.

"Angelique," François called feebly from the other room.

Nicolas lifted a raven-wing's brow but shoved off the wall, allowing her to pass.

She went to kneel before François. His fine linen shirt was damp with sweat, as were the curly locks plastered to his forehead. She smoothed them back, thinking that he was a very attractive man. She should be grateful that she hadn't married a hunchback. She certainly could be worse off. Furthermore, he hadn't forced himself on her.

Sooner or later, as Nicolas had starkly pointed out, that moment would have to be reckoned with.

François captured her fingers and held them to his feverish lips. The intimate gesture startled her, and she tugged her fingers away reflexively.

He managed a faint smile. "I suppose in my condition I'm not quite the gallant I usually am with the ladies."

"No, that's not . . . It's that I'm still adjusting to being a bride," she finished lamely.

"*Eh bien*," he said, closing his eyes again. Then he managed, "Aristocrat for a frontier bride . . . moves like a marquise."

Her breath caught. He couldn't know. He was slightly delirious, that was all. Nonetheless, her innate mannerisms were giving away her background. Soon, she would have to come up with a plausible story.

She chewed on her lower lip, uncertain just where to begin in tending François's wound. Philippe's valet had always dressed him. She knew nothing about men's clothing. She could unfasten the buckle at the knee, she decided, and push the pants leg up past the wound. That way she wouldn't have to remove the pants entirely.

The garter and ribbed cotton stocking came away easily, despite François's moan of protestation. For a moment, she stared at the finely muscled leg, crisply matted with hair. Having never really seen Philippe's body in bright daylight, she felt a little brazen staring at François even though nothing more than his leg and foot was exposed.

There was something sort of improper about a naked foot, she decided, marking the way hair was sprinkled across the long toes. The corners of her mouth crinkled at the humor of the situation. Why did she feel like giggling uncontrollably at times of gravity? Really not at all the behavior of a lady of strict upbringing.

Her smile faded when she pushed the pants leg up over the knee. Common sense told her that the red streaks, radiating upward from the puckered and purple horizontal slash, weren't part of the normal healing process.

"Nicolas," she called, trying for François's sake to keep the panic from her voice.

When Nicolas didn't reply, she told François she'd be right back, but he was drifting in and out of a feverish sleep and wasn't cognizant of her leaving.

She hurried to the front door, where she spotted Nicolas out near the willow racks used for drying the green animal skins. He was dressing a turkey he had killed earlier that day. "Nicolas, come quickly!"

His easy, loping strides covered the intervening distance with incredible speed. When he reached her, she whispered, afraid that François would overhear, "The wound—it doesn't look right!"

He flung the headless turkey on the table and strode into the other room. "What the . . . ?" François said, lifting his head when the other man bent over him to prod the puffy flesh around the wound gingerly.

Nicolas pressed him back down. "Just be still." Then he ripped at the pants leg, tearing the broadcloth up to the groin. His lips tightened at what he saw.

"Bathe the wound in the salt water," he told Natalie, his voice carefully void of emotion, "but forget the salve. I'll be back shortly."

As she tended the wound, François cursed weakly. He seemed rational, but she didn't think he realized how serious his condition was. When the bowl was empty, she rose to leave.

"Stay and talk to me," he said with an irritable scowl caused by what she knew had to be pain. He closed his eyes, adding, "A month abed can drive a man crazy."

Compliantly, she sat on the opposite bed and folded her hands. "Tell me something about Natchitoches, about the people who have settled here," she said, taking the initiative.

"No. I want to know about you. You're my wife," he grumbled, "and I don't even know what part of France you're from."

"St. Maixent. Near Poitiers."

"Your family—were they of the nobility?"

"My father was in the military," she hedged. "My mother died when I was a child."

"But your family must have had money," he persisted. He opened one eye and turned his head to fix her with an accusing look. "You have been brought up to move in *le beau monde*."

"Yes . . . I was."

How could she admit the truth without actually admitting she had married him fraudulently? "My father was a soldier," she improvised, "not a businessman. He made a poor investment, we lost the family estate. So . . ." She spread her hands. "I decided to put my name on a list of the *filles à la cassette*."

"But surely you had a suitor, some *gentilhomme* interested in marrying you?"

"*Tiens!* None for whom I formed a *tendre*. My fancy was captured by the idea of seeking my future in the New World." Her lips twisted ruefully, thinking of John Law's inaccurate representation of the New World. *Ciel*, she couldn't wait for the day it was safe to return to civilization!

François's eyes had closed again, and she wasn't sure if he was merely thinking about what she had told him or if he had drifted off once more. Unaccountably, she felt suddenly guilty about her deception. When that day came for her to leave, how would she explain her deception to François? What she was doing wasn't fair to him, but then what had happened to her had not been fair either.

She could only resolve to do her very best by him while she lived in his house. After all, he had wanted a wife. What if he had taken one, only to have the poor woman die on him, which was entirely possible in such a godforsaken wilderness. He would have been cheated just as much by the woman's death as by her own departure.

She knew she was rationalizing again. She was tired of chasing the problem around like a dog after his tail. For just a moment, she stretched out on the bed, thinking that the mattress of Spanish moss, bolstered underneath by one of cornhusks, was surprisingly comfortable.

Light, seeping through nameless tormented dreams, awakened her. Sleepily, she sat up to see Nicolas hunkered next to François's bed, applying some kind of ointment on the wound from a small leather pouch. A betty lamp burned on the mantel, casting flickering shadows on Nicolas's stern and severely chiseled features.

François stirred and muttered peevishly but didn't awaken completely.

She swung her legs over the bed and went to kneel beside Nicolas. "What is it?"

"Rosehips."

She looked up into the cruel charm of his eyes, liquid black with absurdly long lashes. "Where did you learn about medicine?"

He glanced down at her and went back to rubbing in the ointment. "It may surprise you to learn that Indians have as much medicinal knowledge as apothecaries. Perhaps more, for they don't stupidly apply leeches to an already ailing man. Or prescribe ass milk for an infected leg, as Louis the Thirteenth's doctors did." He frowned. "But I confess I don't know enough. I think it's too late to counteract François's infection."

"What will happen?" she breathed.

He sat back on his heels with a grunt. "The leg will have to come off."

"No!" she gasped. "You can't do that to him."

"If I don't, he will die."

"Can't we wait? The ointment might work."

"We'll wait through the night." His lips flattened over his perfect teeth. "After that . . ." He rose to stand over her. "Go back to bed. You're going to need the rest, no matter what happens."

She tossed restlessly the remainder of the night, with the sounds of François's incoherent mutterings worming through her dreams. It was still dark when she awakened, but dawn was nearing. When she went to kneel before François's bed, she could actually feel, without touching him, the heat radiating off his body.

"Bon Dieu!" she whispered, frightened.

From the doorway, Nicolas said in a tired voice, "He's worse, isn't he?"

She looked over her shoulder, unable to force the truth to her lips. Within the dim room, Nicolas's eyes glowed like black coals. In that long moment of sharp silence, before dawn breaks and nature awakens, they stared at each other, seeing the same agony in one another's expression.

Daybreak's gray-pink light seemed to seep suddenly into the room. "There's always the chance he might get better," she pleaded.

"And if he dies?"

She hung her head and sighed. "What do you want me to do?"

"Heat more water." His gaze swept around the room, searching, then settled on her. "Your petticoats will have to do for bandaging. Tear them into strips. And wait in the other room until I call you."

She rose and set about doing as he had instructed her. Twice he came and went. Once François called to her, but when she checked on him, he seemed to be drowsing again. Then Nicolas closed himself up in the room with François. She could hear occasional murmurs and, two or three times, companionable laughter. One hour stretched into two before the door opened and Nicolas beckoned her. He was naked to the waist, the skin over his torso walnut-brown and taut. She looked away, embarrassed by the sight.

"We're ready." She heard the dry amusement in his voice.

When he moved aside for her to pass through, she smelled the brandy on his breath. He smiled grimly. "François and I have been drinking to His Majesty's health."

She glanced at François. His eyes were closed, but beneath the moustache his mouth was parted in a half smile. He snored softly. A blanket covered his nakedness. She glanced back at Nicolas and only at the moment noticed that an ax dangled in his hand. Her stomach rolled over.

"Let's begin," he said.

"Nicolas, I can't."

His free hand manacled her upper arm. "You will, Madame de Gautier."

He released her and went to François, yanking the blanket from his body. "Not another toast," the man murmured drunkenly. His lids flickered as he were trying to lift them and didn't quite have the strength.

Nicolas reached for a nearly empty bottle that sat on the mantel. Below it, a fire blazed, and the head of another ax was wedged among the pulsating coals. "Give him the rest of the brandy."

She took the bottle, knelt at the head of the bed, and lifted François's curly head to hold the bottle's mouth to the hot, dry lips. More of the amber liquid spilled over the fever-cracked lips than was swallowed. While she did this, Nicolas bathed the wound with more salt water.

"*Bien*," he said. "Now come around to this side. I want you to lie across his chest, to hold him down when he starts to struggle."

"Nicolas, for God's sake!"

"Do it!"

She did as he demanded. When she eased her upper torso over François's chest, he gave a little grunt. His lower lip sagged with the brandy's relaxing effect. She looked from him to Nicolas. He nodded. She pressed down on François, and Nicolas raised the ax. She turned her head and squinched her eyes shut.

She heard the swish of the descending blade, abnormally loud in the room. It sliced through the air with an awful swiftness. Its impact was instantly followed by a violent jerk of François's body. An inhuman, bloodcurdling shriek pierced the air, echoing and reechoing against the cabin walls.

Nicolas grabbed the other ax embedded in the fiery coals. At the same time, she gripped the bed frame so that the writhing body beneath her wouldn't buck her off. She saw that her hands and one sleeve were splattered with blood. Nauseous bile rose in her throat. *Bon Dieu*, if only the ear-shattering howling would stop!

She might have made it through the ordeal, but when Nicolas immediately applied the sizzling-red ax blade to cauterize the open stump, she smelled the reeking odor of seared flesh and the memory of another time, of her own flesh burning, shriveling, smoking from the white-hot brand, flooded into her brain and washed out all consciousness.

When she came to, she saw bright blue sky splotched with leathery green leaves. The magnolia tree she had noticed earlier that week. The few fragrant, hand-wide white blossoms that had surivived the passing of summer had reminded her of her greenhouse cape jasmine in a way.

She turned her head. Nicolas sat in the grass, watching her, his back against the magnolia's trunk. "You carried me here?"

He nodded.

"I'm sorry," she said. "I wasn't of much help, was I?"

"You did what I wanted you to, you held François still."

"Is he going to be all right?"

Nicolas rubbed his jaw. "Probably. Physically, at least."

She sat up. A dead leaf clung to her hair, and she brushed it off. "Physically?"

He fixed her with his obsidian glare. "I mean that his body may heal more rapidly than his mind. With a leg gone, he may feel that part of his manhood is gone also. It happens that way sometimes."

Her brow knitted, and he said roughly, "Do you understand what I'm saying? Do you understand that you may have to help him regain his confidence in his masculinity?"

She nodded jerkily.

"I wonder if you do," he mused irritably. Then, "I'll be blunt, your ladyship. Whatever you've done with other men to entice them, you may have to do with François."

"I have never enticed men!" she exploded.

He sighed and plowed his fingers through the shaggy black hair where it had swung forward across his jaw. "I apologize. If we're to get through the winter together, we must call a truce."

"I am not a prostitute—or a criminal, despite the contrary evidence," she said, staring listlessly at a waxy white flower far above her. "I am innocent. You must believe me. I have only done what I had to do in order to survive."

When he said nothing, she looked at him again, her eyes pleading with his to understand. "Haven't you ever had to do something that on the surface would condemn you before the world, but to do otherwise was unbearable?"

"Yes," he said after a moment, his eyes bleak. "I had to kill my father."

At the admission, her breath rattled in her throat. He laughed drily. "The brandy, I'm afraid, has loosened my tongue. Normally, I make it a rule never to drink anything stronger than table wine."

"Why?" she rasped.

"Because I do and say things I generally wouldn't."

"No, why did you kill your father?"

She knew he was wrestling to control his emotions. It seemed as if several minutes passed. His iron will won. "It was a *coup de grâce*," he said simply. "Better immediate death than slow, tortured death."

CHAPTER

13

Large snowflakes floated like puffs of dandelions against the gray winter sky. Shivering, Natalie pulled the shutters closed. "So much for John Law's tropical paradise," she muttered.

Nicolas looked up from the shaft of wood he was whittling, the fragrant wood shavings scenting the cabin. His close scrutiny made her nervous. Lately, he watched her as if he expected her to sprout wings suddenly. "St. Denis claimed the winters are usually temperate," he said mildly.

"That's because he wants us to become a permanent part of his settlement," François said. He scowled as he shifted his lower torso on the stool so that he faced the fire. "He'd tell us anything if we'd work with him." He slapped his thigh just above where the empty pants leg was knotted and said, "Though just what kind of work I could be expected to do is beyond me."

Nicolas rose and went to hunker before François. He held the wooden shaft next to François's other leg, measuring. "With a peg, you'll do just about all you did before, *mon ami*."

"Ah, yes," he responded with a cynical smile after Nicolas returned to the bench and his whittling. "Maybe even more. With a peg leg, why I could apply for court jester. Just think of the amusing—"

"Stop it!" Natalie spat. She took the bowl of salve and pine resin she had spent the morning preparing and knelt before François. She looked up at him, her eyes snapping. "I find you a handsome, intelligent, and charming man—when you're not feeling sorry for yourself. Now let me look at your leg."

"Leg?" he asked. Beneath the moustache, his mouth twisted in a mocking smile. "What leg? You mean stump, don't you, Angelique?"

She still wasn't accustomed to the name of Angelique, and when she didn't respond immediately, he said, "Say it. Stump. What an ugly sound the word makes!"

She ignored him and set the bowl on the bench so that she could unknot the empty pants leg.

Embarrassment at what she was about to do mottled his face. "I can take care of myself!" he told her, and slapped her hand away. Her fingers caught the rim of the bowl, and it spun and flipped onto the floor, where the salve oozed onto the rough planks.

She shot to her feet. "Then you clean up the mess yourself!"

She grabbed her cloak, stalked past Nicolas, who silently observed the scene, and flung the door open to storm outside. The air was sharp and crystal-fine. Somewhere in the distance, cane cracked with the cold, sounding like gunshots.

Earlier that winter, Nicolas must have taken pity on the loneliness of her isolation, for he had allowed her to accompany him while he checked his traps. Patiently, he had showed her how to move through the tall cane, as thick as a man's wrist, backward, so the face was protected from the sharp, wet blades.

Creeping quietly through the bramble bushes, she dogged his footsteps as he followed his traplines. The first three were empty, but the next contained a raccoon. "*Par Dieu!*" Nicolas muttered, kneeling beside the animal that bared its teeth at them. "Nothing but a coon."

Astonished, she watched him set it free and reset the trap. He looked up and explained, "Its meat wouldn't have been worth chewing."

A smile struggled to her lips. "I think, Nicolas Brissac, that you're tenderhearted."

He shrugged and grinned, one of the few that he allowed himself. "The coons seem almost human."

Living in close proximity with him that winter, she had come to realize that his detachment masked a capacity to be amused by the absurdities of life. His presence made the strain of François's mercurial temperament more bearable.

She held out a palm, caught several soft flakes, and watched them melt. With nowhere in particular to go, she walked down to the stream. The sun set more quickly at this time of year, and already the eastern sky was darkening with dusk. In the stark quiet of the late afternoon, the stream's gentle trickle was soothing. She followed the water's meanderings, heedless of where or how long she walked. Gradually, her anger subsided. In retrospect, she could see that François's actions were understandable, natural.

But, *ciel*, how could she live under such tension for almost a year? She'd go crazy first. What had happened to her cool demeanor that had always amazed everyone but Philippe?

"*Philippe.*" The whispered word lingered on her lips and was gone, swallowed up by that vast wilderness, with no one to hear it. She might never have said his name, he might never have existed.

The months of carrying on the charade were taking its toll on her nerves. Was it only January? It seemed like at least a year since she had stepped onto Ship Island. God, she was so alone. And lonely, with nothing but Nicolas's friendship to ease the days. Even that he proffered sparingly and seldom.

She put her fingertips to her temples and rubbed until the panicky, trapped feeling ebbed. Everything would work out, she told herself. Patience.

The wet snow was seeping through the leather stitching of her shoes, and the sky was darkening rapidly. She forced herself to retrace her steps back toward the cabin. The wick of the oil lamp had been turned down low. François was absent, and the door to the other room was closed. Her gaze went to the floor. The salve had been cleaned up. She crossed to the door and tapped lightly. "François, will you talk to me?"

"Go away," he said, his voice muffled.

Nicolas sat with his back to her, still whittling. At that moment, she resented his calm, his detachment. None of what had happened was of her making, yet remedying it was her responsibility all of a sudden.

"What can I do?" she demanded of him. She circled around to face him, bracing her palms on the table. "You heard François. He won't even talk to me. What else can I do?"

He studied her eyes. Did he expect to find an answer there? "Well?" she asked. "You always know what to do." She knew she sounded childish, but she couldn't help herself. For her, there was no respite, no escape behind a closed door. Night after night, she lay across from François, afraid that he would want her, ashamed of her relief that he did not call for her in the darkness.

"What you have is cabin fever," Nicolas said. "Being penned up for months at a time makes everyone edgy."

"Not you," she bit out.

He set aside the knife and the shaft he was carving and stood up. "Come here."

She tilted her head, puzzled. He nodded reassuringly. She moved around the table until she stood directly before him. His mahogany-colored hands began pulling the wooden pins from her bound braids so that they swung free against the small of her back. She looked up into his face. "What are you doing?" she rasped.

Hands on her shoulders, he rotated her to face away from him. His fingers worked at one braid, loosening it little by little. Then the other. She held her breath, waiting. Then his fingers began to comb through the snarled tresses gently. After a few minutes, what he was doing relaxed her, and she felt the stiffness literally flowing from her bones. Her head lolled back. "That feels so good," she murmured.

His fingers paused. "Your hair—a lovely color, like a tapestry."

Praise from Nicolas was rare. She was always astonished by the nuance and articulation reflected in his voice. She almost turned to look at him but didn't have the courage. "Thank you."

His hands lifted the heavy white-gold mass, sifted through the strands, and let them fall into place once more. "With your hair loose, you don't seem quite the remote queen. Go to François. Now. Go to him and . . . seduce him."

His words were a dash of cold water in the face. Reality washed over her. She turned to stare at him. His expression was unreceptive. "You know what I am, Nicolas? I am one of those Turkish houris. In order to survive, I must please my *maître*, mustn't I?"

"I'll quote you, Madame de Gautier. 'You're feeling sorry for yourself.' "

She felt like slapping him. Her fingers clenched against her palms. She got control of herself and said, "You're right, of course. I'll go to him."

She closed the door behind her and leaned back against it, her breath harsh in her ears. Across the room, she could see François's shadowy bulk, stretched out in sleep on the bed. He was a good man, as Nicolas had told her. She could have been much worse off in marriage to someone else. But she was already married. Philippe . . .

Putting thought behind her, she began to undress, her fingers mechanically working at her basque's fastenings. The gown slithered to the floor, and she stepped out of it. Her undergarments drifted behind her as she crossed to François's bed. The mattress crunched beneath her weight, and he stirred restlessly. She lifted the bearskin and eased herself down alongside him. His naked skin was warm, his snoring a gentle sound in the darkness.

Oh, dear God, how could she do it? She took a deep, steadying breath. Leaning on one elbow, she gingerly laid her hand on his chest. It was broad and thickly covered with hair, unlike Philippe's smooth, velvety skin. What did she do next?

The image of François's severed leg, the reddened skin shriveled and puckered, intruded on her numbed mind. She shivered with repulsion. If she loved him, she knew that it would not have mattered. But she didn't, and it did.

"Your hand is cold, Angelique."

She jumped at the sharp reproval. "François," she begged, her voice barely above a whisper, "I can't be your wife . . . in all ways . . . unless you help me."

His hand gripped hers so that she thought her fingers would crunch. "I don't want your pity."

"It's not pity," she said sharply. "I just don't know how to go about—"

"Making love to a one-legged man?" he sneered, and flung her hand away.

"No! That's not what I meant."

"I assure you, it's no different." His voice cracked, and words poured out in a raw whisper. "I may be an oddity, but, God, oh, God, Angelique, I'm still a man. I'm still a man!" he cried vehemently.

She lowered her head and brushed his lips with hers. His breath sucked in. In that moment, she forgot her own fear, her repulsion, Philippe. Beneath her hand, François's body went rigid. She tentatively stroked the furred chest and kissed his temple, then his eyelids, which were tightly closed.

"Angelique," he said huskily. "Angelique, Angelique. It's been so long." His lashes were wet with tears.

She could pretend.

She took his hand and placed it on one soft breast. He made no move to caress her; she paused, uncertain, then began to rotate his hand over her breast until friction aroused the nipple.

He groaned.

"François, make me your wife."

His fingers closed over her breast, hurting her slightly, but she made no sound.

"Yes, yes," he mumbled, and bent his head to her nipple. She gasped when he pulled it into his mouth. It had been so long for her, too; so long that her breasts had forgotten the pleasure that could be had.

But his mouth deserted her aching flesh, and he rolled over atop her. She stilled, waiting. His breathing was loud, irregular, in her ears. For long seconds, there was only his breathing. Then he threw back his head and let out an unearthly howl. "God! Damn you, God!"

He shoved her out from under him. "Get out, Angelique! Get out!"

The snow melted, but drizzling rain mixed with occasional sleet continued to fall during the following weeks, and Natalie wondered if spring would ever come. The tension in the cabin was stifling. She knew that Nicolas was aware of what had happened the night she had gone to François. How could he not be when François's shouted banishment of her from his bed had rung in her ears. Even if Nicolas were deaf, François's coldness toward her ever since was obvious.

How François must hate her; she was a symbol of his impotence. It would be best if she left, if only for his sake. She knew

Nicolas would be relieved. Her presence had disrupted their friendship. As it was, whenever weather permitted, he stayed away during the daylight hours, trapping or hunting with his bow of acacia wood and quiver of reed arrows. With her gone, he would have his bed back and wouldn't be forced into building a place of his own, come spring.

Spring. Come spring, the chestnut trees would be blossoming in Paris. She yearned for the things she had taken for granted: a night at the opera, a hothouse camellia in winter, *café au lait*, good wine. One day she would go back, one day . . .

Late in February, on a day when the rains had ceased but the sky was left overcast with one last threat of a winter storm, visitors arrived. She stood at the door watching them approach, their red clothing flashing among the dead brown of the trees on the stream's far side.

"François!" she said. "Visitors!"

He looked up from where he sat, fastening the wooden extension to his leg. Uncertainty played across his handsome face. She knew he wasn't ready to face anyone. He had only just managed to walk on the stump without wincing when the wood rubbed against flesh not yet fully callused.

When she turned her attention back to the approaching visitors, she saw Nicolas off to her left, loping from the drying racks toward the cabin. "Did you see—" she began.

He cut her off, saying brusquely, "Four of the men wear the uniforms of the Royal Musketeers."

She blanched. Her fingernails dug into the door's wood.

"What do you think they could want?" François asked, his high forehead wrinkled. "Do you think they're investigating St. Denis's smuggling activities?"

"They want me," she said tonelessly. A terrible fear grabbed hold of her spine and rattled it. Her gaze darted from him to François like a moth in a frantic search for a safe place to alight. They would now be rid of her.

François glanced at Nicolas, then switched his gaze back to her. "Why?"

"Tell him later," Nicolas said. "The soldiers—"

"The furs!" François said. "Hide her beneath the furs."

Stunned by François's unexpected protective attitude, she could only watch as Nicolas yanked the bearskin from the bed and returned to enfold her in it. Sweeping her up, he strode out of the cabin. Even bundled in the shaggy pelt, she could hear the muffled voices of the soldiers drawing nearer. Moments later, she was dumped on a pile of furs in the lean-to. She wiggled about, easing her body's cramped position, and he warned, "Be still!"

Her concealment pressed down on her as he added more furs atop her. "Nicolas, I can't breathe!"

"Shut up, and you'll have enough air."

She didn't know how long she could stand it before panic would make her dig her way out of the furs frantically. She tried to think of other things, wondered what had become of Hervé. And Jeanne-Antoinette. Was Madeleine still imprisoned? And still writing pornography?

With the coming of spring, the smelly pelts attracted flies. One found its way down to where she was burrowed and buzzed loudly near her ear. She tried to swat at it, but she couldn't move her hand up that far. Then she heard voices growing louder and froze.

Above her, the pelts were poked with something, and a high-pitched voice said, "Furs of this quality will provide felt hats for some time to come. His excellency will be pleased to learn that this province is not a total loss."

"*Hélas!*" cursed another man. "My trip was a total loss."

"I don't think His excellency will be too disappointed," said the first.

"*Eh bien*, I suppose you're right."

Their words grew indistinguishable as they moved on. When she didn't think she could stand the physical constraint another second, the pelts were thrown back and she was rolled from the bearskin. She blinked at the sudden light. Nicolas sat on his heels, studying her.

"They've gone?"

"François told them you had not taken to the domestic life of the colony, that you had run off with a Spanish trader."

"They believed him?"

"Who knows? I think they were tired of looking for you."

She shifted uneasily under his scrutiny. Behind him, she saw François hobbling toward the shed. She rose and, with shaking hands, brushed the dirt from her skirts and tucked the loose tendrils about her nape under her comb.

Nicolas didn't relent. "So why would an emissary of the king, accompanied by four musketters, come all the way from France solely in search of a thief named Angelique la Croix?"

"I, too, am curious," François said, joining them. His eyes narrowed on her suspiciously. "You're no mere thief, are you?"

She went absolutely still. Her severe composure fell like a mantle over her. Her head poised on her neck in a way that indicated, as no word could, that the righteousness of her position was beyond dispute. She was finished with lying. "Angelique isn't my name—it's Natalie. And I am the Marquise de Marchesseau."

She saw that the name meant nothing to them, as she had expected. That part of her secret, her marriage to Philippe du Plessis, was safe. "The Marchesseau family estates were taken from me by unusual circumstances. A relative, Claude Fabreville, who wanted control, issued a *lettre de cachet* against . . . my family. I was imprisoned and unjustly scarred with the brand of a thief." Unconsciously, she touched the woolen material between her breasts. "To escape, I signed on as a *fille à la cassette*. That is all there is to tell, all that I wish to tell."

François looked stunned at her revelation. Nicolas—he never allowed his features to express his thoughts, but she was aware that he knew that was not the whole story. He knew that she was not a virgin, that she had borne a child.

How long would he keep his counsel?

CHAPTER

NATALIE ARRANGED THE DRIED lavender in the basket on the table. François had mentioned that he liked the fragrance. When he had been just a name without a face, it had been easy to enter into her deception. Now, every time she sat across the table from him, she felt such awful guilt. One day, she would have to confront him with the truth of her misdeed.

With a basket of laundry balanced on one hip, she stepped outside. The hated country of exile now looked like a fairyland, a veritable Eden. The peach and plum trees were in bloom, and the April breeze animated the waving patches of delicate white and pink. The ripening grapes glistened in the morning dew like scattered jewels, and new magnolias scented the air. Beyond the corrals Nicolas had built, a tangled, sweet-smelling hedge ran wild in a most amiable way.

She lifted her face to the sun, reveling in its warmth. If she must be an exile from Paris, there could be worse places, she decided. Though this No Man's Land was supposed to be dangerous, a haven for outlaws and thieves and cutthroats, she had seen only a few bands of Indians, passing single file across the field on their way to the San Antonio Trace. François had reassured her that they were harmless enough, that they were allies of the French.

She certainly couldn't complain about her life there. After all, she was treated well by her husband. Second husband, she reminded herself with a twinge of conscience that threatened to ruin her perfect mood. And husband in name only.

She also reminded herself that he could have sent her back with Fabreville's emissary and soldiers, and hadn't. She still didn't know if François believed her. Or, for that matter, if Nicolas did. Of course, one never really knew what Nicolas was thinking. To feel that one knew Nicolas Brissac was only to fool oneself.

Even with him off somewhere in Texas, hunting wild horses, the strain between her and François had not eased; if anything, it had intensified without Nicolas's calm presence to serve as a buffer. For six weeks now, she and François had skirted each other, avoided looking at one another as they ate at the same table, and made only the most superfluous comments. He became spuriously irritable if she attempted to ease his tasks in any way, preferring to do everything by himself.

Nicolas's absence was easier on her in a way, for his uncanny perception made it difficult to fool him. Relaxing her masquerade was more difficult around him. She smiled wryly, thinking that sometimes her efforts at pretense only provided him with secret amusement.

She went back to draping the freshly washed clothes over the bushes to dry. She never complained about the hard work, about the way the small of her back ached or about her red, roughened hands. She may have been a *grande dame* and had been waited on by a multitude of servants, but she had also been branded a felon and had lived through that hell on earth at La Salpêtrière.

Over at the lean-to, François worked with the furs, packing them for shipment to New Orleans, and from there on to France. The sunlight reflected off his red-brown curls. He raised his head, and his gaze locked with hers before he turned away. He was a truly handsome man, she mused, and when he smiled, he was charming and disarming.

She tried to imagine Philippe's handsome face—and couldn't. Perspiration beaded on her brow. Her inability to recall the man she loved frightened her. She dropped the wet gray dress and stood erect, looking around her. The land had the power to make one forget. The rolling hills and innumerable, log-jammed rivers and misty swamps and limitless trees blotted out the existence of civilizations beyond.

She wouldn't let it happen to her; she wouldn't let herself forget Philippe and the beauty of Maison Bellecour and the Paris theaters and . . . Oh, God. God!

Reality was here. Reality was Nicolas's splendid height. Reality was the thud of François stomping around the house. She covered her face, drawing deep breaths.

"Natalie? Are you all right?"

She looked over to where François sat, watching her. When she nodded, he shrugged indifferently and went back to his work. She knew, though, that he was not indifferent to her. How long before his injured masculine pride goaded him into making her his wife in all ways?

The neighing of mules in harness interrupted her thoughts. Both she and François pivoted toward the sound. A string of seven mules forded the stream one by one, driven by Nicolas, who was mounted on a sturdily muscled Spanish mustang. He rode the prancing animal magnificently, she thought, recalling her father at the head of his troops, easily controlling his nervous mount.

At once, she and François deserted their work. François, waving both arms above his head, hobbled toward the mule train as fast as the artificial leg would permit. Unaccountably shy, she hung back to watch Nicolas dismount and greet his friend.

François slapped Nicolas on the back, and the two men conversed volubly as they strode toward her and the cabin. She waited until they neared and then said, "Welcome back, Nicolas."

The half-breed's eyes rapidly searched her face. Had he been hoping to find some sign in her expression that she and François had reconciled their differences? If Nicolas was contemptuous of her for passing herself off as a virgin, what would he think if he knew that she was a married woman twice over?

Despite the seriousness of her deception, she had to smile, and Nicolas smiled back, displaying the perfect white teeth, the only thing physically perfect about him. That wasn't true, she thought, as she preceded the other two into the cabin. He had a superb physique that the worn buckskins couldn't hide: tall, lean, with ropy muscles. That realization, something that hadn't occurred to her in all the time she had spent with him, suffused her pale cheeks with a delicate blush.

While François questioned Nicolas with the first enthusiasm he had demonstrated since the amputation, she warmed the stew over the banked embers, adding a pinch of the pungent, ground sassafras plant to it.

No longer did she recall with longing the pleasure of being waited upon and served instead of doing the menial labor, as she now did. If she could have realized the commonplace experiences she had once taken for granted and now forgotten, she would have been astounded, so easily had she accommodated herself to her environment.

"How did you manage it?" François demanded, exhilaration animating his face and brightening his usually lifeless eyes.

She felt the same way; after six weeks of seeing no one but François, six long weeks, day following upon day, without variation, Nicolas represented communication with the outside world. He represented excitement and a change of pace.

"I sold the wild horses the Comanches helped me capture to Mexican merchants in San Antonio," Nicolas explained between bites. "With the profits, after I paid off the Comanches, I bought bars of silver from the Mexican mines, more skins, and, of course, the mules."

Mexican mines . . . Comanches . . . San Antonio. To her, the names conjured societies, people, civilization. Eagerly, she waited for Nicolas to elaborate on his journey, but he was the master of brevity.

"Tomorrow, François, we'll purchase silks and cotton goods from the traders at Natchitoches and resell them either in Nacogdoches or San Antonio."

Impatience got the best of her. "May I go? May I go with you to Natchitoches tomorrow?"

Both men turned to stare at Natalie.

"It's been a long time since I've talked with another woman," she explained, feeling as if she had just asked for the moon.

The Great Raft, or logjam, had helped to determine the location of the Natchitoches post, for the logjam extended more than a hundred miles upstream from the spot that became a rendezvous where the river trade from New Orleans met pack-animal trains from Mexico.

Natchitoches was a frontier outpost of the crudest sort, located at the edge of a boggy forest between the Rivière Rouge and one of its branches that the French had named Petite Rivière à la Bourguignon, sometimes called the Cane River for the thick cane-brakes along its banks. The settlement consisted of storehouses, a stockade, Indian wigwams, and log cabins, where traders lived with their merchandise.

The French soldiers had been sent to Natchitoches to guard that country's hold upon the Red River, but the stockade could not have withstood any kind of concentrated assault. A mere four walls of six-foot-high stakes, the fort contained two dirt-floored barracks, one of which was rotten and beyond use.

The troops had been guaranteed wages of four hundred and fifty piastres yearly, and from that sum each soldier was to provide his own clothing and arms and purchase six horses to help establish a local herd. However, the pay was slow in coming, and a colonial ordinance was passed promising the troops daily rations of stale bread with one pint of wine and a pound of beef or mutton.

Thus, many turned to illegal trade with Spain. The fort's commandant, Louis Antoine Juchereau de St. Denis, was the most adept at the fine art of smuggling.

François meant to be as adept or more so, with Nicolas's help.

Natchitoches's small and motley population included soldiers and ex-soldiers, Indian neophytes, traders, wayward sons of good families whose parents had bought for them positions in the colonies that the youths were not qualified to fill, and a few women—squaws of the Caddo nation, a few wives of the French officers and traders, Saint-Domingue slaves, and, lastly, some of the women evicted from Paris.

At the river's confluence with the wooded Bayou Amulee, François and Nicolas wandered among these people, with Natalie between them. François felt a particular pride for his beautiful wife; Nicolas would have called it his Gascony boasting.

For the visit to the busy shipping port, Natalie had worn her freshly washed gray smock, and her summer-child hair glistened in its crown of braids. So absorbed was she in the provincial spectacle that François was certain that she was unaware of the men and women who stopped to stare, to watch his bride moving majestically among them.

The three of them wandered amidst the trains of pack mules and horses, some of which numbered a hundred or more. Nicolas paused to talk with a muleteer, whose animals were tied to trees along the bayou banks, and François and Natalie strolled on. The little post was a riot of color and gaiety. After months of isolation, the sights and sounds and smells—trilling feminine laughter, the odor of roasting chicory coffee, luxurious silks of royal purple, French wines—François was ready to take his place in the world again.

A mild fracas was in progress between French and African boatmen on one side of the bayou and Spanish and Mexican teamsters on the other, and fractured French expletives rent the festive air.

François noted that his wife was paying little heed, for her attention seemed distracted. "What are you looking for?" he asked. "A length of silk, a lace mantilla?"

She shook her head. "No, I was looking for a familiar face, one of the girls who had shipped over with me as a convict."

"Shhh!" he warned.

She looked at him oddly, and he explained, "No one need ever know you were in a prison."

Disappointment—in not finding her friend?—deepened the pale green of her eyes, but she said nothing. *Merde!* She was so much like Nicolas, so cool, so self-contained. He never knew what she was thinking. Disgust at his inability to bed his own wife seeped through his veins, spoiling the rest of the afternoon for him. When Nicolas suggested they pay a visit to the commandant, he was more than ready.

On the western side of the river, to the south of the fort, commandant St. Denis had built his home on high ground. To the east, across the river, lay the spreading lowlands and swamps of the Red River valley, reaching to the horizon; land matted with cane and reed and willow and webbed by unending bayous and lakes. Towering over all were mammoth cypresses looming majestically from sun-dappled, knee-studded waters.

To the west, toward Texas, were pine hills and streams in

endless variety. Nicolas preferred the rolling hill country, where a man could ride a horse among the trees without bogging or tangling; where flowers, berries, and grapes glowed in the sun; and where streams ran with a merry babble instead of creeping along snakily like the bayous.

St. Denis's house had been built of *briquette entre poteaux*, or brick between posts, and was whitewashed inside and out. Candles set in glass chandeliers swung from crudely fashioned rafters, but the rough board floors were carpeted with fine furs edged so closely together that no boards could be seen.

Madame St. Denis greeted them. Dressed in the style of the French court, Emanuella Sanche de Navarro de St. Denis was a charming member of an old, distinguished Spanish family. There was a mother-of-pearl glow to her complexion.

She stood on tiptoe to kiss Nicolas on the cheek with easy informality, saying, "St. Denis is in his vineyards, but I've sent Jasmine to fetch him."

Tired from so much walking, François sat next to Natalie on the damasked sofa. Nicolas lounged against a wall—or seemed to. Instinctively, he preferred to remove himself from a group, moving off to one side to assess any situation first.

He relaxed his covert vigilance of his partner. He had detected a certain furtiveness in François's eyes as if the man were checking to see if anyone was staring at him.

"François," Doña Emanuella said, coming to tap her fan on his shoulder, "I have only just heard of your accident."

Nicolas liked Doña Emanuella. The two or three times he had been in her convivial presence, he had felt none of the paralyzing power of feeling that François's bride inspired in him.

Doña Emanuella rattled on, and the lines of tension that curved downward with the dip of François's luxuriant moustache eased somewhat under her charming discourse. Although young—in her twenties still—she was a motherly soul with a penchant for conversation. Wisely, rather than to avoid the obvious, she acknowledged his infirmity as a fact of life and nothing more.

"You are a naughty boy for keeping it a secret and depriving us ladies the privilege of nursing you back to health. Although it's obvious your bride has done a magnificent job. You're more irresistible than ever now with the marks of noble suffering etched on your handsome brow. Every female will swear you lost your leg this winter wrestling with an alligator or fighting off Indians or perhaps attacking pirates off the Gulf coast."

Abruptly, the Spanish lady switched her attention to Natalie. "Ah, Madame de Gautier, I hate you already."

Natalie looked startled.

"Not only are you a woman of compelling beauty, but you have captured our settlement's most eligible bachelor. But I am relieved to have another female to grace our largely male-populated settlement."

Natalie smiled. "Thank you, madame."

"I know how you must feel," Emanuella said, "so far from your home, but do not despair. In time, Natchitoches will seem more your home than France ever was, especially since your husband is here."

Nicolas doubted if anyone but himself noted how Natalie tensed at the mention of her husband. He watched her more closely as Emanuella talked gaily on.

"I was but a young girl at San Juan Bautista when my husband arrived to trade with our outpost on the Rio Grande. But outpost though it was, there were still fresh, crisp linens to sleep between; silver to drink from; delicious, highly seasoned food cooked by skilled, patient women; leisurely, clever conversations with men of state and polite small talk with women of breeding.

"When my husband brought me here, there was only the fort. Much has changed since then. Each year brings new settlers and more trade. Give yourself time and you won't find it nearly so desolate here."

"Meeting you has already made Natchitoches less desolate," Natalie said graciously.

"You omitted the romantic part," François told Emanuella, relaxing visibly in her easy company. "About how your grandfather had St. Denis taken prisoner and sent to Mexico City. And how you pestered your grandfather until he consented to the wedding and pleaded for St. Denis's release."

Emanuella dimpled. "Now, how did you know that, señor?"

François winked, and he was once again the roguish gallant. "The people of Natchitoches gossip, Madame St. Denis."

At that moment, Emanuella's maidservant entered with a silver tray bearing goblets. No more than fifteen, her skin was as black as Nicolas's eyes, her hair short and kinky. There was something in her bearing that reminded Nicolas of Natalie—a regal, aloof, and graceful glide that proclaimed that Jasmine could have been a Senegalese princess before she was enslaved.

"Jasmine," Emanuella said, "tell Joseph to set the table for three more guests."

Natalie protested, but Emanuella insisted, decrying the long damp, rainy winter that had prevented such pleasurable socializing.

From behind lowered lashes, Nicolas studied Jasmine as she served François first. Nicolas wondered if his instinct could be wrong in sensing some kind of unspoken beseechment on the part of *la négresse*? When the girl paused before him, he scanned her closed countenance. Her molasses-colored eyes, fringed with thick lashes, watched him warily as if warned by her own primitive instinct.

"Nicolas, François," St. Denis said from the doorway, "what a pleasure."

Twenty-five years Emanuella's senior, the forty-seven-year-old St. Denis looked much younger. Tall, with a bearing of cool, silent dignity, he wore a gaudy vest, cut from the finest velvet, in brilliant blue and green and a yellow taffeta waistcoat with silver braid piping. All those above breeches of bright scarlet. Even in the wilderness, the commandant wore an elaborately coiffed curly wig.

Nicolas did not make the mistake of judging the man as merely a vain peacock. They both had in common their Canadian birth. A man born in the silent Canadian woods had a natural bond with the Indians, who considered the frugal use of words a fundamental virtue. St. Denis also knew that the Indians were more impressed by stately bearing and a bright cloak than by diplomatic phrases. More than once, he had expressed to Nicolas that the man who controlled the Indians controlled the wilderness.

The commonality of their Canadian birth ended there, for Nicolas was a natural son, a bastard, while Louis Antoine Juchereau was the son of a noble Frenchman.

St. Denis now bowed before Natalie, who responded with a deep curtsy that obviously took him by surprise. He glanced at François with approval. "You've been to court, Madame de Gautier?"

"*Oui*, monsieur," Natalie said. Once again, Nicolas detected that guarded look in her eyes. Had she told the truth about a relative imprisoning her? Or had she been a mistress to someone who for some reason had taken revenge? A prince of the blood, mayhap? Whomever, the man had to be highly influential to instigate a search that reached clear to the backwaters of the Louisiana colony.

"François," St. Denis said, "let me offer you my congratulations. You have made an excellent choice."

"It would seem I have," François said with a disarming smile, but Nicolas didn't miss the agonized look of yearning, quickly veiled by his friend's lowered eyelids.

Dinner turned out to be an elaborate affair with capon and a meat pie with truffles and a crust so flaky it melted like the first prismatic flakes of snow, followed by a sponge cake spread with raspberry jam. The food was too rich for Nicolas's taste but he ate a little of everything while listening to the rapid flow of conversation—and watching, always watching.

Natalie sat opposite him, beside François, and St. Denis and Emanuella sat at either end. It was Natalie who attracted his gaze. Stimulated by the company, and perhaps by a little wine, her eyes—her whole face—glowed with animation. She was in her element. And just what was that element? he wondered not for the first time.

"Nicolas," Doña Emanuella said with teasing eyes, "now that François has taken himself a bride, you must be thinking of doing likewise. Surely you found yourself a sultry Spanish beauty to woo in San Antonio?"

Recalling Carmencita, the lusty young wife of an aging *hacendado*, Nicolas said only, "None who compared to your ravishing beauty, Madame St. Denis."

She trilled a pleased laugh but said, "With your fierce chieftain's visage and eloquent tongue, I don't think you will have any problem when you do settle on one."

François lifted his cut-glass goblet and twirled the stem between his fingers. "An excellently light and delicate wine, St. Denis. Spanish?"

St. Denis raised his own glass. "*Oui*, my friend. Xeres from Cadiz, in southern Spain. Acquired through our trade with Mexico."

"Without official government sanction," Nicolas added with a sardonic grin.

"You've started your own trading expedition, I've noticed—without official government sanction," St. Denis retorted amiably, and raised his glass of sherry. "A toast. To your new enterprise—Louisiana Imports-Exports, isn't it? May it prosper!"

Joseph, hovering discreetly, his handsome face bland, refilled the glasses. This time, St. Denis said, "And now another toast. To our new king, long may he live."

"New king?" François asked, and was echoed by the others. "That's right. I heard the news only an hour ago when a boat arrived from New Orleans. Louis the Fifteenth has been king for several months now."

Natalie's hand flew to her mouth. The others were chattering with excitement about the news, what difference it would make politically and what consequences it would have on the affairs of Louisiana, so only Nicolas caught the relief that blazed in her eyes.

"Still, I doubt that we'll see any change in colonial policy," St. Denis drawled. "The Duc d'Orléans may no longer be regent, but Louis has appointed him as minister of the government, so the duc still holds in his hands the reins of power for who knows how long—perhaps as long as a half century, as Crozat did."

Natalie shot to her feet. Her wineglass dropped to the floor and shattered. Behind her, the chair toppled. "No!" she screamed. "No!"

Then she fainted. François barely caught her before she could hit the overturned chair behind her. He eased her onto the fur rug. Immediately, Emanuella bent over Natalie and began patting her bloodless face with a wine-dampened napkin.

"What is it?" François asked, looking at the other woman for some source of guidance. "Will she be all right?"

"François, my dear," she said calmly, "I'm sure it is nothing more serious than the usual. Your bride is probably *enceinte*."

CHAPTER

15

By Natalie's reckoning, it was nearing three in the morning. Another sleepless night. She silently cursed the armada of mosquitoes that circled her, pricking her sensitive flesh and sucking her blood.

The rest of her life! She couldn't do it. She could not survive this kind of existence for the rest of her life!

Her fingers curled into the sheet. Since the evening four weeks before at St. Denises', when she had learned that the Duc d'Orléans—and thus Fabreville—still held the reigns of power and would do so indefinitely, she had been living in utter desolation.

How long? How much longer would she have to wait before Fabreville was out of power and Philippe was free?

The clump of sheet was a damp knot in the palm of her hand, and she released it. She didn't need to peer into a stream's reflective surface to know that dark splotches rimmed her eyes, that her body was growing emaciated, that she looked even more haggard than when she had emerged from the hold of the *Baleine*.

What if the duc ruled as minister for twenty years more? Bon Dieu!

She drew a long, steady breath, afraid that she would start screaming and awaken François and Nicolas. If she started screaming, she'd never stop! The thought terrified her as she recalled all too well the inhumane treatment of the insane at La Salpêtrière.

She forced herself to think of something, anything, to distract her from the growing hysteria locked inside her. About François snoring steadily across from her. Philippe had never snored, but she liked the sound. It gave her a safe, secure feeling there in the isolated wilderness where the only sounds one ever heard at night were the howl of the coyote or the scream of a spotted cat.

She didn't know if Nicolas snored or not; she had never heard him. But then did he ever sleep? Sometimes, she would swear she thought she heard him leave the cabin in the deep of night.

Nicolas's presence lightened the dreary succession of lonely days; he was someone with whom she and François could talk since they obviously couldn't talk to one another. Soon Nicolas would complete the cabin he was working on, then he would be leaving on another journey to San Antonio or Mexico City or Santa Fe. After that, what would be left for her and François? Years of emptiness stretched before her.

She was young! How could she possibly waste away her best years in this hinterland? Seeing few people, toiling all day long, making soap and candles and . . . She would endure it not a moment longer!

Stealthily, she slipped from between the coarse bedcoverings and searched in the dark beneath her bed for the small casket she had brought with her from France. Her fingers located the brass handle on one end and pulled. The casket's metal frame grated against the puncheon floor, and she shot an apprehensive glance at François. His soft snoring reassured her. She dressed quickly, silently.

On cat's paws, she crept into the kitchen, past Nicolas asleep on his Spanish-moss-stuffed mattress spread before the fire-banked hearth. Stretched out on his stomach, he was shirtless, oblivious to the mosquitoes. Her lips pursed with frustration. It wasn't fair that her pale skin so attracted the winged beasts and Nicolas's dusky body did not.

Casket under one arm, she turned and lifted the leather thong from the door latch. She was leaving with no more than she had when she came. Quietly, she eased out the door. The silver stream of moonlight beckoned, and she almost skipped like a child as she hurried to her freedom.

Nicolas missed the northern lights. But that was all he missed. Louisiana supplied the freedom that in Canada the mother country had managed to suppress. The waters to the north whispered of intrigues by France, Spain, and England: a transplanting of ancient feuds to this primeval world, a political seething.

He wondered, though, if he would ever be able to settle down as François had. He yearned for far places, for long trips into the wilderness.

In the other room, he heard Natalie stirring restlessly. He knew it was she and not François by the small sounds she made, by the shifting of her light weight on the mattress. Unwillingly, he let himself dwell on his friend's wife, how she turned in her half-sleep as his running dog used to, turning several times in a circle before settling itself down for the night.

But she wasn't settling down. He tensed, sensing her approach. Eyes closed, he listened as she paused before him, her scent reaching him with the faint rustling of her gown. A combination of scents, really: her own particular one, which he could identify in a room filled with the odor of humans; and the scent of green bayberry wax that clung to her hem, leftover from her candle making two days earlier.

He waited while she slipped into the night, giving her time to put some distance behind her. Then he rose and, thrusting his pistol and tomahawk into his sash, set out on her trail. It led out across the field and into the encroaching forest. Beneath the bright southern moon, her pale hair was easy to spot as she flitted in and out between the oaks and pines like St. Elmo's fire, that apparition created by marsh gases.

She was fleeing, he realized, and had no sense of where she was going or the danger in which she was placing herself. Stubby palm fronds grew like mushrooms over the soft earth. Bordering them, just beyond, were cypress knees that protruded above inch-high water. Farther into the forest, the water was imperceptibly deeper.

He lessened the distance between them. The leafy branches filtered out the moonlight, and his eyes refocused, absorbing every bit of refracted light. Once or twice, he almost caught up with her with the intention of halting her flight, but he knew she'd have to halt of her own accord, return of her own free will.

She seemed to skirt the swampier areas instinctively. She took no precaution to soften the noise her feet and skirts made against the undergrowth. A thin fog swirled off the swamp bottom but didn't completely conceal the coral-blotched viper curled up beneath the fan-shaped ferns. Natalie paused to look around her, perhaps realizing for the first time that she had no sense of where she was going. She was breathing heavily, and he doubted if her untrained eye had noticed the venomous reptile. Its bullet-shaped head swung close to her ankle and drew back to strike.

Hissing like the coral snake, the tomahawk winged through the air. Its impact rustled the fronds. She whirled, her hand at her throat. A scream trembled on her lips, then died as a muskrat scampered away through the undergrowth.

She moved more slowly now, more carefully, yet more uncertainly. He figured the casket had to be getting a little heavy. He retrieved his tomahawk, not far from the twin halves of the colorfully banded, deadly snake, and moved off in the wake of his quarry.

The pulse of pounding drums reached his mind's core, vibrating along his bloodstream, before she even became audibly aware of their rhythmic noise. Unknowingly, she let her footsteps carry her toward the primitive music that seeped like fog through the trees.

She paused at the edge of a clearing, which was starkly lit by the moonlight, and he halted several yards behind her. Before them, fifteen to twenty black people, arranged in a haphazard circle, swayed in unison to the steady, irresistible beat of a drum. Their shadows danced on the ground before them like drunken spirits.

In the center of the circle was an impromptu stone altar. The opiatic incense that smoldered at each end of the altar cloyed the night air. He recognized the ceremony. The Conjure religion. It was a heritage of black Africa and the West Indies. The magic had become entwined with a sort of perverted Catholicism like the Black Mass. The low mumblings of the African slaves accompanied the roll and thump of the drum.

Upon the altar was a piece of black wax in the crude shape of a snake. If he correctly recalled what Jean-Baptiste had told him, the symbol of the snake was similar to the phallic worship found among other primitive nations of Africa and India. The snake represented the all-powerful supernatural being from which all events derived their origin. The creature was vast and terrible, not unlike the God of the Old Testament; all-powerful but at the same time frivolous and malicious. The participants of such orgiastic rituals had to be intensely emotional and possess a childlike credulity and an imagination easily inflamed in order to understand the black magic.

The adoration of the serpent started when the king, or shaman, began a weird African chant. His shiny black loins were girded with red handkerchiefs, a blue cord encircled his muscled stomach, and a cloak of multicolored feathers mantled his shoulders. Nicolas recognized him—it was Joseph, St. Denis's house servant and Jasmine's brother. With a high, intelligent forehead, flaring cheekbones, and strong, albeit tatooed, chin, the Senegalese prince was handsome.

Nicolas's gaze moved among the worshippers and located Jasmine. Her slender figure, clad in a guinea-blue wrapper, twisted sensually to the mounting tempo of the vodu drum.

Joseph stepped before the altar and held aloft a large rooster that beat its wings frantically as it squawked with terror. The drumming ceased, and the chanting lowered to an underlying hum. From the scabbard attached to his blue cord, Joseph withdrew a long, slender blade that glinted in the moonlight. The knife slashed the struggling rooster time and time again. Blood squirted everywhere. A chorus of muttering approval arose from the worshippers.

Joseph held the dying but still faintly struggling bird over the upturned face of the nearest worshipper, a stoutly built man with the mashed-flat features of the Congo tribes. Avidly, the man opened his mouth to catch and swallow the warm gore.

Nicolas heard Natalie's startled gasp. She whirled to flee, her blind steps directing her toward a thirty-foot wall of nearly impenetrable and brittle cane brake. Once in there, she would make as much noise as a cow loose in a cornfield.

Sprinting lightly after her, he leaped forward and dragged her down with him into the tall grass. At the impact, her dowry chest thudded against the soft earth at the same time as all the breath *whoosh*ed from her lungs. His hand clapped down on her mouth before she could scream. Her darting eyes, wide with fright, stared up at him without immediate recognition.

"It's Nicolas," he whispered. Her eyes focused on him with concentrated effort, and he said, "Don't make any noise. Do you understand?"

Her frightened gaze clung to the movement of his lips; she nodded.

"They mean no harm, but they are emotionally overwrought. They might unintentionally react dangerously."

She nodded again, indicating her comprehension. With the motion, loose hair about her temples fell across her eyes, and he brushed away the silky strands. At the intimate gesture, her eyes locked with his.

His temples tightened. He gathered her against his length. Her rich golden color was a counterpoint to his swarthy skin. Beneath him, he felt her heart beat an erratic, rapid tattoo against her fragile rib cage. A mighty yearning was reborn in him after a long period of quiescence. His manhood stirred at the pressure of her warmth against him: not aggressively, just a growing— quiet and sure—even as he sensed a subtle change in her breathing.

He simply could not give her what she wanted. He rolled away from her, his features controlled, expressionless.

"Why were you running away?" he asked quietly. He lay stretched beside her, one hand holding her wrist to keep her from bolting.

Behind them, the drums started up again, their irresistible, syncopated beat of tribal and primeval passion punctuating the air.

Her face looked numb; her lips moved uncertainly. "Nicolas . . . Nicolas . . ."

He released her hand, and her little fists began pounding ineffectually on his uplifted shoulder. "I can't stay here," she whispered brokenly. "I can't. Not the rest of my life, all the years to come, I can't."

"Why not?" he asked piteously. "Where else would you go? If you show your face in France, what do you think this Fabreville will do? Do you have any family—anyone—left to turn to?" He caught both her wrists in one hand and gave them a little shake.

She stiffened. Her mouth set in rebellious lines.

"No," he answered for her. "That's what I thought. And what about François? He's in love with you, you know. He married you and took you in, knowing nothing about you—neither that you are a felon nor that you have known other men. Don't you owe him loyalty, at least, if not a wife's love?"

Her rigid body went limp. Wet lashes dropped over the beguilingly sad eyes. "Help me, Nicolas," she whispered. "Help me. I'm so alone, so lonely!"

"Why should I? I don't like you. I don't like you one damn bit."

At her deep, shuddering breath, he felt a moment of exasperation, mainly with himself. His eyes glittered, reflecting something savage in his face. He bent his head and lightly brushed her lips in a kiss meant to comfort. It was the wrong thing to do.

Beneath his lips, hers moved pliantly, languidly. The crescendoing beat of the distant drum lit a fire in his blood. The fecund scent of the moist earth and grass—and that emanating from her body, which was hot, damp with sweat—stirred a powerful desire in him. Her mouth tasted salty; her lips were soft, yielding.

Sensing all would soon be lost, he groaned and set her from him. She stared up at him, dazed, as mesmerized as the vodun worshippers. "This is wrong," he ground out darkly. "Do you understand?"

Did *he* understand? Really?

She nodded dumbly, and he rolled to his feet, pulling her upright along with him. Whatever he expected to happen next, it certainly was not the manner she evinced. Sweeping past him to retrieve her chest, head held regally high, she declared in that husky contralto of hers, "*Merci bien* for saving me from an indiscretion, *Monsieur le Sauvage*."

CHAPTER

16

With a woven basket under one arm and a broom in her hand, Natalie moved among the oaks that peppered the pine and other trees surrounding the clearing. In the hot July sun, her motions were mechanical. She knocked the moss from the drooping limbs with the broom and gathered it in her basket for drying, after which the soft, blue-green plant would lose its color and turn black. Its horsehairlike texture was perfect for cushions and mattress stuffing.

She would have preferred a chore that called for greater concentration. Too often her thoughts returned to Nicolas. Her attempted flight the night of the voodoo ceremony had changed everything—or perhaps clarified everything would be a better way to put it, she thought. No, the feelings she had certainly couldn't be termed "clarified," not when she felt such confusion, especially in his taciturn presence.

She couldn't be falling in love with him. She yanked viciously on the beardlike moss. She loved Philippe.

Was she lying to herself?

She couldn't even recollect Philippe's features. Concentrating, she could remember other, nonvisual things about him: his contentment with life, his joyous energy. Then, too, she had always admired his absorption in the moment without the tiresome prudence that always requires one to look ahead.

Yet he was completely of the Old World; how would he fare here in this bawdy and unformed New World? If she were honest with herself, his contentment with life had been accompanied by an irresponsible streak. His joyous energy had alternated with his love of indolence. If one were ever imprudent in this unforgiving wilderness, if one didn't look ahead even in planning the next footfall . . . why, there was no "next" anything.

She stuffed the moss into her half-filled basket. Ducking her head to avoid a limb, she moved onto another spot where the moss draped like a green cascade. Beyond the shadows of the huge oak, on the far side of the stream, she could just barely make out the forms of François and Nicolas. Both were shirtless. Nicolas, his skin a gleaming mahogany, knelt atop the frame roofing of his cabin, hammering cedar shakes into place. Below, François hacked the shingles from slabs of cedar. Every once in a while, Nicolas's voice reached her, a richly melodious baritone that prickled her mind with forbidden images.

Dear Lord, couldn't she at least be true in thought to one man?

Farther across the field, she could just make out a lone figure approaching. As the person drew closer, she could distinguish the blue guinea wrapper the woman wore. Jasmine. An image of the African slave swaying sensually during the occult ceremony filtered through her thoughts, causing revulsion to rise in her like bitter wine in a glass.

The black woman stopped to speak to the men, then continued toward François's cabin and Natalie. She glided effortlessly through the tall grass like a sleek black panther stalking its prey. When she paused before Natalie, her head was proud atop the long, graceful column of her neck.

"Madame St. Denis wishes that I give this to you." Her French was flawless, but then she and her brother had been born into the French household of a Saint-Domingue sugar planter.

Natalie took the folded parchment. Actually, there were two sheets, both beautifully scripted. The first gave Jasmine, the fifteen-year-old female Negress slave of Louis Antoine Juchereau St. Denis, permission to travel between Natchitoches and the concessions of François de Gautier and Nicolas Brissac. In order to limit attempted slave runaways, the travel letter was especially prevalent those days since the attempted slave uprising south of Natchitoches at the military trading post at Poste des Attakapas. That settlement, on the Bayou Teche, smack in the heart of the reputed cannibalistic Attakapas Indian nation, had been established, like Natchitoches, by the irrepressible Louis Antoine Juchereau de St. Denis.

The second sheet invited Natalie, François, and Nicolas to a festivity in honor of Louis's birthday the following week. "Tell your mistress the wife of François de Gautier accepts her kind invitation on behalf of the three of us."

Jasmine's wide nostrils flared at Natalie's intentionally accented "wife." Gravely, she nodded her head as if accepting the homage of a subject, but her lips set in a surly thrust and there was an adversarial quality in her stance.

Watching the girl leave, Natalie felt reluctant sympathy for her. She was obviously hopelessly in love with François. She had seen it in the proud girl's face that first afternoon at the St. Denis home. She knew the African slave would have been furiously indignant, had she been aware of Natalie's sympathy.

François sat, head bent over the enterprise books, as he scratched out the latest entries. Natalie briefly assessed the trimming she had given his queue and found it to be, everything considered, not too bad a job.

Shears in hand, she stared at Nicolas, who sat, shirtless, on the stool. He braced his hands outward on his knees and eyed her warily with a skeptical lift to his arrow-straight brows. Her fingers ached to trace the heavy ridges of muscle that bunched beneath the velvet skin of his shoulders.

"I don't suppose reminding you that I'm opposed to being scalped is going to do any good?" he asked.

"Stop behaving like an infant, Nicolas," she grunted, moving behind him. Their banter, almost siblinglike in its outward lightness, masked the intensity that struck sparks between them like iron wheels against granite cobblestones. At least the bantering did so on her part. She wasn't quite sure just what Nicolas felt, he was so good at concealing his feelings. That he wanted her was quite likely. But beyond that . . . Did he still hold her in such utmost contempt?

As she wielded the shears through his coarse black hair, she wondered where he found the release men were so driven to seek. He was so private. So hidden. She had a thousand questions, yet to ask even one would put them at the threshold of an entirely different relationship. As it was, their relationship was as tenuous as a spider's web.

Or was it? He was more stable, more self-assured than any man she had ever met, and he could offer her a bond of friendship as strong as manacles. But what if she wanted more? There could be no more; they both understood that implicitly.

Fiercely, she clipped away at great sections of his hair. Within a few more days, he would be moving his effects into his cabin. Once he was gone, what would she do? Lying in bed at night, she invariably thought of him, only a few feet away. She yearned to be held. She was a woman; she needed the love of a man.

Her lips smiled wryly. She had the love of a man. Two men. Both Philippe and François adored her, both from afar.

"Natalie," Nicolas drawled in that sonorous voice that caressed her very soul, "I don't want to be bald."

"You have a long way to go before that happens," she said, smiling. Her free hand ruffled through the shorter hair, amazed at how the clipped locks took on a life of their own and curled around her fingers. When he tilted his head to look at her inquiringly, her breath almost caught in her throat. No longer did he resemble a fierce chieftain. With the shorter hair wreathed about his ears and nape, he could pass for a full-blooded Frenchman.

Someday, she would learn the full story of his French-Indian heritage, not just the bits and pieces she had gleaned from conversations between him and François.

"You've washed the shirts?" François asked from the table. He rarely looked at her if he could help it; yet she could swear that she felt his eyes on her when he thought she was unaware.

She tossed him a glance over her shoulder. "They're outside drying."

For St. Denis's birthday festivities, both men were donning their best. In François's case, best meant yellow satin breeches and matching coat with an embroidered brown waistcoat for contrast. For Nicolas, she had washed a pair of soft deerskin trousers along with a collarless linsey-woolsey shirt bloused at the wrists.

François would be wearing jackboots of a rich cordovan leather; Nicolas, his beaded moccasins.

For herself, she had spent her spare time mending the badly tattered and faded velvet-trimmed emerald silk dress. Her needlepoint training at Poissy had stood her in good stead. Even freshly washed, though, the dress was lackluster after all the time and wear, and doubtlessly would hang limply on her thin frame.

When her fingers brushed the wisps of clipped hair from Nicolas's shoulders, she felt him tense beneath her lingering touch. "We'd best begin to ready ourselves if we're to leave by this afternoon," she said brusquely.

In the privacy of the bedroom, she washed the grime from her body and hair with two buckets of water drawn from the stream. Thin crescents of dirt lay under her nails, and it was some time before they were completely removed. With the dirty water, she washed her cracked leather shoes. The water swelled the leather so that the fine cracks weren't so obvious.

As she rebraided her hair, she thought of how odd it was that she was so excited about attending a party at a frontier post when before—before La Salpêtrière—her life had consisted of nothing but one party following another.

When she was ready to dress, she found in her casket, instead of her refurbished emerald gown, a satin dress the color of French champagne spangled with tiny pearls at the hem and along the low neckline. Her hands moved lovingly over the exquisite material, and tears at possessing such a luxury welled in her eyes.

Only after she drew it forth from the casket did she notice the length of folded netting. A mosquito *baire*. Immediately, she knew which man was responsible for which gift. François would have provided the dress, for Nicolas would never by word or gesture indicate any feelings of a personal nature. He would have selected something more practical.

When she joined the other two, they all stood staring at one another, stunned by the difference in appearances. François looked incredibly dashing in his curled wig and satins, a dress sword fastened by a gold sash. Nicolas looked . . . She couldn't put her finger on it exactly. Dressed as he was, he didn't seem quite the backwoodsman, but the improved clothing could not conceal the underlying primitive essence he possessed—that same strong primitiveness she had unaccountably felt the night she had witnessed the vodu ceremony.

"Your ladyship." Nicolas bowed, but the usual mockery was absent from his voice.

François flashed one of those rare, roguish smiles that had the power to snare all females. "I knew you'd be beautiful in that dress."

She planted a brief kiss on his cheek. In his eyes glowed the unquenchable wanting of her. Looking at his attractive face, her heart went out to him, along with her gratitude. "It's so lovely, François! Thank you! Thank you!"

Then she turned to Nicolas, who was watching the scene closely. With him, she felt an even greater silence. "I can't tell you how much I will value the *baire*." Before she could lose her courage, she stood on tiptoe and brushed his smooth jaw with her lips. The mere act left her breathless.

"Shall we be on our way?" François asked, his mood gay.

Gallantly, he lifted her into the saddle of the waiting Appaloosa. The tension that had formerly marked his conversations with her was noticeably absent. Why hadn't she realized earlier that the elegant dress of a gentleman would help to restore François's damaged masculinity?

Though François had a little difficulty mounting his steed, Nicolas wisely made no offer to assist him. Once astride, François handled the horse well. Earlier, Natalie had assured the two men she could ride, but in the course of the trip their dubious expressions changed to approving looks at the way she controlled her mount.

They passed other couples journeying to the party afoot. The women had doffed their shoes and stockings, tying them carefully in handkerchiefs so that they wouldn't dirty their attire trying to cross the innumerable little *maraises*, small depressions filled with summer rainwater.

By the time they neared Natchitoches, the dusky sky was flagged with gorgeous pastels, pinks, mauves, and purples. Several other saddled horses and a lone calèche, a lumbering carriage swung on rawhide straps, stood outside the long, L-shaped cedar trading post, which was the only place large enough to contain all the people coming from the surrounding countryside for the birthday ball. Opportunities to party were rare, and the festivities would continue until sunrise the next morning.

Natalie watched in astonishment as barefoot women halted at the open door where a tub of water had been provided. They shook one foot after another in the water. After repeating the process a half-dozen times, their feet were freed of the accumulated mud. A slave posted at the door held towels and wiped their feet dry. Then the silk stockings and satin slippers were put on, the cloaks thrown aside, the tucked-up trains were let down, and the ladies sashayed inside.

Cane torches lit the interior. A long table graced one wall and on it were fruits, candied orange peels, Charlotte Russes, custards, jellies, cold meats, smoked game, and salads. A variety of chairs and stools, obviously donated from other households, flanked either side of the table. A few hungry men had already helped themselves to food and taken seats, while others were sampling the various wines offered.

Natchitoches might be a rude little frontier settlement, but as a port and a distribution center to the West, it had access to the best to come out of France's growing mercantile industry.

A dais girded another wall, where a stocky young man in a brown-curled wig was taking a violin and bow from a deerskin sack. Some of the bachelors were already engaged in *vingt-et-un*, their shot bags filled with doubloons used in the game.

Looking around her, Natalie realized there were no older people present. Louisiana was a place where only the young with their dreams dared to come, where only the strongest survived. For the first time, she felt a little thrill at being a part of the beginning of the history of this new land. What tales she would have to tell her grandchildren—if she and Philippe ever had the opportunity to have grandchildren. They would! She must never give up hope for his release. To do so would mean accepting her fate in Louisiana.

Surreptitiously, she glanced at Nicolas standing at her side so commandingly tall above the others. When she left Louisiana, would she ever be able to forget this gentle savage with his chieftain's visage? How could she love one man and want another so badly? Each night her dreams were a betrayal of the vows she and Philippe had once exchanged.

While the violinist warmed up, the guests amused themselves with animated conversation. The lovely Emanuella, with the dignified St. Denis at her side, stood just inside the door greeting the swelling crowd of guests. When she caught sight of Natalie, Emanuella's eyes took on an added sparkle. *"Ma chérie!* How absolutely beautiful you are. Don't you know it is an impertinence to outshine the hostess?" A charming smile tempered the rebuke.

The violinist began to play a gay contredanse of faraway Paris, and Natalie recalled her days at court, the monotony of the same people, the same fêtes. Even *chocolat à triple à vanille* grew tedious when that was all one ate.

At that moment, though, she wanted badly to dance. It had been so long since she last had. She yearned to dance with Nicolas, to be close to him, to have an excuse to touch him as she had when cutting his hair. However, she doubted that his mentor, that eccentric priest-soldier, had also acted as a dance master. To dance with François was, of course, an impossibility.

After Emanuella greeted François and Nicolas with affectionate kisses, she drew Natalie aside to introduce the settlement's newest member to the citizens of Natchitoches who were not yet dancing—or drinking. Natalie was slightly surprised by the homage paid her. Wherever she paused, the women, dressed in their finest, curtsyed low, and the men made a leg and doffed their feathered hats in deep bows. She looked inquiringly at Emanuella, who explained, "They have it in their heads that you are of the royalty."

Something went still inside of Natalie. "Why would they think that?"

"Well, *ma chérie*, you don't exactly exhibit the mien of a servant girl. Your every move, every gesture, gives you away. And . . ."

"And?" Natalie prompted.

Emanuella looked around, then, taking Natalie's arm, drew her a little apart from the others. "And, besides, secrets can't be kept in the Red River valley. Everyone knows that soldiers came all the way from France to look for someone of your description. They would come that far only for someone of importance, a comtesse at the least!"

"Hardly," Natalie managed to say with a look of insouciance. "True, I appeared at court, but on the fringes of the *noblesse*. So did hundreds of other young ladies with dreams of grandeur, only to be lost in the shuffle of intrigue."

Emanuella patted her arm. "I understand. The year before I met my Louis, my grandfather took me to the Escorial in Spain. Unlike Versailles, black was mandatory at the Spanish court. However bleak the court life, though, political connivance abounded. Beauty, wealth, power—any of these, or all three, can often draw unwanted jealousy and resulting intrigues."

The contredanse over, the dancers drifted off the floor, and it was then that Natalie came face to face with her past in the form of her shipmate Solange, who was grasping the arm of a balding young man who had been introduced earlier as the St. Denis bookkeeper.

At seeing Natalie, the pretty prostitute halted abruptly. "Well!" she said loudly, too loudly. "If it isn't *la comtesse!*" She grinned, displaying her badly spaced teeth, and glanced around, making certain she had everyone's attention. "Be careful of your purses, gentlemen. We have a thief in our midst!" At the surprised mutterings, she said, "Oh, yes. Right here. Our comtesse, or is it baronne or marquise?"

The faces around Natalie were a blur. Shame reached down through her cracked-leather shoes and pushed through to take root. Was she safe nowhere?

"Has our comtesse shown you her brand yet?" Solange jeered. Her escort, the bookkeeper, tried to tug her past Natalie, but the woman continued to rile, "It's the brand of a thief—burned between her breasts!"

Gasps arose from the guests, and a smile of satisfaction crossed Solange's narrow face. Emanuella stepped forward and said bitingly, "You're one to be calling the kettle black—a prostitute."

"At least I work for my money!" Solange countered.

Natalie whirled and began to push through the crowd, but Nicolas's solid frame arrested her abruptly. "Would you care to dance, Madame de Gautier?" His deep, melodious voice was like a balm.

He bowed over the hand he had taken, his crushing grasp giving her no further opportunity to bolt. "Always running away, aren't you?" he said under his breath as he led her out onto the dance floor. The first strains of an English minuet signaled another round of dancing.

Other couples hurried to arrange themselves in lines facing each other for the stately and formal dance. Her lips compressed, Natalie went through the motions of the steps. Nicolas, for all his usual pantherish grace, performed the steps woodenly. Great concentration showed in his face. A half-wild savage and a branded thief dancing together. The effect had to be farcical, but not one person present dared to laugh.

She knew he had made the gesture of requesting the dance in order to preserve her honor. Still, she was furious. When she met him in the center of the parallel lines, she hissed, "Staying can only ruin François's name!"

"Half the people here are former convicts." He flashed her a cold, deliberate smile, for her and for all those watching.

It was not the dance she had yearned for, but somehow she got through it. When it was over, François waited to escort her to the buffet, a husband's loving look on his face. Below his moustache, his mouth was set in a stiff smile. "Nicolas did what I should have done," he said under his breath.

She knew, though, that the incident was only a secondary irritation to François. He had known about her past, almost all of it, anyway. Solange's taunting words bothered him less than the evidence of his infirmity. He was suffering from the realization that dancing was just one more thing he could no longer adequately perform.

"You're doing it now," she pointed out. "You're defending my honor merely by being at my side. That is all I could ask for."

The muscles in his jaw worked. "Don't lie to save my feelings, Natalie," he snapped in a low voice. "At least spare me that. To begin with, you could ask for a husband in all ways."

She could tell he had been fortifying himself with deep drafts from the wine casks. She lifted her shoulders in a tiny shrug and fanned herself, all the while looking for Solange, but the woman had doubtlessly slunk off to entertain her escort since she hadn't accomplished anything with her outburst about Natalie's sordid past.

Some of the strain went out of François's face. He escorted her to one of the ubiquitous rush-bottomed chairs, where others had already adjourned to eat, and went to fill a plate for her. Jasmine stood behind the table serving, yet her demeanor was more like that of a queen receiving her subjects. At François's approach, a desperate passion suffused the girl's face so that her complexion became that of a black rose. Natalie wondered how François could be so blind to the love engraved on the girl's naked face.

Not wishing to witness their private but different agonies, Natalie turned elsewhere, anywhere. As usual, Nicolas's commanding height caught her attention, and she felt again that sharp tug deep inside, where she had locked away her own passion. He stood talking to Emanuella, and for once the vivacious woman was silent, charmed, as Natalie had been from the first, by that musical voice. It was so unexpected, coming from that craggy face.

François stepped into her view, walking with his badly uneven gait. He bore his refilled glass in one hand and in the other a plate with a green salad, *galantines* quaking in jellied seclusion, and little towers of nougats. "Aren't you going to eat?" she asked.

He shook his head. "No." He looked sourly into his glass. "I probably should. At this rate, I shall become quite drunk. I'd like that."

"I wouldn't, François," she said evenly. "You'd only feel worse tomorrow morning."

"You don't give a damn how I'd feel."

She stiffened at the harsh reproach. Laying her fork on her plate, she looked up and met his challenging stare. He wanted her to tell him she loved him. "I do care about you, about what happens to you. Very much."

"Yes," he said, a rueful smile tugging at the ends of his moustache, "I was afraid that would be your answer." He took another deep swallow, emptying his glass. "Pardon me, Madame de Gautier, while I refill my glass and seek oblivion."

Miserable, she picked at her food, finishing only the leafy salad. Later, when other men requested dances from her, she acceded. To refuse would only annoy François that much more. She knew he continued to watch her. So she danced the night away, even as he kept his vow to get drunk, although there he shared the companionship of quite a few other men. Come sunrise, she and Nicolas would have a time of it getting François home.

As it turned out, it wasn't François but she who had to be borne home semiconscious. She wasn't quite sure exactly when she began to feel a little queasy, but toward dawn pains began wrenching at her stomach. Once she had mounted the Appaloosa, she thought she might just make it home; after all, she was neither dancing nor walking.

But the pains became more and more violent. The last thing she remembered was calling out "Nicolas!" before sliding, sliding, into a deep void.

CHAPTER

17

"PERISTAM SANCTAM UNCTION-
em . . ."

Something deep within Natalie's brain dimly recognized the Latin litany.

". . . and His most loving mercy, may the Lord forgive you whatever wrong you have done by the use of your sight . . ."

Gradually, she became aware of what was happening. She was being given the Extreme Unction—the last rites! She tried to open her eyes, but her lids were as heavy as if they had already been weighted with gold coins.

Where was she? As the heavy voice intoned its ritual, parts of her brain assimilated bits and pieces. Louisiana. She was in Natchitoches. But the settlement didn't have a priest.

She wasn't going to die! She couldn't! Not before she saw Philippe again!

"You're only making her worse! Get the damn thing over with and get out!"

François's voice. He had been drinking, she could tell.

"Mi hijo, podias que tener . . ."

The priest had reproved François in Spanish. A Spanish priest? Was she hallucinating? What had happened to her? Her body hurt so, everywhere.

She felt the warm, moist pressure of his thumbs against her lids. The priest was anointing her with olive oil. *Mon Dieu!* What if they buried her alive?

She summoned the last particle of her depleted strength and willed her eyes to open. In a blur, she saw the priest leaning over her, then straightening, receding from her in a dark tunnel. The wide sleeves of his brown robe swung in and out of her vision. From somewhere she heard soft weeping mixed with slurred, muffled words.

Another pain twisted through her, leaving her gasping, too weak even to cry out. Everything darkened.

Time and space weaved patterns in and out of her subconsciousness. Then a point came where she faced the brink of infinity. She struggled against the soft earth being shoveled over her, against the inexorable suction pulling her down, downward, through the bottomless swamp. Morass filled her ears and nostrils so that she couldn't breathe. She opened her mouth to scream, and slimy ooze gushed in. She was strangling!

Someone screamed. "Nooooo!"

Words completely foreign to her were being spoken in a low, resonant voice. Slowly, with difficulty, she opened her eyes. Nicolas's cinnamon-colored face swam above her. He was speaking in some Indian dialect, almost crooning to her. When he saw that she was fully conscious, he ceased stroking the hair at her temple, and the strange Indian chant halted.

She fixed her gaze on the inky pools of his eyes, clinging to the promise of life she found there. "What has happened?"

"You've been very ill—you ate something poisonous at the birthday festivities."

She blinked, trying to assimilate what he had told her, but she found being cradled in his arms a much more pleasant experience to contemplate. Unlike François, his swarthy chest was smooth, devoid of hair. "Where's François?"

"He took the *curé* back to Los Adais."

"So I wasn't just imagining it. There was a priest." She looked about her, saw that she was in her bed, that the dying sunlight filtered anemically through the linen window covering. She noted that a mosquito net was draped from the ceiling, enveloping the bed—and her and Nicolas. She also noticed that her hair lay unbound over her shoulders.

"You were on the point of death. You mumbled about absolution. François rode like the hounds of hell to Los Adais to fetch the priest for you."

"Did I—did I mumble anything else?"

"You mean, did you enlighten him about your past? No. Your secrets are safe."

His contempt hurt. But she was too weary, too weak to try to remonstrate with him. She closed her eyes, gathering strength from the blood that pounded through her heart at such a furious pace at Nicolas's nearness.

"What did you eat the night of the party?" he asked her.

She opened her lids again. "Mostly salad."

"What you ate could have contained hemlock."

A disgruntled sigh fluttered past her lips. "Someone's carelessness could have cost a lot of lives."

He frowned and shook his head. In the time she had been ill, his hair had grown, and the heavy curls were loose about his nape. "Except for quite a few nasty hangovers, no reports of illness or death have reached St. Denis."

Her eyes flared. "You're saying I was deliberately poisoned?"

He held a wooden spoon to her lips. "I'm not saying anything. Swallow."

She lifted her head, trying to see what the spoon contained, and he said, "It's not hemlock. It's a Chipewyan antidote I've been giving you for the past ten days."

"Ten days? I've been sick that long? Who—"

The spoon, prodding her lips open, cut off her questioning. Helpless, she swallowed. She gagged and screwed up her nose. "*Tiens!* That's wretched-tasting medicine!"

His lean lips widened to emit reluctant laughter. "An apothecary couldn't do better."

She liked his laughter. It had the sound of the wind rustling through the trees. She looked at him, really looked at him. The eyes were the entire man, she thought. An opaque flat black set in the fierce face, they were nevertheless luminous, eloquent with the gentleness inside the man. It was true, she thought, that nothing was so strong as gentleness, nothing so gentle as real strength.

She had seen only the rough-hewn face, but now she perceived the deep character sketched in its lines. So much he had never talked about—and so much he knew. And so much time she had wasted, pinning for Philippe, when she could have been getting to know Nicolas better.

As Nicolas had gotten to know her, she realized suddenly and uneasily. "You took care of me all of this time?" she asked.

"Most of the time."

A deep flush rose like the tide, flooding her wan cheeks. He had to have performed the most intimate of tasks for her. Her hand crept up to her throat where the tie strings of her woolen nightrail lay loose, exposing the expanse of soft, white flesh that was faintly veined.

"The branding must have been horrible for you," he said quietly.

Now was her chance to tell him the entire truth, that she had known only one man, her husband. Yet she couldn't bring herself to mention Philippe. He belonged to another world, another time—and she was here, now, held in Nicolas's arms. Her racing blood whispered that, for just a little while, it couldn't be such an act of infidelity to lose herself in this small pleasure.

Unconsciously, she traced the fleur-de-lis atop the nightrail's fabric with her fingertips. "You must believe me, Nicolas," she said in a voice even more husky than usual, "I have not been an immoral woman."

He released her and rose, his features harsh. Under the straight slash of his brows, his eyes smoldered with the tension that coursed between them. "Did a rejected lover issue the *lettre de cachet*?"

Wordlessly, she shook her head and looked back up at him. "That was unfair, Nicolas. There's been only one man in my life."

"And it wasn't François, was it?"

"I refuse to answer that!" Shakily, she pushed herself to her feet and faced him, swaying, her chin jutting. "How many woman have there been in *your* life?" she countered.

"None that I deceived."

Jealousy coiled in her stomach. She hadn't expected jealousy to strike; in fact, she had never experienced it before. Its impact staggered her. Her knees gave out, and Nicolas's hands shot out to catch her before she collapsed. He lowered her to the bed, but his hands released her arms at once, as if she were aflame. She lay there, the white frost of her hair cascading over the mattress.

"Were you in love with any of them?" she asked in a whisper.

A tight smile lightened the dark face that hovered over hers. "The first one was the most memorable."

"I really don't want to know any more."

He sat down beside her again. "Yes, you do. When I reached thirteen years, Jean-Baptiste decided it was time I became a man. He took me to the nearest trading post, more than four hundred miles away, and solicited the fattest, oldest, and ugliest Indian whore he could find. She was toothless in the bargain."

One corner of his mouth crooked. "Shall I continue?"

She tried to make her voice light, knowing that anything else endangered the platonic relationship that had been carefully established. "If you don't, Nicolas, I'll never forgive you."

"She left me with a host of crotch vermin that kept me scratching for months—and the vow I'd never take another woman."

She raised a skeptical brow and said, "I don't believe you."

"Nevertheless, it's true. I was genuinely astonished that more men didn't elect to lead a priest's celibate life-style. However, the instinct to mate was irrepressible, and at the next opportunity— almost six months later—I was driven to bed another woman. I searched and found a somewhat younger one this time. At least she had teeth."

He paused, then said, smiling, "Jean-Baptiste had been a wise old man. The first time was so bad that after that every time had to get better."

She knew she should act shocked, but unavoidable laughter escaped between the fingers she pressed against her lips. "Oh, Nicolas!"

At the stringent lines that abruptly deepened at either side of his mouth, her laughter dissipated. "Natalie, when François returns tomorrow, I'm leaving for the Natchez Trace. I'll be gone for some time."

The name meant nothing to her. "You don't have to go."

"I have to. I want to establish trading relations with the Cumberland settlements."

"You know that's not what I meant."

"I want you to listen to me," he said, ignoring her statement. "You must be careful when you visit the St. Denis household in the future. Eat only what François or the St. Denises themselves eat."

"It's Jasmine, isn't it? She wants François's love for herself."

He stood and went to the door. She felt the distance between them as more than just a matter of space. In the darkness, his sensuous baritone voice reached her. "François loves you; you are his wife."

"Yes," she whispered, her fingers plucking at the sheet listlessly. "A wife chosen by his best friend."

CHAPTER

18

$\mathbf{A}$CROSS THE BAYOUS AND through dense forests, the pack train traveled. Hummingbirds sparkled among the honeysuckle. Serpents tattooed by nature slithered through the flowers. The scents of summer exuded from the profusion of wild roses and azaleas. Crepe myrtle was bejeweled with its pink pastel bouquets, and acacias waved feathery green and gold leaves.

In some places, the juice of wild strawberries reddened the legs of the horses up to their knees and crimsoned the hem of Natalie's apple green broadcloth riding habit, brought upriver from New Orleans. François had insisted on buying it, "to go with your eyes."

The land seemed too intoxicating for her. Or perhaps it was being so close to Nicolas. Sleeping on the ground with only a few feet separating them . . . Touching his fingers when he passed her the fish or game he had prepared . . . Watching the play of the firelight on his splendidly barbaric features. It was almost like that first journey she had made with him—except that this time François accompanied them. Armed with a French fowling piece, he brought up the rear of the train, with her between him and Nicolas, who was riding scout.

She was fortunate even to be going. François had wanted to

make the trip, and she suspected the only reason Nicolas had agreed was because of the poisoning incident several weeks earlier. Perhaps, he felt, as she did, that if Jasmine had indeed been responsible, time and distance might ease the girl's bitterly jealous hatred.

As the pack train drew closer to its destination, Natalie grew more impatient. The Natchez Trace Nicolas had spoken of started at Fort Rosalie, and she was anxious to learn of Jeanne-Antoinette's fate.

Fort Rosalie crowned a two-hundred-foot bluff. Its early settlers had chosen the spot as the river's finest for a permanent settlement: healthful, exposed to a gentle breeze, and well above the murky swamps of its vicinity. Next to it was the concession of St. Catherine, patron saint of wheelwrights and mechanics, some of whom had been among those early settlers.

All of Fort Rosalie turned out for the pack train's arrival, and among the soldiers and civilians who crowded outside the stockade's open gates was a face she would have recognized anywhere. Those sloping eyes widened in disbelief at the sight of her.

"Hervé!" she called, and pulled up on her reins to wave a gloved hand.

At that same moment, a girl pushed past the soldier and two blanketed Indians in front of her and shouted, "Angelique!" She grabbed the stirrup latigos. "I can't believe it's you!"

"Jeanne-Antoinette! I'm so relieved! You're all right!"

The dark-eyed girl blushed. "I'm a married woman," she said, a little proudly. She nodded over her shoulder at the blond Atlas, who strode up behind her.

A droll smile lightened Hervé's face. "I did as you asked, Marquise, and—"

Natalie saw Nicolas haul up on his prancing mount and wheel it back to join her. "Please," she said, "my name is Natalie. Natalie de Gautier." Then, in an easier tone, "I'm here with my husband and his partner."

By the time Nicolas and François joined her, Hervé was bidding the three of them to stay with him and Jeanne-Antoinette while they were there at Fort Rosalie.

She introduced François and Nicolas, explaining to them, "Hervé and Jeanne-Antoinette were passengers with me on the ship that brought us to Louisiana."

She knew what François was wondering: first, how the young girl came to be a wife and, second, if the couple had been criminals. As for the inscrutable Nicolas, one never knew what he was thinking.

Hervé, who was apprenticed as a carpenter at the fort, had constructed a two-room French cottage that was admirably suited to the tropical climate. Single-story, it was built *poteaux enterre*, raised a few feet above the ground on piers. His high-pitched, thatched roof was modeled after those found in the West Indies. That night, the five of them sat drinking chicory coffee, with an excited Jeanne-Antoinette doing most of the talking.

Watching the thirteen-year-old wrinkle her nose in an adorable little gesture or toy with one of her fat braids, it was difficult for Natalie to realize that Jeanne-Antoinette was married, and to that brigand Hervé. Even so, the couple exchanged the intimate glances of lovers, the stolen glances that Natalie had once shared with Philippe, the kind she would never know with Nicolas.

Not if she valued the salvation of her soul.

She tried to shake off her melancholy and fastened her attention on the conversation. "I don't understand," Hervé said to François, his brow furrowed with a bloodhound's multiplicity of wrinkles. Marriage had added a maturity to his demeanor. It was obvious to Natalie that he had the respect of François and Nicolas, which didn't come lightly. "Why go all the way to the other end of the Natchez Trace to trade with the British colonies? Why not establish another trading post and warehouse right here?"

François fingered his moustache. "I suppose there's enough traffic to warrant it."

"Would you be interested in running the place?" Nicolas asked, one of the few times he had spoken that evening. Always, those narrowed jet eyes watched and evaluated. She longed to untie the leather thong that he used to catch back his hair, which had grown long again. The queue, however, did civilize the ferocious power of his features.

Hervé looked startled. "I don't know . . . I'm not sure I know how to do—"

"Of course you do," Natalie said. "You smuggled salt when to do so was unacceptable in France. You could sell smuggled goods when to do so is acceptable, in Louisiana."

"As a minor partner, you would receive a percentage of the profit," François said expansively.

From under sloping brows, Hervé glanced at his wife. She nodded enthusiastically, her braids bouncing against her little breasts.

It took four days to arrange the complex details needed to establish a subsidiary post of the Louisiana Import-Export Company of Natchitoches. On the final night before their return trip, the deal was consummated with several toasts of taffia, a crude rum made from the fermented juice of sugarcane. As usual, Nicolas abstained from drinking.

Apparently, Hervé and Jeanne-Antoinette did their own celebrating later that night in the bedroom, for Natalie, stretched on a pallet in the kitchen–main room, overheard the soft cooing and pleasurable growls of the girl and Hervé.

Natalie lay close to François, but in the confined area she had only to roll over and stretch her arm to touch Nicolas. How could she explain it, that just being near him made her blood swirl and eddy through her arteries so that she was alternately weak-kneed and exuberant—she, who had been so cool, of such even temperament, always composed. This primitive land did strange things to its inhabitants. It was like the lunacy that seemed to possess some people in the full of the moon, except this was always and everlasting.

Monsieur le Sauvage.

Her name for him was a sigh on her lips. At once, she stiffened, afraid that his acute hearing might have detected that sigh, but she could hear only his steady, even breathing of sleep and François's gentle snoring. Unable to withstand the intimacy of lying so close to Nicolas, of yearning to be held possessively against that lean and so decisively muscled frame, she quietly rose from her pallet.

Outside, the moon drenched the exotic landscape and the sultry summer night drew forth the intoxicating fragrances of wild roses and cape jasmine, her favorite flower. But here no orangerie was needed to enjoy its languorously sweet scent. The entire terrain was a hothouse.

Picking her way carefully down a shrubbery-strewn, rolling

incline, she reached her destination, the cape jasmine clump. Its white flowers beckoned in the moonlight, and she leaned close to inhale their fragrance.

"You're not running away again, are you?"

She spun around, at the same time stifling an inadvertent scream. Nicolas stood behind her, clad only in his buckskin breeches. The moon silvered the high, prominent bones of his cheeks. "No." She swallowed and said huskily, "I was restless . . . couldn't sleep."

His heavy-lidded look seemed to linger on her lips as she spoke, and when his eyes raised to meet hers, she felt a great spasm of wanting ripple through her. "Neither could I."

She could think of absolutely nothing to say. He was so close. Too close.

He reached around her, his arm brushing her shoulder and plucked a flower. With his mahogany skin, he could have been descended from the night. "They are wasted on the bush," he said, and tucked it in her hair behind her right ear.

She closed her eyes, quivering uncontrollably at his touch, at the flower's intoxicating scent. "Nicolas . . ." she breathed. Her eyes opened, her gaze locking with his dark, passionate one. Something hot and elemental passed between them.

"Nicolas . . ." This time it was almost a sob. "This mustn't happen!"

A muscle along his jaw flickered. Then his hands closed over her shoulders, and he drew her against him to bend his head over hers. His mouth marauded her trembling lips, crushing them, as his hands, cupping her head, crushed the flower, releasing its aphrodisiacal fragrance.

Hungrily, she returned his kiss, not caring that his mouth bruised hers. She pressed her breasts and loins against the length of his lean muscles, needing urgently to feel a oneness with him.

With a shudder, like a great beast in fever, he pushed her gently from him. His dark eyes, glazed by a mixture of barely repressed passion and self-disgust, stared down at her. "*Par Dieu*, you're married to my friend, my partner!"

A despairing gasp struggled up past her throat. Her deception was hurting so many innocent people. She shook off his hands. Tears welled in his eyes. Her clefted chin was inclined staunchly.

"Then we must do everything we can," she said in an almost inaudible voice, "to make certain this doesn't happen again."

His eyes held a wintry gleam, and his lips twisted in a contemptuous curl. "Do you really think it won't? I don't think you're that naive, Natalie."

CHAPTER

19

Jasmine left Mass before the commencement of the Spanish *curé*'s tedious and disagreeable sermon, delivered for two to three hours on end in atrociously mispronounced French idioms.

Once a month, since the summer before last—since delivering the last rites to Natalie de Gautier, the reverend father had been coming to Natchitoches to the military post where a large room had been fitted as a chapel. The good priest had two faces. While he preached against avarice, he also indulged in it. No longer did he affix to the church door the customary tax on burials, thereby concealing what he charged.

That the young Capucin priest was determined to obtain the salvation of her soul surprised her, for his blazing eyes glared at her with what she could only think of as utter hate instead of the compassion and fatherly love of a priest for his children.

Jasmine was only one generation removed from African civilization, where her parents had been herded onto a slave ship. Christianity had been forced upon her parents, then on her brother and herself, by the masters who had owned them. Though she fulfilled the duty required by St. Denis of attendance at the Christian Mass, she still clung tenaciously to the man she loved in defiance of Father Hidalgo and his Christian precepts.

Father Hidalgo preached of salvation and a glorious life to come. Jasmine simply yearned for the glory of her freedom—and François de Gautier. After almost a year of giving herself freely to the sophisticated French gentleman, she had finally convinced him to persuade her owners to hire her out—or "lease" her to him. In payment for her "services," François had promised St. Denis to provide her room and board.

François had paid to have built a little house of *bousillage*, which she had designed. It bore a striking resemblance to a mushroom, with its bottom floor of massive slave-made bricks and the hip roof of cypress shingles with a twelve-foot overhang. Verdant Spanish daggers flanked the doorway. She called it her African House.

Natchitoches settlers looked upon it, separated from the other dwellings, as something mysterious, something hoary with age, though it was only recently constructed.

The bitter October winds buffeted her as her long strides took her with feverish anticipation to the little African house where François was waiting. Her public concubinage scandalized the good priest and some of Natchitoches's more upright citizens. Even if François had not had a wife, a beautiful wife, Jasmine would never have been permitted to marry him. The law forbade either a Christian or an African marriage between the black and white race, referred to as a "natural" marriage.

Jasmine had other plans this time. On this particular day, she meant to implement them.

She closed the door behind her and leaned against it. François lay on the sleigh bed waiting for her. She wondered that he never noticed the image of the devil that was engrained in the rosewood head and footboards.

"Take off your clothes, Jasmine," he said, and swilled another drink from the bottle beside the bed. He was naked to the waist, and he wasn't wearing his peruke.

Her head held proudly, she crossed the nearly bare room to stand before him. Slowly, her fingers worked at the bodice laces of the black broadcloth, her Sunday dress. She wore no undergarments, and the dress slithered down her long, supple thighs to reveal the glossy, ebony body. As she knelt by the edge of the bed, her elongated breasts swayed low against her rib cage. Hungrily, like a child, François took one into his mouth.

While he suckled, she began to unbutton his breeches, seductively running her slender fingers along the muscled stomach and lower to the kinky, dark thatch. Her fingers wrapped around him, and he groaned. But she wasn't about to pleasure him yet. First, she would tease and tantalize him until he was out of his mind with wanting her.

"Wait, *chéri*," she told him, gently withdrawing her nipple from his mouth. Her tongue traced the veined length of thick flesh, even as her hands worked his pants gingerly over the mangled leg. Sometimes François's attitude infuriated her. He felt no embarrassment at her seeing or touching the unsightly stump, yet he wouldn't allow his wife to do so. His wife was a grand lady, while she—while she had François all to herself, she thought with a thin half smile.

Natalie was a fool to give up her husband so easily. Perhaps the close brush with death had put fear into the heart of the aristocratic Frenchwoman. The half-breed had saved Natalie de Gautier, but Jasmine was too smart to attempt the same thing twice. She wanted her freedom—and François—not the French whipping horse. There were other ways to get what she wanted.

François's breeches joined her dress on the stone floor. She slid up over him, slowly, sinuously. Her tongue flicked out to taste his salty flesh. His hands cupped her head and drew her down onto him. "Jasmine, you're a viper," he rasped. "You would entwine yourself about me until you crush the very life from me."

Her lips deserted his tubular flesh, and she stared up into the passion-wracked face. "No, *chéri*, I want you to put life into me. Now." She sat up and, fitting herself onto him, began to rotate her hips, tightening vaginal muscles that possessed the strength of youth. She had been a virgin when François first bedded her.

Afterward, she lay beside him. His skin, the same shade as her palms and soles, glistened with the sweat of their lovemaking. His eyes were closed, but she knew he wasn't asleep. Her finger played with one end of his neatly clipped moustache. He might get drunk some nights when he was with her and use the vile language of a sailor off a slaver, he might vomit all over himself the next morning, but in public he was always the immaculately dressed, well-bred Frenchman.

·   ·   ·

In June, François brought Natalie into Natchitoches in the new
calèche he had had brought up by barge from New Orleans.
While Natalie visited at the St. Denises, he went to see about
completing the shipment of recently rendered bear grease.

Watching Natalie embrace a joyous Emanuella, he felt an inex-
tinguishable desire rising in him for his beautiful wife. He thought
of how he should be a happy man. He was half-owner of a highly
profitable business, he was married to a woman most men could
only dream about, and he had for a partner a friend he cherished
deeply.

In addition, he had as a mistress a young Negress who was
nothing short of incredible in bed. Her devotion to him was
something he hadn't expected.

But as he drove the calèche into the Natchitoches business
district, he reflected that somewhere his life had gone awry. With
the one woman he loved, his own wife, he was impotent. A
morbid smile lifted the ends of his moustache. How ironic. The
old Greek dramatists would have appreciated his dilemma. His
hands clenched around the reins. The worst of it was, he was
beginning to suspect that Nicolas was falling in love with Natalie,
and she with him. He felt at once like weeping and cursing the
fates that had brought his life to this impasse.

The oblong-shaped log cabin that served as the offices for Louisiana Imports-Exports squatted on a ridge along with the rest of
the mercantile establishments, overlooking Rivière Rouge's placid
arm, Rivière aux Cannes. Watching the slow-moving ripples in
the brown water, François felt some sense of calm being restored
to his warring soul. He had grown up on the coast and had served
in the navy, and the love of water was ingrained in him.

Inside the office, two male slaves, Samuel and Jeremiah, worked
at a table. In the large jars he had obtained from the Mediterranean, they sealed the grease taken from bears trapped in the
wilderness beyond Natchitoches. Bear grease in Europe was a
valuable commodity, vitally needed to keep coaches, wagons, and
artillery working smoothly.

The idea of exporting it had been his, and Nicolas had agreed
to put it into effect. That winter, Nicolas had hired trappers and
Indians to prod the bears out of hibernation. He and Nicolas had
always worked well together, complementing one another.

However, between establishing a lucrative trade route to both

Mexico and the English seaboard colonies and setting up a *vacherie*, grazing land for the wild cattle driven back from Texas, Nicolas was now away from Natchitoches more often than not.

The few times Nicolas had visited him and Natalie, the unspoken tension was so strong that everyone felt uncomfortable. François was certain that nothing had happened, that Natalie was faithful to him, that Nicolas was his friend, a man of integrity, a man he admired.

But how long could it continue like this for them?

His wooden peg thudded hollowly against the floor of the back room as he moved among the crates of pelts and barrels of tobacco due to be shipped the next day. He was counting and marking on a ledger when the door of the front office slammed and Father Hidalgo shoved aside the curtain that partitioned the two rooms. Within the pointed hood, the young *curé*'s complexion was mottled with zealous outrage.

He pointed a trembling, bony finger at François. "I command you to put away your concubine and I forbid any further resumption of this unsanctioned—scandalous—alliance with the Negress Jasmine!"

François set down the ledger and stared at the young priest in mild surprise. French society considered the Africans more or less exotic, and even the illustrious King Louis XIV had reportedly had a Negress for his mistress in the amorous days of his youth. "Is there some reason why you should just now consider this a great scandal?"

"At confession, she admitted to carrying your child!"

François concealed his astonishment. "Is the reverend father ready to accuse all masters at the post whose slaves have produced such children?"

"That is not the point," the priest said indignantly. "Furthermore, you have not complied with the requirement of annual confession and communion."

François shrugged. "Before the priests came, we didn't do so, and I don't think our souls were any more jeopardized than they are now."

Father Hidalgo sputtered, "If you don't do as I command, I shall take this matter to higher authorities. To Bishop Remant in Quebec, if need be!"

Sudden comprehension dawned on François. The poor priest

was waging his own inner conflict. He himself lusted after Jasmine! François's spark of sympathy immediately evaporated. "You might consider well at this point the matter of the furnace and mill that Louisiana Import-Exports donated to the parish."

The priest spun around to leave, and his brown robes swished past the rustling curtain.

François finished his inventory and drove over to the African House. Jasmine met him at the door, slipping her arms up around his shoulders and pressing her hips against him suggestively. He grasped her wrists and removed them from about his neck, stretching them out to either side of her. He looked down into her face. Her nostrils flared with his scent, and her wide lips parted in hunger. Her eyes flashed challengingly up into his. The primitive savage inherent in her fascinated him—and for a while had superimposed itself over his unconsummated love for Natalie.

"Why didn't you tell me about the baby?"

Her teeth gleamed against her black skin. "I was going to. It just occurred to me at confession how enjoyable it would be to shock the young priest."

He let her wrists drop and went over to the small commode, where he uncorked a half-empty rum bottle. "Well, you seem to have stirred up a hornet's nest, Jasmine."

She came up behind him and looped her arms about his shoulders again. She nibbled at his neck, raising little goose bumps of pleasure. "François, *chéri*, our child must not be born with the stigma of slavery."

He swallowed a mouthful of rum and said, "I will buy the child from bondage, Jasmine, but do not expect me to acknowledge it publicly as mine. The child will never inherit my assets."

Fiercely, she sank her pointed little teeth into the flesh at his nape. With a yelp of pain, he dropped the bottle and spun on her. She jumped back out of reach of his lashing hand. Her eyes narrowed to slits, her teeth bared, and she spat, "Just what children of yours do you think will inherit your assets? Your children by your wife? Ha! You can't even manage to make your manhood ready for her!"

Her venomous outburst distracted her momentarily, and the back of his hand slammed against her cheek. "I'm sending you back to the St. Denises and selling this house," he gritted. "I don't ever want to hear of you—or the child—again!"

Tears of pure rage glistened against the whites of her eyes. "What other woman do you think could bring herself to touch your hideous deformity?" She hurled the words after his departing back. "Not even a paid whore!"

An early-morning breeze rustled the orange and brown leaves along the winding little dirt street that paralleled the Cane River. Besides the unsightly warehouses and stores that banked one side of the river road, a few stylish homes had actually sprung up, boasting wide porches, or galleries, laced with wrought iron imported from France and tall doors and windows to capture cooling breezes. Louvered shutters, called *jalousies,* protected against sun and rain, or other *jealousies,* because a lady might look through the slats without being seen.

Natalie stood behind one louvered window of the recently completed house and watched François limp up the shrub-bordered path. His gait was unsteady, not because of his wooden leg but from drinking. She knew where he had been. With the lieutenant's widow, Marie Duclos. Thin, intense, and pretty, the well-born woman from Normandy had the morals of a bitch in heat. Like the others, she had fallen under the spell of François's charm and tried her best to seduce him away from Natalie.

As ever, a deep surge of pity for François welled up in her. She knew he would soon drop Marie, just as he had the other women, Solange included, in the year since he had broken with Jasmine. He amused himself with them, treated them rather shabbily, and then deserted them for a new face. Somewhere there was always a woman ready to be his mistress, but none of these would-be mistresses seemed to realize that it was François's frustrated love for his wife that drove him to them in the first place.

Natalie didn't bother to move from the tall, narrow window when he entered the parlor. "Ah, the devoted little wife waited up for me," he slurred, and attempted a clumsy bow.

"Do you want any breakfast?" she asked calmly.

His hand came up to stroke her throat. "Do you never worry that I might not return from my nocturnal forays?" he asked softly. "Or do you hope that I won't?"

"You know that's not true."

His fingers tightened at the base of her throat. "I wonder." He pivoted from her and started toward his bedroom, which he had converted from the Stranger's Room: originally intended in the colonial homes for any sojourner lacking a place to sleep, the Stranger's Room had a separate entrance. "Don't go out today. Last night the slaves on the Poydras plantation butchered him and his wife and children. The slaves were planning on mounting an army of blacks and marching downriver to New Orleans."

She followed him into his bedroom. "Then they were stopped?"

"St. Denis caught twelve of them. His soldiers are still looking for the rest. They've fled to the swamps with their leader." He removed his sword belt and laid it across the shaving *duchet*, then shrugged out of his ruffled linen shirt, before he continued. "Joseph."

"Jasmine?" she asked.

He pulled off his boot. "She's with them."

"The child?"

François looked up at her. "Her child's with her also."

Her child. Did François really believe she didn't know who the father of Jasmine's daughter was? Father Hidalgo may have reluctantly recorded the father as unknown, but Natalie knew the father's identity, as did everyone else in Natchitoches.

She wondered why it was that there was a word for a husband whose wife was unfaithful—cuckold—but no term for the wife whose husband kept other women. People might pity the wife, but she wasn't scorned. An unfaithful husband was acceptable, expected.

In the days that followed, Natchitoches appeared deserted but for the mangy dogs and an occasional chicken or pig that had escaped its owner. At nights, even François slept at home. Emanuella came over to visit once, accompanied by two soldiers from the fort. Dressed in their shabby blue uniforms, they stood guard on the gallery. With the Company of the West Indies bankrupt, they were going as much as a year without pay; it had been that long or more since a French ship had put into New Orleans. They existed only on what St. Denis managed to eke out and on their own small grants of land.

"Would you believe," Emanuella said, "Solange has given up her calling and married our bookkeeper. Charles Didier is such a bland, unprepossessing young man. Myopic and balding to boot."

Natalie poured lemon-scented punch and passed a cup to Emanuella. "His myopia will be good for the marriage. It might make him blind to her past."

While the women chatted, the guards shifted from one foot to another, uncomfortable in their roles as escorts. They much preferred to be in on the chase, scouring the woods and swampy areas for the bloody insurrectionists.

Eventually, as the days dissolved into weeks and no arrests were made, the settlement was forced to conclude that the slaves had made good their escape. Life resumed its normal pace, unhampered by a mild winter.

Natalie's days were filled with occasional visits and domestic chores. She could have had a maidservant to perform the menial duties, but she remembered her own freedomless days all too well. So she preferred the chores and neighborly visits that kept her busy and pleasantly tired.

Sometimes, in the deep of night, though, she would awaken, a terrible loneliness gnawing at her body, which was as white and wracked as a martyred saint's. She ached to be held, to be touched. The ache was not sexual. Over the years, her body had nearly forgotten that need. No, it was a purely human need to be touched. In some cases, if that need went unfulfilled, a person had been known to die eventually. Natalie felt as if she had already died and was shriveled up inside.

Whatever beauty her features were proclaimed to have certainly didn't permeate through to the core. Inwardly, she felt old and ugly and haggard. Life was slipping by, and she was astonished to realize she really didn't care. Rarely did her thoughts ever turn to Philippe. He was part of her ancient past. She even doubted whether he was still alive after all those years. Her indifference frightened her.

One January afternoon, when a burst of sunlight finally drove away a dismal, week-long drizzle, Emanuella arrived, full of news. "Solange has left poor Didier! Now ask me, just ask me, who she ran off with!"

With a curve of amusement twisting the ends of her mouth, Natalie arranged dried rosemary, lavender, and thyme in a delicate porcelain Sevres vase. "I give up, Emanuella. Who?"

The Spanish woman's lips made a little moue that Natalie had put forth no effort to guess the identity of Solange's lover. "She ran off to join our former slave Joseph no less!" she said, triumphant at having elicited a lift of Natalie's finely defined brows, which were darker than her hair. "I swear it's true. Heard it from Madame Duclos, who saw them together not six months ago. They were, well, doing you know what in back of the old market house."

"Well, Joseph is undeniably a handsome man," Natalie commented idly, "if one could overlook the hideous tattooing on his chin."

"And his color!" Emanuella said.

Natalie bristled slightly but made no rejoinder to her friend. Color mattered little when one was in love. Didn't she herself love a redskin, as the Indians were called there in the New World?

But Emanuella's next statement did bring her up short.

"Nicolas is back. He stopped by the house to talk with Louis. From what I overheard, it seems Nicolas has established a lucrative trade with St. Genevieve in the Illinois country. Your husband is going to be very happy at that news. You know, I wonder that Nicolas has never taken a wife. Probably too much the *coureur des bois* in him. Even when he's in town, he holes up out at his cabin. I'm so pleased, Natalie, that you and François finally moved into town."

Nicolas!

As Emanuella continued her recitation of local gossip, Natalie's body clock had ceased to function. Seven months ago when last she saw him, he had presented her, in François's presence, what appeared to be an inconsequential gift. A tiny looking glass suspended on a thin gold chain.

"The Apache counts it a great privilege to stare in the looking glass and see himself reflected there," he had told her and François at dinner. "He believes this means that the wearer always keeps him in his—or her—heart."

She wore the necklace constantly. Seven months may have intervened since she last saw him, yet the excitement that curled deep within her was as powerful as that last kiss they had shared . . . how long ago? Years before.

"Natalie? Are you listening?"

Natalie blinked, trying to whisk away the passionate thoughts that surely glistened in her eyes. "I'm sorry. What were you saying?"

"Only that I'm expecting another child." She sighed. *"Toujours coucher, toujours grosse, toujours accoucher!*" Always being bedded, always pregnant, always bearing babies!

A twinge of jealousy twisted through Natalie. Ever since the night she gave birth to the stillborn son at La Salpêtrière, she had felt that her female organs were condemned to barrenness.

That night, after she donned her gauzy nightrail, she studied the reflection in the tiny looking glass suspended on the thin gold chain about her neck. Smoky green eyes stared back at her. Was there truly a woman inside that body? Or was she as lifeless as the wooden statue of the Madonna at the little church?

A scraping noise from the direction of the parlor spun her around. François never returned from his *amours* until nearly sunrise. Wild hope flickered in her. What if Nicolas . . .

The door swung open, and Jasmine stood there. The candles in the socket flickered off her sleek black skin, the short, kinky, glossy hair, and the blade of the wickedly curved knife she held in her hand. Jasmine's eyes gleamed in the sputtering light of the candle that dwindled in its socket. Natalie imagined that the Angel of Death must look just so. But it was more than that. The blood lust Natalie had witnessed the night of the vodun crazed the woman's face.

"You turned François against me," the black woman purred, stalking closer to Natalie.

Natalie looked frantically about the room. Jasmine stood between her and the bedroom door. The only other escape, the gallery door, was on the far side of the room. "That's not so, Jasmine," she countered in a reasoning tone. "Your name was never mentioned between us in that context."

"I have borne François a child. You never will. I mean to make certain of that. I mean to make certain François's daughter inherits what is rightfully hers."

Jasmine slid nearer. The knife she brandished before her swished back and forth through the air like a snake's head prior to its strike.

Natalie whirled and swatted blindly at the candle stub in the wall socket. The flame hissed and sputtered out. At first, the room was as black as the *Baleine*'s hold. Then as her eyes adjusted, slivers of moonlight slipped through the jalousies to limn the dim silhouettes of the two adversaries.

Jasmine laughed softly and advanced. "Perhaps I shall slit your throat as I would a chicken." Her knife carved the air. "And watch the blood seep out until you're as white as wax."

Step by step, Natalie retreated until her thigh brushed the bedstead. Her fingers clutched at the blanket. Fear strangled her throat, but she suppressed the urge to flee. So she waited. Jasmine's small white teeth gleamed triumphantly in the dark. She took another step forward. Natalie's nostrils detected the musky scent of the young woman. At that moment, Natalie whipped the blanket from the bed. Like a net, she tossed it over the black woman. Jasmine screamed a snarl of fury.

Before she could throw off the blanket, Natalie hurled herself at the woman. They rolled on the floor, entangled in the blanket. They grappled for possession of the knife. The nails of Jasmine's free hand raked crimson tracks down Natalie's cheek. Natalie grasped a handful of wiry curls and jerked. The black woman's head arched backward, and she screeched with pain. Both hands came up to tug at Natalie's wrist, and the knife clattered to the floor. Natalie swooped down on it and came up in a crouch over Jasmine.

Common sense told her that it was either her or Jasmine, that if she didn't kill the woman now, the woman would yet find a way to kill her. Yet Natalie couldn't bring herself to do it. She struggled to her feet and pushed the hair out of her face. "If I ever see or hear of you in Natchitoches, I swear I'll find a way to have you killed."

Jasmine's slow, contemptuous smile made a razor-thin line of white in the darkness. "You are weak-willed," she spat.

"Get out! Now! Before I change my mind."

The black woman backed out of the room, her cat's eyes never leaving Natalie's face.

Natalie stood at the top of the stairs and watched until Jasmine was gone. Then she collapsed against the wall, her knees buckling as she slid downward. Shaking with deep sobs, she buried her head between her knees. Why did she stay? Why didn't she try to find refuge elsewhere, in another country? But she knew the doublefold answer.

Guilty gratitude to François; abiding secret love for Nicolas.

CHAPTER

20

NATALIE ACCOMPANIED EMAN-
uella and her young daughter, Marie des Neiges, to what had
been intended originally as the house of the commandant within
Fort St. Jean Baptiste. Used by St. Denis as an office, the commandant's house was a mere frame packed with adobe mud with
earthen floors. A powerful odor pervaded the stockade, seeping
from the latrine that ran along the staked wall nearest the barracks.

"Now you can understand," Emanuella said, holding a scented
handkerchief to her nose, "why I insisted Louis build our home
outside this fort!"

Natalie wrinkled her nose. After all the years at Natchitoches,
this was the first time she'd set foot in the fort and hoped it would
be her last. She had only entered the fort because, while browsing
with Emanuella at the small shops and temporary stalls that had
sprung up along Bayou Amulee, word had come that Joseph had
at last been arrested and was being held at the fort. With a shudder, Natalie recalled her fight with Jasmine nearly six months
before. After that, it was many nights before Natalie was able to
fall asleep without wondering if Jasmine was waiting in the dark
with a knife.

"Where is my husband?" Emanuella asked pleasantly of Charles

Didier. The poor, balding bookkeeper seemed more harassed than usual. His little mouth was quivering.

"What is it, Monsieur Didier?" Natalie asked.

"My wife, madame. They found Solange beneath the brush of Bayou Amulee. She had been . . . strangled."

Emanuella gasped. Natalie asked, "Do they think that Joseph is res—"

Outside, a sudden jabbering and shouting in the direction of the guardhouse drew the two women and the bookkeeper to the door. At the thunderous roll of drums, the fort's raggedy troop of soldiers stood at attention. "Natalie, look! That's Joseph between those two soldiers!"

Natalie followed the direction Emanuella's parasol was aimed in. The handsome black man stood tall and stiff, his hands bound behind his back. He was naked to the waist, and his skin was crisscrossed by thin, red stripes. About his neck was a two-inch spiked collar. It was difficult for Natalie to believe that the dignified Joseph was capable of butchering humans, but the blaze of hatred in his eyes was irrefutable.

St. Denis, dressed as brilliantly as a parrot in a lime-green satin coat and purple knee britches, stepped before the man, said something to the soldiers that Natalie couldn't hear, then moved out of range.

"*Bon Dieu!*" Natalie breathed. "The soldiers are going to execute him!"

Emanuella looked at her as if she were out of her mind. "Why, you sound regretful, Natalie. Joseph ordered the deaths of scores of people. Women and children were hacked to death in their beds. Why, it could have been Louis and I and our children who died in our sleep!"

"Joseph's death will only stir up more resentment among the slaves. His execution is not the way to solve the problem." Against the relentless July sun, she raised her blue-striped parasol, which matched her organdy bodice. "Let's leave, Emanuella. I don't think either you or I, or your child, should watch this."

"Maybe they won't actually kill him," Emanuella offered tentatively.

"Ready . . ."

Natalie gathered up her skirts and shoved her way through the gathering of the fort's contingent of Indians and other men and women from the settlement. They reminded her of carrion birds, waiting avidly for the final throes of an injured animal to end before feasting. Emanuella and Marie followed her as far as the warehouse, where the warehouse keeper jostled them in his haste to witness the rare spectacle.

". . . aim . . ."

Natalie shuddered at the command.

". . . fire!"

When the rifle fire boomed, she had to swallow hard to keep the rising nausea in her throat. "I'm going home, Emanuella. François and—" Again she nearly gagged. "—and I will see you at supper tonight."

She circumvented the dispersing crowd, carefully keeping her head averted from the execution site. She got no farther than the newly constructed St. Francis chapel, where more and more of the men and women had drifted, eagerly sniffing the scent of additional bloodletting. Father Hidalgo, his cadaverous face aglow, held a bound Jasmine before him. Like her brother, she carried herself proudly.

"Harlot! Jezebel!" the priest declared in stentorian tones. "Renounce your wicked ways!"

The slave woman laughed and spat on his brown cassock.

A gasp went up from the throng of watchers at what was tantamount to desecration.

A black child, no more than eighteen months old, toddled out of the church to cling to Jasmine's leg. The hooting and jeering of the people drummed out whatever Jasmine told her daughter.

"What's going to happen?" Natalie asked of the bewhiskered man next to her.

"The whipping horse." He spat tobacco juice on the dry, baked earth. "A slow death for de Gautier's whore." Only then did he look at Natalie, and she saw the dawning recognition in his eyes. "Please excuse me, madame," he mumbled sheepishly, and scurried away.

Between the shoulders of the people in front of her, Natalie watched as two soldiers prodded the barefoot woman over to a wooden edifice that did, in fact, resemble a horse. What happened next Natalie could only think of as something obscene, something

out of one of Marguerite's pornographic stories. The woman was
stripped to the waist and tied hand and foot to the horse's barreled
torso.

The child, sensing the threat of danger, began to whimper.
Father Hidalgo swooped down on the toddler, his wide sleeves
flapping like a giant crow's wings, and lifted the child high. "This
slave's daughter shall be redeemed from the life of sin her demon-
worshipping mother has instilled in her. She shall be raised in
the church to glorify the Almighty."

Jasmine lifted her head. Her eyes flashed fire. "You do that,
Priest, and I curse you, I bring Satan and all his demons down
to hound you for the rest of your life!"

"Put the lash to the wench!" a muleteer shouted. Others joined
in until their demands became a rising chant for Jasmine's torture.

Natalie should have taken some kind of pleasure in the dem-
onstration of justice meted out, but the memory of her own public
torture was still as fresh as the day it had happened years before.
She could almost smell her own flesh burning again, feel the
hideous pain that welled with the blistered, seared skin. Now
there was the shriveled purplish patch between her breasts to
remind her.

A corpulent soldier stepped up to the whipping horse to lay
on the bullhide lash, complete with tail, and an excited murmur
ran through the spectators. The lash flicked through the air. A
collective intake of breath from those watching rustled the stillness
of the moment. When the lash descended, Jasmine's back arched
with the impact. No sound escaped her lips. A thin red line
appeared. Once more the lash came back. The procedure would
be repeated until the spine and rib cage were stripped of flesh.
Afterward, her ears would be sliced off, and the victim would be
left to endure the harsh sun and chill night air until death ended
her torturous pain.

The lash sliced downward several more times before Jasmine
screamed out, an animal's agonized wail, then fainted. Nevertheless, the whipping continued. The skin was flayed until only
a mass of raw flesh dotted with flecks of white bone could be
seen.

Glancing around at the tense mob, Natalie knew there was
nothing she could do to stop the torture. Her impotency infuriated
her. Then her gaze landed on the fear-stricken face of Jasmine's

daughter. The toddler cowered at Father Hidalgo's feet. Natalie knew the child didn't understand what was happening but sensed in some way that it threatened her security.

Natalie pushed her way through the people around her. The young priest watched the lashing with an almost celestial enrapture and didn't notice as she scooped up the child and fled.

"What's she doing?" a soldier's aproned wife called out.

A few turned to see what was going on, but most were so intent on the whipping that they missed the abduction of the child.

With the infant cradled against her chest, Natalie fled through the empty streets. Her mind worked feverishly. Though the priest was Spanish, he still wielded influence through the papacy. He could conceivably demand that she return the child.

Where could she go? Skirting a lumbering wagon, she turned her feet in the direction of Emanuella's house. Legally, the child belonged to Louis Antoine Juchereau de St. Denis since it was an offspring of a slave he owned.

But in the mood the crowd was in, a confrontation between the priest and the commandant could bring problems down about St. Denis's head.

Mired by indecision, she instinctively redirected her steps away from the settlement. In the twilight, she started south along the riverbank, always keeping herself in the shadows of the leafy trees. On a bluff, she paused once, breathless. The little girl was heavy in her tired arms. Somewhere along the way, she had lost her parasol.

She looked behind her. A faint reddish glow appeared in the area of the settlement. Torches were being lit, the better to watch the whipping—or to find her and the child?

The tiny girl was squalling now, and Natalie tried to quiet her as she hurried through the dusk. Three more miles; safety couldn't be much farther. Then she saw it: Nicolas's cabin, crowning a hill that sloped off to the willow-bordered Red River. His log house, set against a backdrop of mulberrys laden with Spanish moss, wasn't as large as the original one he and François had built. Now, though, Nicolas's cabin served only as a layover when his travels brought him back to the base of operations for Louisiana Imports-Exports. The smoke curling from the clay chimney told her he was at home.

Even as she approached, a wedge of light showed at the front, and she knew that he had sensed a visitor and stepped out to investigate. A long rifle was cradled in one arm. When she drew near, within a yard, she looked up into the formidable face. His inscrutable eyes were black coals against the toast color of his skin. She marveled at his shoulder-length hair. He had to be nearing forty, but no gray threaded through the raven strands.

What if he turned her away?

The girl whimpered, and she shifted her in her arms. As usual, Nicolas said nothing, only waited for an explanation. "The child is Jasmine's daughter." Her breath labored in her ears.

Apparently, her simple statement was enough for Nicolas. He stepped aside, saying, "Come in."

The hearth's small fire reflected here and there, giving the place a reassuring warmth. Nicolas laid the rifle in the bracket of stag's antlers anchored above the fireplace, then crossed to her to pry the child gingerly from her protective embrace.

"Sit down," he told her, nodding toward one of the two rush-bottomed chairs before the fire. Its light cast into shadow the dark skin stretched tautly along his jaw.

She felt sudden shyness before this fierce-looking man who knew more about her than any man, even Philippe. Nicolas knew *almost* everything about her. And he understood her all too well.

Grâce à Dieu, though he might know she wanted him, she didn't think he knew that she loved him.

She watched him hold the toddler with the same gentleness and assurance with which he cradled his rifle. "What is her name?" he asked.

"Deborah. At least that's the name Father Hidalgo baptized her with. I think Jasmine calls her Quin-Quin, or something like that."

He took the other chair and balanced the girl on his knee. Her pudgy fingers reached in fascination for the shiny, worn quills that decorated his soot-blackened buckskins. "Tell me what happened, Natalie."

She inhaled deeply to steady herself, and the pungent odor of brewed coffee reached her, along with the tempting odor of cooked meat. She should have been hungry, but the day's earlier events made even the thought of food repugnant to her.

"Joseph and Jasmine were captured sometime during the night.

Joseph was shot this afternoon." She paused, waiting until the words came more easily. "But Father Hidalgo had Jasmine tortured on the whipping horse. I don't even know if she's still alive."

"*Par Dieu!*" Nicolas muttered.

"Ba-ba," Quin-Quin cooed, turning one of the quills in her tiny hand.

"And the child here?" Nicolas asked.

"Father Hidalgo was going to turn the child over to the church. If he had his way, the child would be a cowering fool by the time she is ten."

"I've always thought the church had too much control," he murmured, pushing the child's curls out of her moon-shaped face. "I had hoped here in the wilderness of Louisiana it would be different."

Anxiety propelled Natalie out of the chair. She walked about the room, carefully keeping her face averted from him. "I didn't tell you everything. You're gone so much of the time that I'm not sure how much you're aware of. Quin-Quin's father is François."

"Yes," he said quietly, "I know."

Her hands rubbed against each other. To conceal her agitation, she lightly fingered the stag's antlers. "We both know that my marriage to François has only brought pain to everyone. It was the wrong thing to do at the time, but it seemed the only solution."

Nicolas said nothing. The little girl had fallen asleep, and he rose and took her into the next room to lay her on the bed. Natalie browsed about the room, trying to think of a way to phrase what she really meant to say.

"You can't change past mistakes, Natalie."

Startled by his voice, she looked behind her. He stood with a shoulder braced against the doorjamb, watching her.

Her fingers deserted the antlers, wandered past the powder horn and bullet pouch suspended from a peg, then traced the tattered binding on a copy of *Ovid*. She lowered her voice to little more than a whisper. "If I could make something good come out of all the terrible things that have happened . . ."

She whirled on him. Now the words spilled out of her mouth. "I know it sounds insane, Nicolas, but I have this desperate notion that the redemption of François's bastard daughter, a slave at that, will somehow be my own redemption. By purchasing Quin-Quin from St. Denis and obtaining her manumission, I might somehow be purchasing my own way back to my former life."

He shoved off the oak door frame and crossed the room in two strides to catch her shoulders. He shook her with rough impatience. Her head bobbled, and her mirror necklace bounced against the hollow of her throat. His eyes were slits of anger that burned fear into her. "You're still thinking of yourself! Going back—leaving François. Damn it, Natalie, you've married him! For life!"

"And what if"—her teeth rattled with the shaking— "if I was still legally married to someone else when I married François?" she blurted out.

The shaking stopped, but his powerful fingers dug into her shoulders. "My God, what kind of woman are you?" he said between clenched teeth.

His contempt knifed through her. "You do what you have to do at the moment! I had to survive—you had to kill your father."

His breath hissed in. "There's nothing you wouldn't stoop to, is there?"

"And you?" she countered. Tears blurred her eyes. She saw only the grim scythe of his mouth. "Are you so virtuous? Do you lie to yourself, Nicolas, denying that you want me? Do you run from yourself and run from the truth? That you love your best friend's wife?"

"I could want a trading-post whore," he gritted, "but that doesn't mean I could love her."

She slapped him. Sudden silence sizzled the air in the room. Aghast, she stared at the white imprint that gradually mottled his swarthy skin. Her mouth opened to form some sort of apology, but his hands fastened around her upper arms. He jerked her against him, and she whimpered in anticipation of unidentified fear. His mouth silenced her outcry. Like those days of starving in La Salpêtrière, her lips opened hungrily against his. She pressed against his length, seeking his essence, seeking the source of his power, seeking recognition of a mutual need in him.

His tongue invaded her mouth, striking little sparks in the core of her. Her arms wrapped about his neck, and her tongue invited him farther. *Bon Dieu*, she couldn't help herself. She loved Nicolas Brissac like she had never loved another man. She loved him as a fully enhanced woman, not as the child-woman who had married Philippe.

"God, yes, I want you," he murmured against her feverish lips. "I want to do all the things to you that a man does to a woman." His mouth stroked the hollow of her neck. At the touch of his lips on the bare flesh where one breast burgeoned, her entire frame trembled with the yearning that rippled through her. "I've loved you . . . all these years."

Her head lolled to one side, allowing his lips access to that forbidden part. Instead she felt only the slip of air over her skin as he set her from him.

She looked up into his face for a clue and saw there the self-disgust she had glimpsed there several times before. She was sickened by what she had allowed to happen. Before, her love for Nicolas had been her own secret. Now, not only was it exposed, but it had been made to appear cheap.

Her regret at her weakness thundered in her ears, drowning out everything . . . drowning out the creak of the cabin's door swinging open on its taut leather hinges.

François's glazed pupils slid from his friend to his wife. What he saw . . . it could be misconstrued. Nicolas's big hands clasped Natalie's shoulders. The dress's neckline looked askew. François wasn't certain if it was passion that ignited their expressions or anger.

He braced his weight on his good leg and closed the door behind him. His free hand held a corked bottle, a quarter full. The rich brandy he had consumed to blot out Jasmine's torture had not helped his equilibrium. The slave woman had loved him, really loved him, which was certainly more than he could say for his dear wife.

"I drove over to talk about old times, Nicolas." He tried to make out what lay behind the sudden screen that dropped over the half-breed's eyes. He felt sprouting in his guts an ugly suspicion that had lain dormant in his mind since the day Nicolas returned with the bride he himself had arranged for. "It looks like you're already busy talking about old times."

Natalie ignored his sarcastic innuendo. "I saw the execution today, François." She moved to put distance between herself and

Nicolas. In the candle's faint light, her hair sparkled like *louis d'ors*. God, but she was beautiful! "I saw Jasmine lashed on the whipping horse."

François glanced at Nicolas for a hint as to what was on Natalie's mind, but his partner had turned his back to kneel at the hearth and stir the embers. François knew that Natalie had been aware of his *affaires* all this time. He had wanted her to hurt like he hurt for her. If she had made a scene, cried or begged or gotten angry, she would have been in a class with other women. That he could deal with. Maybe, just maybe, he could have made her . . . Hell, he was getting maudlin.

He said bluntly, "Jasmine died about half an hour ago."

Natalie bowed her head for a brief second, then looked him directly in the eye. "I brought her child here—your child, François."

Anger stirred his liquor-steeped blood. "You are never to meddle in my business!"

"Don't you mean meddle in your *affaires*?"

His gaze went from her to Nicolas, who had risen to stand beside Natalie. François wasn't certain if it was a protective gesture or not, but the mere action riled him. "We're going home."

"Your daughter goes with us," she said defiantly.

Frustration knotted in him. "Why?"

"Because," she said in an empty voice, "the child may be the only hope left to bond us."

The preposterous statement staggered him. His mistress's child, a slave child, bonding them. He almost laughed, but the laughter turned to a sneer. "Do you think a child will bring me to perform my husbandly duties—which you could not inspire?"

Natalie blanched.

Nicolas said, "The child is asleep. Leave her for the night."

Damn Nicolas and his logic and wisdom and—damned complacency with the world! As for his own self, his life was spinning dangerously out of control. He shrugged and limped to the door. "Are you coming?" He tossed the question carelessly over his shoulder to Natalie.

The ride back into Natchitoches was tensely silent, with only the rumble of the calèche's great wooden wheels and the chorus of bullfrogs to rile thoughts that were already highly agitated. Initially, Natalie's interference had infuriated him, but once more the insidious serpent of suspicion slithered through him. Had Nicolas and Natalie been carrying on their own affair the entire time? His mind flashed back over the years, sorting out images of them. Those interchanging glances he had intercepted—had they held nuances he had missed?

He pitched the empty bottle out into the night, immediately wishing he had another. The brandy might blot out the image of their bodies entwined, an image that tortured him, spinning through his brain in tempo with the carriage's wheels over and over. By the time they reached Natchitoches, the settlement's lights had been snuffed—and his supicious had magnified. An instant's cold sobriety flashed through the darkness. Had he been cuckolded? There was only one way to find out.

As if sensing his suddenly resolved purpose, his wife seemed to flee up the stairs to the gallery and down the hall to her bedroom. Her pale blue dimity skirts swished like the tail of a Thoroughbred in heat. Promising. He trailed after her. His wooden leg thudded on each stair, declaring his intent. When he opened the door, she spun around to face him. Her arms were lifted to remove the combs in her hair. The position provocatively thrust her breasts taut against the blue-striped organdy bodice. Something in his face must have given him away. Slowly, her arms lowered to cross protectively before her.

"What do you want?"

He unbuttoned his vest. "To consummate our marriage, Natalie."

The cornered look of the animals that Nicolas trapped edged into the silver center of her green eyes. She had no excuse. She was his wife. With a boundless sense of satisfaction, he felt himself harden, thrusting against his breeches as her breasts did her bodice.

"Why now, François?"

His smiled wryly, even as his fingers worked at his cravat. "The obvious. Because I was unable to before."

"With me, yes," she countered, her voice huskier than usual. "But not with every other female in the Louisiana territory."

He started toward her, discarding his shirt on the settee. He reached out and fingered one of her wispy side curls. "All that has changed."

She turned her head away. "I've changed. I'm not the same

woman you married. Whatever love I might have had for you,
you destroyed with your whoring."

He brushed her gardenia-white cheek with the back of his
fingers. Her sharply indrawn breath pleased him enormously,
even excited him. "I'm not asking for your love or affection." His
hand dipped down between her breasts and located one taut nipple. "I want *foutre*, my dear."

Her head swiveled around at the obscene word. "No!"

"You're my wife, remember?" With that, he ripped the bodice
down the front, and her breasts spilled out over the camisole.
Her hands fought him, and she tried to shove him off balance,
but he was larger and forced her backward to the bed. His free
hand opened his breeches. Never, with even the most practiced
whores, had he felt the excitement bursting in his groin as he did
now.

Natalie tried to scramble across the bed, but he caught one
hose-encased calf and dragged her back. She kicked out at him,
and her fingers arched out to claw his face. He dodged and then
leveled himself atop her. His hands thrust her skirts over her hips.

"Not like this!" she begged.

"It's the only way."

He knew that now. His hands anchored her hips to the mattress. He used the space between her thrashing thighs as a channel
to guide his thrusting organ up into her. At his entry, she arched
off the bed with a strangulated gasp. Otherwise, there had been
no obstruction, no maidenhead to pierce. Only her surprise and
outrage. With that knowledge, his own rage mounted. He plunged
into her time after time, and then came too quickly. With a
muffled groan, he fell across her.

"You've had what you came for," she hissed, pushing ineffectually at him. "Now get out!"

He raised up off her, his arms enclosing her at either side. Her
unbound hair, meshed over the tapestried cover, framed her dead-
white face. A great sadness welled in his soul. "No, I found out
what I wanted to know."

He shoved away from her and rebuttoned his breeches. Something in his expression must have warned her. She struggled from
the bed. Pushing mindlessly at her skirts, she followed him to
the door. "Where are you going?" she asked in consternation.

He retrieved his sword and started down the stairs. Whatever sadness he had initially felt was rapidly being diluted by his anger. He had been betrayed. He ignored Natalie's anxious questions and stalked from the house. He might have been unfaithful to Natalie, but he had never tried to dupe her or to skulk around behind her back. Yet she and Nicolas had done just that. Nicolas, his partner, his best friend.

He would kill the bastard.

Nicolas, his partner, his best friend.

The catchphrases chased each other round and round in his rage-smoked mind as the calèche's gray picked its way through the deep night. The fresh bottle of rum François gulped from periodically only intensified his seething hatred. Shakespeare was wrong, he fumed. There was no fury like a man cuckolded.

He should have known that that half-breed's sixth sense would have alerted him to a trespasser's approach. François, silhouetted by the moonlight, descended from the calèche and stalked toward the cabin door. Nicolas waited just inside in the shadows. Just like the half-breed had always done—waited in the shadows, waited to take his place in Natalie's bed!

François stepped into the darkened room and drew his sword. He could just barely make out Nicolas's eyes. "I've come to kill you, *mon ami.*"

Nicolas's voice held the calm and patience of a priest. "You want to tell me why first?"

"*Merde!* Do you and Natalie take me for an absolute idiot?"

In the silence, he wasn't certain what Nicolas was doing. He heard movement, that was all. He didn't trust the son of a whore.

"You're wrong." Nicolas's voice came from a different part of the room.

François spun toward it. He squinted, trying to focus on the differentiating shades of black.

"Nothing has happened between Natalie and me, François."

"Liar!" He moved toward the shadowy figure. "I've known all along."

The figure evaporated, and François swung around. He cursed the wooden leg that gave his position away while Nicolas moved silently, stealthily. If he couldn't conceal himself, then he would distract Nicolas, his enemy.

"Don't you think I've seen the way you two look at each other, touch each other?" His sword scythed the air. It made no contact, but he heard Nicolas, dodging from its path, bump against something.

"I tell you, François, you're wrong." This time Nicolas's deep voice came from Nicolas's right.

François's sharp blade cleaved the darkness. Nothing. "Am I wrong about the bloodless sheet tonight?" He swung with both arms. *Whoosh. Whoosh.* Emptiness. The damned half-breed had the advantage in that he saw better in the dark.

"You're wrong about everything. Go home. We'll talk about this tomorrow when you're sober."

"Oh, but you're wily, *mon ami.*" Where the hell was the bastard? Keep him talking. "While I was away, did you hang your bloodied sheet out for all to witness the defloration? You assume too much, *mon ami.* The privileges of the proxy over that of the husband, eh?"

"The proxy marriage was your idea, François, when you hurt your leg."

"Perhaps I didn't have to lose my leg." Even as he said it, the suspicion became certain knowledge. Nicolas and Natalie had conspired against him from the first. Take his manhood, and what was left?

"You know that's asinine, François! You would have died if we hadn't amputated."

François's smile was lethal. He stabbed at the traitorous voice. The sharp blade sheared an unobstructed arc. "Goddamn you to hell, Nicolas!" he cried.

He hacked again and again at the unseen enemy and found each time only a void. Sweat and tears mingled in his eyes. "Damn you, Nicolas," he said, weeping, "can't you fight like a gentleman instead of a *sauvage?*"

Suddenly, Nicolas's arm locked about his throat. François's free hand clawed at the constriction. "Bastard!" he wheezed.

"Drop the sword, François."

François felt the vital air seeping from pores. He had to strike now! Wrenching his wrist, he raised the sword and drove backward and downward with it.

CHAPTER

21

Lt. Armand Scoraille tucked
his tricorn under his arm and bowed low over Natalie's hand, his
lips brushing her gloved fingertips. "I will call again tomorrow,
madame, if I may."

Natalie withdrew her hand, held by the handsome lieutenant
just a fraction too long. Having arrived only several weeks before
from Paris, his uniform was in immaculate condition. Soon the
sultry heat, even though it was almost October, would convince
him that the heavy woolen blue jacket, along with the brown
bagwig, was unnecessary for another couple of months at least.
However, St. Denis still managed to turn out in splendid array
after all those years. "Perhaps another time. I leave tomorrow for
Fort Rosalie."

A frown furrowed the brows over the lieutenant's light brown
eyes. He was merely one more among the throng of men already
courting the widow. "Surely, Madame de Gautier, you're not
planning on making the journey yourself?"

She lifted her shoulders prettily. "And why not? I'm half-owner
in Louisiana Imports-Exports, I keep the books and select the
merchandise to be bought and sold."

"Well, *naturellement*, I have heard of this business you run so
successfully."

Natalie didn't bother to inform the officer that it wasn't so much business that sent her to Fort Rosalie as it was a message from Jeanne-Antoinette, who was expecting her first child in a month and wanted Natalie to be there to help with the delivery.

Lieutenant Scoraille continued, "But to travel to the Natchez Trace, madame, it can only be *très dangereaux* for a woman."

Her mouth curved in a wry smile, and, stepping from the company's overhanging porch into the blistering sunlight, she raised her yellow lace parasol. "Two of my employees will be with me. Besides, Lieutenant, I have seen and been through more danger in the last few years than most soldiers see in a lifetime."

A lifetime. She felt as if she had lived several lifetimes, and she had yet to see her thirtieth year. Nevertheless, she felt terribly old.

"Ah, yes," the lieutenant said, touching her elbow sympathetically. "I have heard the tragic circumstances of your husband's death. My condolences." He bowed again, annoying her slightly with his solicitous attentions.

"*Au revoir*, Lieutenant Scoraille," she said curtly, starting homeward. It was impossible for her to feign sorrow at François's death. The real tragedy had been François's life, not his demise. She felt his death had at last set him free. Oh, the settlement still gossiped about his suicide.

All of Natchitoches had known that his depression had driven him to drink and other wild excesses, so the fact that he had died by his own hand wasn't so farfetched. Only St. Denis and herself knew the full accounting given by Nicolas—that he had sidestepped François's driving sword, and François, still immobilized by Nicolas's arm, had inadvertently impaled himself. However incredible, she believed the story. St. Denis hadn't felt it necessary to call for a court of inquiry, although Father Hidalgo had been incensed that the commandant had ignored his accusations that the peculiar circumstances pointed to skulduggery.

She passed by the hotel, stagecoach depot, and the theater and ballroom, all of which had sprung up in the past year due to the town's booming trade. All roads led to Natchitoches. It was the outfitting point for the thousands of people going West. It was the terminus for the eastern end of El Camino Real or the San Antonio Trace. Another route led eastward to Fort Rosalie, where it connected with the Natchez Trace.

Arriving home, she handed her parasol and gloves to Thérèse, who met her at the door. "Is Quin-Quin napping?"

The freedwoman's jowls wattled with her nod. "Yes, madame, but there's—"

"And my baggage, did you have a chance to pack it?" She knew she sounded short-tempered. The conversation with Lieutenant Scoraille about the past had triggered her bad mood. "If not, don't worry about it, Thérèse. I can do it tonight before I go to bed."

"Madame, Monsieur Brissac awaits you in the parlor," Thérèse managed at last.

Natalie's stomach fluttered like a hundred hummingbirds. "How long has he been here?"

"About a half hour, madame. I served him the château wine."

"Good. Please see that no one disturbs us."

Thérèse's large, raisin-brown eyes gleamed with wicked good humor. "They'll have to cross my dead body first, madame."

Natalie closed the parlor doors behind her and leaned against them, waiting for her legs to regain some stability. Her eyes searched the room and found Nicolas, his back to her as he stared through the jalousies. He was fashionably dressed in a dark blue suit with wide skirts and silver-buckled shoes. The silken hose displayed his muscled calves. His black hair was neatly tied back in a queue.

She was glad she had worn the yellow silk damask with the white satin quilted petticoat—but regretted the mobcap that hid her hair.

"I see the English colonies have civilized *Monsieur le Sauvage*," she said quietly.

He took a drink from the footed glass he held. So he drank more easily now.

"You could at least have let me know where you were," she said, this time vehemently. "I worried—"

Without turning, he said, "You've done well with the business, Natalie."

She crossed the parlor to stand behind him. Her fingers ached to caress that broad back. "I heard once you were in Williamsburg's countinghouses—that you had bought shares in a three-ton merchant vessel."

She had also heard he had purchased an indentured servant from Ireland and scandalized Williamsburg by setting the comely lass free. The last Natalie had heard was that the young woman was living with him.

He set the empty glass on the sideboard and turned to face her, his hands at his hips pushing back the front panels of his finely tailored coat. Inwardly, she shrank from the sulfurous eyes. "I kept account of your half of the company, Nicolas," she rambled. "It's all deposited at the Royal Bank of New Orleans."

"As I've said, you've done very well. Much better than I expected."

"You resent my independence, don't you?"

He tossed back the remaining wine in his glass. "I want to sell out to you."

She drew in a deep breath. "I don't deserve your hate, Nicolas."

The corners of his lips curled in a bitter smile. "Oh, I don't hate you. I still want you as much as I ever did, damn you, Natalie."

She reached up to touch the muscle that throbbed in his jaw. He said tightly, firmly, "Don't."

She dropped the threatening hand to her side, blurting suddenly, "Nicolas, I love you!"

He caught her arms and shook her with exasperation. She didn't care. At least he was touching her. "God, Natalie, are you so determined to have your own way that you can't see François would always be between us!"

"François is dead! We're alive!"

His angry glare left her to sweep around the parlor, taking in the damask wall hangings, the silver tea service, the spinet in the corner. His eyes returned to settle on her parted lips. "You and I are mismatched, Natalie. I'm not François. I could never settle down for long. The freedom of always moving on is strong in my blood. The lure of the horizon would soon beckon me like a siren."

"I've waited for you for all this time. I would wait for you to return the next time, however long it might take to exorcise the wanderlust in your blood."

The nostrils of his high-bridged Indian nose flared. "Are you so certain? How do I know that while I'm gone some handsome officer won't keep the lonely nights away from your bedroom? Perhaps the Lieutenant Scoraille already has."

She wanted to slap his barbaric face, to remind him of the indentured servant he had kept and all of the other women he had undoubtedly possessed over the years. Instead, she flung her arms about his neck and pressed her feverish lips against him. He grasped her arms to remove them, but she clung to him. "Nicolas, please," she murmured against his mouth. "Don't make me grovel."

For an answer, he caught her face between his hands and kissed her ruthlessly, his mouth controlling hers. His teeth ground against her soft lips, and his tongue thrust between them with cold, brutal passion. Her bruised mouth returned his savagery. This was what she had waited for.

When he scooped her up in his arms and deposited her on the settee to thrust her dangling legs apart, she felt a liquid fire burn through her in anticipation. "Nicolas, I've waited so long for you. So long."

What matter that his passion was ignited by anger rather than love? What matter if he hurt her? At least she was feeling something at last, if even it was pain. Years . . . years since she had even been kissed. Her breasts had forgotten their need to be touched by a man.

He straddled her with one knee and ripped the panel from her bodice. Her eyes closed. Her breathing thundered in her ears. His swarthy hands cupped each breast, his fingers biting into their milk-white softness. She entwined her fingers with his. "Nicolas, tell me . . . please tell me you love me."

His breathing was harsh. "If I said no, Natalie, would you stop me from taking you?"

The moss-green depths of her eyes glistened. She shook her head. "No," she said huskily. "No, I would still want you."

Dark passion ignited in the depths of his pupils, and he lowered his head over her breasts. She arched her back and gasped when his tongue touched the purple welt of the fleur-de-lis between her breasts, burning his own brand over the old one.

His hand deserted one breast to push up her skirts, but his fingers discovered that she was already ready for him, already moist with the seepage of wanting him so desperately.

His hands came up to cup either side of her face, his fingers digging brutally into her scalp. The scent of her clung to his hands. Bitterness warred with misery for dominance in the set of his mouth. "Do you understand that I won't be coming back after this?"

"Yes, *mon sauvage*." Tears welled at the outer corners of her eyes at the certain knowledge, but her body demanded him no matter what the aftermath.

Again his mouth ravished hers, and she responded in kind— this would be the first and last time she would surrender herself to the man she had loved so long. Her hands worked frantically at the buttons of his breeches. Abruptly, she turned her head from his kiss and propped herself on her elbows. She pressed her face against the smooth skin that sheathed his muscled chest and hard stomach, inhaling deeply of his singular masculine scent.

When she nuzzled over, his hand anchored in her curls and pulled her head backward. "I want you now, Natalie."

She nodded, feeling the pull of her hair at the temples.

With that, he took her, filling her aching cavity with himself, a slow, sure plunging that increased in tempo until she felt engorged, close to bursting. She held on to the feeling growing in her. Too soon what she had waited for so long would be rapidly spent. The moment had to last forever. Oh, God, don't let her forget the exquisite pleasure of this moment, united with Nicolas, at one with her own Nicolas.

Afterward, she lay still on the settee, her eyelids shut tight, and listened to him dress. She waited for him to leave so that she could cry, but he surprised her. He came over to her and rearranged the skirt that was bunched about her thighs, dampened by their lovemaking. Through a tangle of wet lashes, she stared up at his face. "Nicolas, please stay. Please."

He bent over her and kissed the salty tears that spiked her lashes. "*Adieu*, Natalie."

This time Natalie found the journey to Fort Rosalie less pleasant. For one thing, the caravan didn't leave until two weeks later because of unseasonal rains. For another, everything seemed flat— the taste of food and wine, her usual joy in the autumnal colors, her anticipation of being with Hervé and Jeanne-Antoinette again. The company's two freedman, Jeremiah and Samuel, did their best to ease the hardships of the journey, but by the time she had spent three weeks on the trail, with only an oilcloth to keep off the rain, she was thoroughly miserable.

A half-galley out of New Orleans, loaded with merchandise, was anchored below Fort Rosalie's soaring bluffs. At word of the pack train, the soldiers mounted Fort Rosalie's parapet to watch the stream of mules plod toward the village of St. Catherine. The musical sound of the bells tinkling on harnesses brought the people of the concession to their doorways.

Jeanne-Antoinette, leaning against the wooden balustrade on her narrow gallery, spotted Natalie astride the Appaloosa and waved one arm enthusiastically. The young girl started down the steps toward the pack train, her arms outstretched in greeting. Natalie realized that she was very pregnant, all stomach with two thin arms and a round, little face attached and, somewhere below, two feet.

Natalie waved Samuel and Jeremiah on to the company's trading post and reined up before Hervé's little house. Dismounting, she hurried to give Jeanne-Antoinette an affectionate hug. She stepped back, still holding the girl's shoulders, and looked her over. "It appears you're carrying a son as big as Hervé," she teased.

The girl blushed. Natalie realized this was no longer the child who had come over as a casket girl with her on the *Baleine*. She was . . . Natalie mentally paused to figure Jeanne-Antoinette's age. The girl was nearly twenty now.

Bashfully, Jeanne-Antoinette touched her mounded stomach. "Oh, Natalie, I was so afraid the rains would keep you from coming in time."

"I'm glad I didn't wait any longer," she said with a pointed glance at the girl's stomach.

During the rest of the afternoon, the two women gossiped, but when Hervé arrived that evening for dinner, the talk turned to a heated discussion about the newest restrictions France was placing on trade.

"Our business is off," Hervé told her, his sloping brows furrowing down over the usually droll eyes. The hominy that Jeanne-Antoinette had cooked with rabbit might have been tasty, but Natalie's stomach had been queasy for the last few days. "The British are besting us along the Natchez Trace for the trade of the Chickasaws."

She laid down the wooden spoon, unable to eat another bite. "I understand your commandant's stupidity and stinginess is not helping matters."

Jeanne-Antoinette said, "Sieur de Chopart has demanded more land from the Natchez, including even White Apple Village, where their ceremonial pyramidal mounds are."

"Did they surrender their village?"

"Their leader, the Great Sun," Hervé said, "has said he would think about it." The former brigand shrugged his shoulders. "Who knows, but a soldier who came to the post today said he had heard from his Indian sweetheart that the Choctaws were conspiring against us."

"Why, the Choctaws have always been friends of the French," Jeanne-Antoinette said with a dismissing motion of her little hand.

Over after-dinner brandy, talk turned to problems with the Indians at the trading post itself. Natalie, tired from the trip and sleepier than usual, went to bed early—this time alone on a box chair that folded out into a narrow bed.

Sleepy as she was, she lay, wide-eyed, tossing from side to side. Reluctantly, she let her thoughts drift to Nicolas. Abruptly, she bolted upright. Perspiration beaded her temples. With painful clarity, she realized she was pregnant. The queasy stomach, the inordinate sleepiness, the monthly flow that was several days late—the signs were all there. She counted back to the afternoon in the parlor. A little over a month. *Sacré bleu!*

She lay back down and, arm thrown across her forehead, considered the changes the baby would make in her life. Naturally, the fanatical Father Hidalgo would be up in arms about an unmarried white woman having a baby—a woman of property at that. It would be quite a scandal, but she knew she would be able to depend on friends like the St. Denises to rally around her.

Nicolas's child!

She smiled to herself. Whether Nicolas liked it or not, he had given her a part of himself forever.

She would have to be careful. That first time, when she carried Philippe's child, the trauma of the branding had caused her to miscarry. She had been a child herself then; this time, she swore to herself, would be different.

CHAPTER

22

Before the geese had honked southward that autumn, the corn dance was celebrated. It was the most joyous of traditions, one the Natchez had brought with them ages before when they migrated eastward from an Aztec-influenced west.

The Great Sun of the tribe was borne swiftly on his litter by relays of bearers, taking him to the harvest celebration. Feasting and laughter, stately speeches and games filled the afternoon. Then as evening descended, cane torches blazed as brightly as the last rays of the sun on the lowlands beyond the river.

A drummer began to beat a skin stretched across a pottery bowl. Around him circled the young Natchez females, then the warriors. Each carried a gourd filled with pebbles. The women moved from left to right and the men in the opposite direction. During all this, they kept time with their bodies and their gourds to the beat of the drum. When the dancers wearied, they dropped out into the darkness beyond the torches and other men and women took their places.

Celebrating the harvest, fulfillment, and fertility, the dance continued until dawn. But this year what the Natchez Nation celebrated most was a harvest of hatred.

. . .

The Great Sun's plan went into effect on the 28 of November
1729, reckoned by the Natchez as the ninth moon, that of the
buffalo. By European concepts, the time specified for the attack,
the fourth hour, would have been the fourth hour after midnight,
but for the Natchez the time was the fourth hour after daybreak,
or about nine o'clock in the morning.

Natalie was sitting on the gallery with Jeanne-Antoinette, shell-
ing peas, when three Indians approached carrying baskets of dried
and husked corn. Smiling broadly, they spoke with Jeanne-Antoinette in a mixture of French and Indian, and she explained to
Natalie what she understood about the tribute the commandant
had demanded.

"They carry arms for hunting, for a great feast, they say."

Natalie couldn't shake an uncomfortable feeling. While the
Indians talked, she noted that small groups of other Indians entered other houses. Suddenly, from the commandant's quarters,
came musket shots. As if it were a signal, the three Indians fell
upon Jeanne-Antoinette and Natalie. What happened next seemed
to occur all at once.

From the basket, one Indian whipped out a wooden head-
breaker and, with a mighty swing, brought it down on Jeanne-
Antoinette's head, caving in her skull as if it were an eggshell.
Blood and brain matter flew everywhere. Natalie screamed and
shot to her feet. The bowl in her lap thudded onto the wooden
floor. Shelled peas rolled across the gallery like marbles.

One of the Indians, a short, stocky brave, pinned her arms
behind her and prodded her down the gallery steps, but not before
she saw one of the warriors take his hunting knife and slit open
Jeanne-Antoinette's bulging stomach. The red-fleshed baby was
still kicking when the Indian swung it by its tiny ankles and
bashed its head against one of the gallery's cedar posts.

After that, Natalie's body responded to the grunted instructions
of her captor, but her mind was hazed over like the morning fog
off the swamp. When she finally took note of where she was, she
wasn't certain just how much time had elapsed, perhaps a full
day, maybe two. She only knew that she blinked and looked up
from the hands that lay palms up in her lap to see that she was
in another house much like that of Hervé and Jeanne-Antoinette's.
Other Frenchwomen, along with some Negresses, sat in the room
with her or paced the floor. They all wore the same vacant look.

Natalie recognized a woman Jeanne-Antoinette had introduced several days earlier, the German widow Schneeweis. "I see you're coming to yourself," the stout woman said in her mildly accented French, leaning down to peer at Natalie.

Up close, Natalie could make out the widow's faint moustache. "What time is it?"

"About four in the afternoon." The widow nodded her head toward the window. "The massacre looks to be over. The red devils are dividing up the spoils among themselves."

Natalie rose from where she sat on the planked floor and crossed to the window. She felt a sharp pain grind through her at what she saw. The heads of all the French dead were being brought into the public square. Disbelieving, she watched as Hervé's houndlike face was mounted on a staff. Most of the heads lacked scalps. In the center of the square, the mutilated bodies, some of those children, were piled to be left to the dogs and buzzards.

Sometime between that grisly moment and the forced march to the Grand Village, Natalie miscarried for the second time in her life.

A woman's blond scalp tied to a tree limb was the first of a series of gruesome warnings that Nicolas encountered on his trip downriver to New Orleans. A full scalp, taken just above the ears, could be made into several smaller ones, equally negotiable for ten écus, if the scalp looked to be Indian. But a blond one . . . Clearly, an Indian uprising was in the air.

Three days after, word of the massacre at Fort Rosalie reached the capital along with a more accurate tally of the dead given by Father Philibert, Capuchin priest and missionary. Of about 500 settlers, 144 men, 35 women, and 56 children were killed.

Nicolas, sharing confidences in one of the New Orlean's seedier rum houses with a member of Virginia's House of Burgesses, heard the story as it passed in French from slurred lips to slurred lips. "To Governor Perier—and revenge," toasted an older Frenchman whose wig was askew.

Nicolas, though seeming to have hefted his share of mugs, had actually drunk very little, yet the room seemed to expand, the customers and the walls fading away to be replaced by Natalie's face. Often he had put miles and months between himself and Natalie, yet she still managed to claim corners of his mind at the most unsuspecting times. He would love her as long as there was breath in him. All his wanderings would never change that fact.

With painful clarity, he realized that as long as he had known she was alive and all right, he had been able to remove himself from her life. That independent woman with her cool, regal beauty, hadn't she always been able to take care of herself, to adapt, even in the midst of a wilderness? But now . . .

It didn't take him long to gather the few facts and learn that the governor was planning to unite the French forces with the Choctaws and attack. While revenge might be sweet, it could endanger the lives of the captives. Nicolas knew he had to reach the Grand Village ahead of the French and the Choctaws. *Le bon Dieu* willing, Natalie had either escaped, though few had, or she was a captive. The chances of the latter were good since it appeared that for the most part the white women and the slaves, both men and women, had been spared.

He left at once, taking a pirogue, which, even going upriver, was faster than trying to guide a horse through the mire and swamp and tangled underbrush of the trackless forests. Fringed leggings had replaced his satin knee breeches and deerhide moccasins his gold-buckled pumps.

Before he drew near the village, he rechecked his musket's firing pan and priming pin. His knife and tomahawk were fastened to his side like old friends but hung loosely enough. For nigh half a day, he patiently reconnoitered the area, gliding over the withered grass and brown leaves like a light bark canoe over water so that his passing left no trail. The woodsman in him summed up all in his field of vision as either being normal or else unnatural. When his woods sense sounded no alarm of suspicious signs, he at last approached the stockade.

The Natchez houses were made of mud and cane and were dome-shaped like the windmills of La Cadie. Those occupied by the nobility were approximately thirty feet square; those of the lower class were about half as large. The main temple faced east, squatting on a mound of earth about eight feet above the rest of the terrain. On another mound, the house of the Great Sun stood facing the temple.

The Great Sun emerged from the low doorway of his hut. His face was painted vermilion, and he wore a half-crown of flamingo feathers and a loincloth, along with a fur robe mantling his shoulders. In his head, he carried a red stick decorated with not white but red feathers—symbolic of war.

A war dance was already in progress. The warriors had painted different parts of their bodies with various colors of mud—black, red, yellow, gray, smeared from hand to foot. Their belts were ornamented with bells or shells filled with pebbles that clicked and clanked. The braves cavorted about the village's central plaza. Meanwhile, the old men were coloring war clubs red, obviously preparing for a large-scale attack.

Nicolas had learned enough about this particular tribe to know that captives were usually made to sing and dance for several days in front of the temple before they were delivered as recompense to the relatives of persons who had been killed. With the time that had elapsed, he figured that Natalie was no longer held in a communal building but had integrated into one of the households. Which?

Occasionally, a bedraggled Frenchwoman crossed the compound, weighed down with an armful of logs or toting heavy kettles of water. None of them was Natalie. Time was running short, and a stealthy search of each hut was out of the question.

A frown creased the high bridge of his bladed nose. He was attacking the problem as a white person would, looking at the problem from the aspect of the difficulties rather than searching for the simplistic approach.

It would be his *manito* against theirs.

He rose from his surveillance spot at the base of a twenty-foot canebrake and sauntered boldly into the village. At first, no one took note of him, but as his confidence-proclaiming strides took him nearer to the plaza, heads started to turn. The naked Natchez children ceased playing *pelotte* with the fist-size ball of deerskin packed with Spanish moss and stared at the buckskinned stranger. A weathered old woman grinding maize paused and flicked him an impassive glance. The village's mangy curs snapped at his heels, and scrawny chickens pranced quickly out of his path.

Two painted warriors halted their dancing and descended on him. Ignoring their hostile looks, he walked directly to the temple and removed the white-clay peace calumet that hung from the tall red pole near the doorway.

"*Mikilish hatak!*" shouted the chief, demanding he halt.

Pipe still in hand, Nicolas, looking down from his greater height,

asked guilelessly, "Am I not covered by the smoke of peace?"
Purposely, he spoke in English.

The warriors slowed their charge. With the British as allies of
the Natchez, they assumed he was an English trader. Safe for
the moment, he launched into Creek then, which the Natchez
understood for the most part, at least better than English. "I have
trade goods that are both superior and cheaper than the French
stock, and the English rum is as potent as the best French brandy."

Invited into the Great Sun's cabin, he accepted the calumet's
bowl, which was passed from the chief to four or five of the more
distinguished princes. Atop their heads, they wore a tuft of longer
hair, which hung over the left ear. After Nicolas inhaled and
passed the pipe to the malodorous prince on his left, he proceeded
to relate that his trade goods were in his canoe cached upriver
beneath the riverbank underbrush. Deftly, he turned the discussion to the white captives he had noticed in the village.

The chief launched into a wordy description of the coup the
Natchez had performed on the French. For all the Great Sun's
boasting, Nicolas could see that the chief was concerned about
the consequences of having defied the mighty French nation.
Eagerly, he questioned Nicolas about the possibility of support
from the Cumberland settlements, which were English.

Nicolas let a suitably lengthy interval pass in which he seemed
to be giving much consideration to the Great Sun's question. At
last, he drew dramatically on the calumet's stem, exhaled, and
replied, "Great Sun, I'd be willing to act as one of your emissaries
on my travels back through the Cumberland to the English seaboard colonies. If I take one of your French captives with me, I
could better convince my government of your magnificent feat
against our shared enemy, the French dogs."

The suggestion did not work quite as he had hoped, for the
Natchez chief clearly meant to make the choice of the captive
who would accompany Nicolas. After all, the chief explained,
relieving one of the warriors of his reward could result in bitter
feelings. The choice would have to be considered and Nicolas
would be informed the following day.

That evening, he ate a rancid stew of dog meat and watched
the monotonous ceremonial dancing about the smoky fires. The
warriors wore water-repellent swanskins about their shoulders as
mantles. The bucks were growing inebriated with the plunder of

wines and liqueurs taken from Fort Rosalie. Syphilis, smallpox, and alcohol were gradually decimating the native population.

Casually, his gaze moved beyond the pall of smoke to the doorways of the various cabins. Did Natalie watch from within one of those cabins?

The pain of loving her and never having her had filled him with rancor over the years, making it difficult to think of her without anger. Now, all he could think was that she had to be alive. Or else he faced the yawning emptiness that had been his life before she came into it with her imperious little gestures and those quick flashes of humor that had wedged between the panels of emotional armor he had donned as the son rejected by Sieur Damien du Plessis.

When the earlier group of dancers withdrew beyond the ring of firelight and others took their places, Nicolas thought it time to seek out the cabin appointed to him, smaller than those of the nobility. Inside waited the Natchez maiden who was designated as his for the night. A banked fire gave off subdued light. He saw that she was tall and comely despite the tattoos that marked her chin. She wore a soft deerskin skirt that was beaded at the hem and a tunic banded with shells—and the mirror necklace he had given Natalie.

Pushing back her back curtain of hair, she rose from the fur-covered platform and crossed to him. *"Tsĭshia?"* she asked. Her brown fingers indicated the area of her groin. Unself-consciously, she took his hand and drew him back to her bed.

He lay beside her and stared into her sloe eyes, but it was pale green eyes and sun-drenched hair spilling over the platform that his mind's eye saw. Nevertheless, the Natchez maiden was going to be insulted if he did not take advantage of the gift offered a guest by the host. And an insult wouldn't prompt her to talk about the necklace.

Tentatively, she touched his crotch and said, *"Átcha,"* referring to his sex organs in general, then asked, *"Mishmish-kip táma'l?"*

"No," he told her, she wasn't a homely woman. That wasn't the reason for his soft manhood.

Satisfied, she set out to rectify the problem. Even with Natalie's face haunting him, his body responded to her seductively manipulating hands and lips. He took her at once, feeling the intense but fleeting pleasure of muscle contractions that convulsed his entire frame. Afterward, she curled up, her back to him, prepared to sleep, but he began to talk to her, stroking her nape and occasionally plying her with seemingly aimless questions.

At last, he had the information he sought. A brave had given her the necklace. Four or five women with blond hair and of Natalie's height and slenderness had been taken captive. Their ages could vary; it was difficult to tell from the Natchez descriptive term of years. Two captives were lodged with the same warrior and his family. Two or three more were distributed throughout the huts of the lower ranks of the Natchez. One was housed with a prince of the tribe.

Seeing that the Indian maiden was becoming aroused again, he ceased his stroking, which she dutifully accepted and went off to sleep.

He stepped out into the frosted moonlight and marked the hut where Natalie might be. Once again, he opted for boldness. He began to sing drunkenly in English and staggered along. At that time of night, few were sober enough to question him. At the predetermined cabins, he introduced Natalie's name in a slightly louder singsong.

The first of the described huts elicited no response, but from the second he heard, "Nicolas, here!"

Abruptly, he halted before the hut. She was alive! A smart slap came from the cabin's exterior, followed by the cursing of an old woman in the Natchez language, something about Natalie awakening the dead. Nicolas wasn't that fluid in the Tunican dialect.

He sang again, introducing the French word *patience* several times between two bawdy English stanzas. He could only hope she understood. After a while of rambling drunkenly about the area, he circled behind the hut where Natalie was. Recalling the cabin he had just quitted, he tried to judge where the platforms would most likely be situated in Natalie's hut. With his knife, he passed a good hour and a half sawing as quietly as possible at the cane-and-mud wall. He dared not go any slower, for fear the cabin's resident warrior would return from the dance. A two-foot square took shape, large enough for a slender woman to wriggle through.

Carefully, so carefully, he removed the loosened portion, hardly daring to breathe. When he perceived that a human back blocked the hole, he lost all his breath. Then Natalie's face appeared. Incredibly, she was smiling, with tears glistening on her cheeks. He took her outstretched hands and pulled her through the aperture.

When she could stand, she flung her arms about him and wept silently, her narrow shoulders quaking convulsively. He held her for a moment and caressed her matted hair. She would need to draw strength from that small comfort before they began the arduous undertaking of making good their escape. That they would escape offered no problem; he was that sure of his capabilities. What he would do once he reached Natchitoches with Natalie, or without her, was the problem. The woman that had fascinated him from the first, and continued to do so after all these years, possessed a *manito* equal to his.

He wondered if she expected him to show a typical male's concern for any possible violation that might have been inflicted upon her by one or several of the bucks. That she was alive was all that mattered; the white man put too much of a premium on a woman's chastity. Still, around her he had to make himself think as a white man would.

"Are you all right?" he asked softly, his blunt forefinger soothingly stroking the intriguing cleft of her chin.

"I knew you'd come," she whispered between breaths, still clinging fiercely to his shoulders.

He sighed. "Damn you to hell, Natalie." But for a brief moment, he permitted himself the enjoyment of her lithe body molded against his.

CHAPTER

23

With abstraction borne of absolute exhaustion, Natalie squinted against the unforgiving sunlight, watching the sweat beads roll down Nicolas's cinnamon-colored flesh to seep into his belt line. The Natchez, she knew, would not give up a single captive easily. Their headlong escape from the Natchez Grand Village had taken five full days—and sapped her strength. For most of that time, the need for silence and haste had overshadowed all else. Only a few words were exchanged—mostly orders given tersely by Nicolas. Not until he was paddling the canoe up the Rivière Rouge did the tension lines about his mouth fade into their usual impassivity.

He wedged the canoe between the reeds and cattails. Unsteadily, she rose to her feet from her perch at the prow of the birchbark canoe. The hem of her calico dress hung in tatters with the skirt split up the front, exposing a thigh encased in a ripped and stained white cotton stocking. Nicolas was waiting for her, holding out his hand, but when she stepped onto mushy landfall, her stiff limbs gave way, and he caught her up in his arms, carrying her up the partially wooded, partially sandstone slope to his cabin.

At the kick of his moccasined foot, the door swung open. She hated for him to reach the bed. This moment, cradled in his arms, was one that she wanted to stretch in her memory. Yet the moment her head touched his mattress, her lids involuntarily closed.

When next they opened, candlelight softly lit the room. Nicolas was standing at the foot of the bed, his forearm braced against the bedpost. He was still naked to the waist, but his dark face had been freshly washed, and his hair and lashes glistened with waterdrops. Those black eyes were staring at her with the old wanting—and frustration.

"Marry me, Nicolas."

"No."

She gambled. "I was carrying our child. During the Natchez raid, I lost it."

His eyes flared in astonishment. His arm dropped from the bedpost and he straightened, arms akimbo. His eyes perused her as carefully as he would a war trail, searching for trickery. Then exasperation tightened the muscles about his mouth. He looked as if he wanted to shake her. "And what about that insignificant detail back in France—your first husband?"

She pushed herself up on one elbow, and her hair, matted with dirt and twigs, tumbled over one scratched, bare shoulder. Her hands knotted into fists, and her eyes stared up into his beseeching him to understand what she had to say. "Nicolas, I was scarcely sixteen when we married. We were both of the aristocracy—the Golden Couple, we were called."

Nicolas turned from her and picked up his knife, brushing both sides of it across a whetstone in preoccupation. She understood Nicolas; she knew that he didn't want to hear her story, and yet did. The velvet skin stretched over his broad back where two dark curves marked the ridges of strength in his shoulders.

"I was married to him for only four years!" she went on relentlessly.

It was now or never, for she knew he would drift out of her life, this time for good, unless she could somehow convince him otherwise.

"After Philippe's uncle issued a *lettre de cachet* against both of us, we were never to see the light of day again! And I—" The words caught in her throat at the memory of the terror.

Nicolas put aside the knife and whetstone and paced before her, his fine lips taut. Impatiently, he ran his fingers through his damp, shoulder-length hair.

"I can't tell you the horror that each day brings in one of those prisons. If Philippe is still alive, after almost eight years of being caged like an animal, he's not the same man I married." Her hands covered her face in an effort to hold back her old fear and anguish. "God, Nicolas, I'm not the same woman. Natalie du Plessis died the day she was branded."

Abruptly, his pacing halted before her. He thrust aside her hands and jerked her chin up so that he could see her face exposed in the candlelight. The sinews of his neck stood out. "Du Plessis? Your husband is Philippe du Plessis?"

She nodded, her brow knit in perplexity. "You know of him?"

A bitter smile cracked the hard cast of Nicolas's expression. She felt something as dangerous and silent as a grudge hovering over her. "He is my half brother." His voice had the brightness of a little boy's knife.

She felt the lime-washed walls go liquid. They began to ripple and flow past her. A current tugged her down.

Not like this! she wanted to scream. *Not out of anger and retribution.*

The wedding was being held in the St. Denis home. As commandant of the settlement, he had the right to perform all ceremonies in the absence of the priest. Of course, Father Hidaglo wasn't absent from Natchitoches, but Natalie quailed from taking religious vows of matrimony when the church refused to recognize divorce.

Nicolas was derisive and needled her while she dressed for the wedding. "You seemed willing enough to violate the tenets of the church the first time," he said mockingly with a sardonic arch of one brow.

She whirled on him and hurled her pink damask slipper at his chest. He dodged it agilely. "I had no alternative, damn you!" she spat.

He crossed the room in two quick strides and grabbed her wrists, pinning them against her chest. He glared down into her ashen face. "Marrying you is going to give me great pleasure, your ladyship. I feel almost that *le bon Dieu* has a sense of justice."

She had stretched on her toes and kissed him with a woman's savage need to strike back in the most effective way she can. Only the gentle way his mouth dominated hers made her capitulation to the impending wedding bearable—that and the full, incredible story of Nicolas and Philippe. Now she could understand and forgive Nicolas his reprisal.

For the wedding, she wore an open robe of antique pink silk damask with a petticoat of silver lace flounces over a domed hoop. The silver lace also adorned her three-quarter-length sleeves and her stomacher. A furbelowed pink ribbon necklace graced her slender neck, and Emanuella's silver lace mantilla, anchored in her upswept tresses, trailed the ground.

Natchitoches had never seen such a beautiful woman as on that day.

Nicolas was more sedately dressed in a black satin frock coat and knee breeches, but his waistcoat was of intricately embossed and embroidered scarlet velvet. He dominated the roomful of dandies.

When she and Nicolas knelt before St. Denis, her hand was icy in Nicolas's. His warm fingers caressed hers reassuringly, as if to impart a message of love despite the circumstances of the solemn rite.

Behind her, she could hear the rustling of broadcloth and silks and the occasional clank of a sword. After all these years of waiting for Nicolas, she secretly feared that someone like Father Hidalgo would step forward to protest the marriage. She forced herself to listen St. Denis intone the words of the marriage ceremony.

"As Commandant of the Upper Cane River and by virtue of the power granted me by the King of France, His Majesty Louis XV, I do hereby declare Natalie du Plessis de Gautier the wife of Nicolas Brissac."

With that, she looked up into the stern countenance of her half-breed husband and glimpsed the light of love shining in his dark eyes before the Indian in him erased all expression. Somehow, as she offered herself up to his gentle kiss, she felt certain that their love would make everything come right.

"You have my love," Nicolas said. "Do not make me regret it."

So different had Philippe and François been from Nicolas. She had been able to deal with the first two men in her life through the potent combination of intelligence and feminine wile. Nicolas she could not so easily manage, even after a year of marriage.

"Do I?" she countered. His face above hers was barely distin-

guishable in the dark of their bedroom. "Are you so certain I have
your love? What if you don't return from Williamsburg? What
good then is this love of yours I have?"

"There is not—nor ever was—any woman in Williamsburg who
had the love I give you."

Her fists thudded his shoulders. "I'm not talking about other
women, Nicolas! I'm talking about danger and death. I'd swear
that you men think with your—"

"*Oui?*" he drawled.

She ignored the amusement in his voice. "Damn you, Nicolas,
why must you act as a—a—"

"Espionage agent for certain English colonies?" he supplied,
and she could imagine that sardonic lift of one black brow.

"*Mais oui!* As a spy! What happens in the English colonies is
their business, not ours. You'll end up getting your neck stretched
at the end of a rope—all for some foreigners!"

She felt the mattress give as he rolled from atop her and strode
to the open French doors. That summer, Nicolas had added two
more rooms to his cabin, one this spacious bedroom designed
expressly by herself and the other a bedroom for the child she
desperately hoped for.

His back to her, hands on his hips, he casually watered her
recently planted cape jasmine. Exasperation filled her. "Nicolas,
you're not listening to me!"

He half turned, his jutting shaft silhouetted against the moonlit
night. "Frenchmen, Englishmen, Germans—we all have to live
together on the same continent, Natalie." Amusement no longer
tinged his baritone's voice. "The only way we can do that is as
free men, not under the thumb of another country."

"What about me? What about us?"

He padded over to her. "We have now. We have this moment.
Can anyone say for certain that he has more than that?"

He was right, this man of hers. In reply, she took his callused
hand and drew it down to that part of her that evidenced her
want of him.

CHAPTER 24

New Orleans,
Colony of Louisiana   May 1744

IN THE GOVERNOR'S IMMENSE
ballroom, gaily uniformed officers danced with bejeweled women
dressed in satins and silks. The glittering light of hundreds of
candles shimmered off Natalie's fuschia taffeta. Lustrous pearls
beaded the ball gown and lace draped from its sleeves. Additional
pearls were looped through her elaborately arranged and powdered curls. Though she was nearing her forty-fourth year, she
still drew the masculine approval of every man in the room.

She wanted only one man's approval, and that wasn't likely to
be forthcoming under the circumstances.

The new governor of the Louisiana colony, the grand Marquis
de Vaudreuil-Cavagnal, flirted outrageously with her as he paraded the slender beauty through the steps of the minuet. Angry
with Nicolas, she laughingly encouraged the governor's attentions—and studiously ignored Nicolas.

In less than two years in the post, Vaudreuil had set a new
precedent for graft and corruption under a lax and venal administration. He was accused of favoring the soldiers, who bullied
and insulted the citizens, and was said to surround himself with
a small group of favorites who flattered him and thus received
many economic privileges.

When dinner was served, Natalie covertly appraised him from

her end of the immense rosewood table, adorned with the best silver and crystal. He seemed of a genial and kindly nature, and she thought it paradoxical that the man was capable of the vile acts rumored about him. Especially when he had established a court where court dress for his grand balls was *de rigeur*. She counted his soldierly courtliness and great dignity a plus for the backwoods capital. He had created out of the far-flung outpost a fashionable little court closely resembling that at Versailles.

He was fond of pomp and splendor, especially in military display. The upper class of the colony vied for an invitation to his sumptuous dinners. The fact that he had issued an invitation to two of Natchitoches's Canadian entrepreneurs, St. Denis and Nicolas, amused her. The governor would have been astonished to know that Nicolas Brissac's lovely wife of fourteen years had been a felon at La Salpêtrière—and even more surprised to learn that the erudite Nicolas was a half-breed. Over the years, most of Natchitoches had managed to forget the fact, not that Nicolas gave a damn.

Emanuella, who sat two people away from her, swore she had heard that Vaudreuil took money from the city treasury to deal in liquor, which he sold to the lazy and undisciplined soldiers, Negroes, and Indians.

"Madame Vaudreuil keeps right here in her house every sort of drug," Emanuella had whispered when the two women were having their hair powdered before dinner. "They say the drugs are sold by her steward."

Natalie lifted the powdering mask over her face, and the Vaudreuil family's hairdresser sifted the powder from the dredger over Natalie's crown of white-gold curls, which was now invaded by strands of silver, giving her hair the appearance of sun-streaked highlights. "Whatever Vaudreuil's done in Louisiana," she mumbled from behind the mask, "it's an improvement over twenty years ago."

She could still remember her first sight of the dismal little settlement of huts that was suppose to be the capital of the vast colony.

"Bah," Emanuella said. "New Orleans is notorious as a town of loose morals. Why, murder and robbery are commonplace here!"

"Is that why you pleaded with Louis to take you to one of the gambling dens along the riverfront?"

Emanuella's lightly painted lips pursed in a moue. At forty-three, the Spanish aristocrat had plumpened but still possessed a sultry Latin beauty that was counterpoint to Natalie's slender, golden loveliness. "Arguing with you is futile, *chérie*."

Natalie recalled her friend's words as she partook of one of the little candied orange peels topped with sugared rose leaves. Nicolas had said almost the same words to her the evening before as they dressed for dinner. They had disagreed over something unimportant, so unimportant she couldn't remember what, but underlying it all was her continual worry for his safety. His work as an agent for the English colonies had led him even deeper into espionage.

"What good will it do me if you're hanged as a spy?" she had demanded. It was the same argument, the old one, between them. Their life together certainly wasn't placid, would never be so.

He had paused in unbuckling his stock. His black eyes had passed scathingly over her. "As a wealthy citizen of a French colony, you lead a fashionable, social life of ease, Natalie. Have you forgotten what it was to be an outcast, to enjoy no privileges—especially freedom? At least the English courts feel that a person is innocent until proven guilty."

Wearing only her camisole and pantalettes, she had whirled on him, hands anchored about her wisp of a waist, and spat, "I haven't forgotten anything, especially how it felt all the times when you were gone on those—those secret assignments, not knowing if I'd ever see you again!"

He had grunted with exasperation. "You knew I was in the English colonies."

"Nicolas, you're not English, you're French! Why must you hobnob with these English colonists?"

"I'm neither English nor French. I am a free man. And until every man is a—"

"You are a married man, a detail I sometimes think you'd like to forget!"

"It's impossible to argue with you," he had snapped. "You're irrational and illogical when you argue."

"You think this—this spying is rational? What do you think will—"

"Shut up!" He had grabbed her arms and shook her. "Do you want every servant in Vaudreuil's household to hear you?"

At that, she had flounced into the adjoining dressing room and had refused to speak to him since.

Now her eyes sought out his leonine head, three seats away. At her glance, he made some excuse to the flirtatious brunette on his right and rose from the table. Despite the voluble conversation about the table and his discreet leave-taking, more than one feminine glance followed the departure of that broad back.

Age had rendered his formidable features impossibly handsome. The white that streaked his hair made him appear terribly distinguished. Unlike most men of fifty-odd years, he had not added a paunch but was still lean and hard. In comparison, Louis St. Denis, on her left, looked peaked and unwell. The great man was getting on in years, she realized. He was nearing—what?— sixty-eight?

"Do you know," gossiped the heavily rouged woman nearest her, "that the king's mistress is said to be frigid?"

Natalie forced her attention back to the pretentious matron. "Ah, well, a man can be happy with any woman as long as he doesn't love her," she said, and reached for the cut-glass goblet of wine.

"*Oui,*" replied the woman, slightly flustered by the non sequitur, "but La Pompadour only keeps her place by procuring the king's numerous mistresses. Imagine!"

"Imagine," Natalie parodied. She watched Nicolas return to his seat, wondering what it was that could have taken him from the room for less than the span of two minutes.

The painted woman seemed unaware of Natalie's disinterest in continuing the conversation. "Why, it is said the king prefers the very young and preferably virginal because he fears diseases. And I have been told firsthand that he houses the young women who serve his pleasure in a hotel he keeps on rue Saint-Merderic in Deer Park."

"Our cloven-hoofed king should call the place Stag Park," Natalie replied distractedly.

The woman tittered behind her swishing fan. Natalie was relieved of continuing the conversation by the gentle prodding of St. Denis's elbow. When she looked down, he was holding a folded scrap of parchment. "For you," St. Denis said with a sly smile. "From your husband."

She took the note and opened it, holding it below the table, out of sight of her feminine neighbor's prying eyes.

I think you are being unreasonable, and I think days from now you will agree. However, I am thoroughly miserable at being out of sorts with you. I confess that I love you, you bitch!

She looked up and caught Nicolas's dark eyes watching her. She flashed him a glorious smile. Tonight, somehow she knew with a certainty that tonight she would conceive.

The wild peaches were in bright, casual bloom, and the soft spring breeze played with the fuzzy puffs of dandelions. Gently, Quin-Quin blew on the dandelion held between her fingers, and the laughing eighteen-month-old Reinette toddled on dimpled legs to catch the floating puffs.

From the cool shadows of the gallery, Natalie watched the two playing. An affectionate smile nudged at the corners of her lips. Quin-Quin was as handsome as her mother. Natalie thought it strange that the young woman carried herself with the same regal command her mother had, yet the twenty-two-year-old Quin-Quin had never really known Jasmine and thus had no example to follow.

It never occurred to Natalie that she also moved with that same stately grace peculiar to aristocracy or royalty.

Her gaze drifted to Reinette, and a deep surge of love tugged at her heartstrings. Nature had been contrary, leaving her infertile that night in New Orleans she had been so certain she would conceive. Instead of giving life, nature had taken that of their old friend, St. Denis. For nearly two years, she remained barren, until a night when Nicolas had roused her from her sleep and she barely recalled the coupling the next morning. So unfair. Yet looking at the results, that adorable mite of humanity, she forgave nature the trickery.

She thought, If only I can hold this moment in my memory, my daughter's pudgy little hands grasping for the elusive dandelion puffs.

Late in life had come Natalie's greatest blessings. First Nicolas—or, at last, Nicolas, she rephrased her musing—and then her daughter. After all the heartache of her earlier years, she realized that a person could only appreciate the miracle of a sunrise when he has waited in darkness.

She wanted to tell that to Nicolas. He would understand, after wandering through the darkness of his childhood. As always, at the thought of her *sauvage*, she felt the urgent welling of love and wanting deep within her.

"Quin-Quin," she called out joyously, "I'm going down to the river. Keep an eye on Reinette."

"*Oui*, madame," the pretty black girl called out, and waved.

Concern wrinkled Natalie's brow with lines as faint as those crow's-feet at the corner of her eyes. Quin-Quin's future was uncertain. The girl was neither fish nor fowl. As a *gens de couleur libre*, she had the right to put the initials F.W.C. after her name—free woman of color—but she wasn't accepted by the rest of her race, enslaved there in Louisiana's wooded wilderness. The few Negro males of her own age who managed to obtain manumission early in life were usually sent off to France by their benefactors for further education. Such a step was unheard of for a female.

Natalie shook her head. She would not let the slight shadow of worry invade her jubilant mood. Picking up her crepe skirts, she strolled across the well-manicured lawn toward the dock, out of sight below the roll of the wisteria-wooded hills. Beyond, the pink tailfeathers of the day were fluttering at the western horizon.

Through the fragile wands of cattails, she glimpsed the dock and knew that Nicolas was somewhere close by fishing. She had practically pushed him out the door that morning, insisting that he take the day off. Between the demands of the export-import-business empire they had created and that "other activity," as she uneasily referred to his subterfuge work with the English colonies, he had little time for relaxation.

Rustling among the crepe myrtle brought her spinning around. It would be just like the Indian in Nicolas to sneak up on her. She saw not Nicolas, however, but a stooped, bony man. The upper half of his face was a colorless membrane stretched over the skull. He looked old and young at the same time, like a hundred-year-old newborn infant. A scraggly beard concealed the lower half of his face. A stained red cravat drooped about his scrawny neck like a noose about a skeleton.

"Natalie." His voice was a croak.

A small frown creased two vertical lines between her brows. Something about the man was familiar. *Bon Dieu!* She felt as if she were wading through a nightmare. Distance and fog rushed in on her.

"What do you want?" she rasped.

"My wife. I've come for my wife."

She saw in his eyes the insanity, turned down like a lamp wick but ready to ignite. She was looking at a man who, after years in prison, was twisted in body as well as soul. "Philippe . . ." A silence trembled with her whisper. "I'm not the same Natalie you married. I'm no longer your wife. Forgive me."

His eyes glowed in the sockets cratered by time and torture. "I know. I know about your bigamous marriage!" She shrank back from his windmilling arms. "And that half-breed you're living with." From somewhere, the wildly flinging hands produced two pocket pistols.

"Philippe," she said shakily, "let's talk about this."

"I didn't spend a quarter of a century in prison waiting to talk! Fabreville died before I could take my revenge, but did you know his son has been granted my title of Marquis de Marchesseau— and my estates of Maison Bellecour?"

"No, I didn't." If she could keep him talking . . .

"I have nothing left but you, and you—even you have deserted me!" He backed away from her, walking jerkily like a puppet moved by unseen strings.

For an eternal moment, she stood rooted, staring past him, past the present moment toward the dark future that tapped insistently on her temples, begging to be let in.

Reaching the line of cattails, Philippe turned and lurched toward the dock with a celerity surprising for the rickety frame.

Nicolas! He was going to kill Nicolas! "No!" she screamed as she hurtled down the slope after him.

For years, Philippe had apathetically accepted his imprisonment in the Bastille's almost luxurious cells, those reserved for victims of *lettres de cachet.* He had been allowed to shave and bathe regularly and was served good food.

One day, he had always told himself, one day he would be free. One day he and Natalie would return to his beloved Maison Bellecour, once again they would be the Golden Couple . . . one day. That thought had been his lifeline. Something he could cling to. One day the political situation would change. Nothing ever remained status quo. Things could be much worse, he had told himself. For instance, if he forced a prison break and was caught.

One day. Be patient. One day.

Then word had filtered through the fortress walls of the Bastille that Louis XV had at last been crowned king. Philippe's joy was short-lived. He had learned the Duc d'Orléans had merely exchanged the powerful position of regent for that of minister.

The days slipped into weeks and months and on into years. Always he worried: What had happened to Natalie? Had she escaped Fabreville's talons? Often he had awakened in the night, her name on his lips, his sheets soiled like those during his puberty.

Rumor came that the duc had died of apoplexy some time before in his mistress's arms. In truth, he had died of excesses—too much liquor, too much food, too many and too varied bed partners.

Philippe had learned that the opposition, theDuc de Burgogne had taken d'Orléans's place as minister and advisor to Louis XV. For a while, Philippe had held out hope that his *lettre de cachet* would be rescinded. Then he had learned that his archfoe, Fabreville, had inveigled himself into the intimate confidence of the Duc de Burgogne.

Someday became forever.

He knew then that his period of apathy had ended. Someday, somehow he would escape or die trying—just as the half-breed who now called himself Natalie's husband would die.

Philippe pushed Natalie's grappling hands away and shoved through the undergrowth toward the riverbank. If he had hoped to take the half-breed by surprise, Natalie's scream, as well as his own noisy approach, brought the Indian spinning where he knelt on one knee.

"She's mine, not yours," he told the man called Nicolas. It was all he could do to control the fury that palsied his hands so that the two pistol barrels waved erratically.

The half-breed merely watched him with steady eyes, but prison life had taught Philippe enough about cornered men to know that this one looked like a caged cat about to spring. At once, his thumbs cocked both pistols—at the same time that Natalie thrust herself between him and the savage.

The pistol shot that blew a hole in her breast took the breath from his own. Stunned, he watched his beloved slide to the ground—and the damned savage cradle her against him with a cry that curdled the blood.

Red and gold sparks went off behind Philippe's eyes, eyes that gave false witness to a soundness of mind that wasn't there. He aimed the other pistol at the great Indian and finished what he had come for. No, not everything. There remained one more thing to do.

From the lush lawn above the river, Quin-Quin paused in the game of puffing on the dandelions. She thought she had heard gunfire. The old man who had talked to her and Reinette and told them he was looking for his wife—he looked crazy enough to shoot himself. But, no, listening, she heard only the river's wind rustling in the trees. Her imagination, nothing more.

She turned back to Reinette's chubby, inquiring face and blew softly on the dandelion, watching it vanish in the wind just as if it had never existed.

PART

3

CHAPTER
25

Louisiana Colony   *July 1751*

A SECTION OF THE RIVIÈRE Rouge meandered into a wild and swampy region. People found the area excessively creepy and stayed away. Bleached skeletons of long-dead trees seemed to take on a ghostly glow in the fading light of day. Wispy strands of moss reached down for trespassers from overhanging limbs like long, gray fingers.

Nearing six, Reinette du Plessis was not a trespasser. Her earliest memory was of magical swamp lights that danced for her. Père Philippe called the fairy lights "gases." She preferred the less prosaic term of fairy lights. For Reinette, the treacherous swamp held only beauty: floating beds of lilies and shaded tunnels of tupelo gums and wisteria that lead to thick groves of feathery bamboo. The only thing that could possibly be more lovely was Maison Bellecour.

The way Père Philippe described what should have been her estates, so he said, made Maison Bellecour seem like some sort of magical castle. One day, he promised her, he would take her there—"home," he called it.

A family of egrets lifted their heads in a stately attitude to watch the old man and young girl in the bateau. A screech owl blinked solemnly at the girl's soft, joyous laughter and took flight when she leaned near the base of a tree trunk to pluck a wild orchid and tuck it into her tangled mane of tawny hair.

Stillness permeated the tropical air, broken only by the sounds of water burbling against the raft and the splashes of her and Père Philippe's poles in the water as they drove the bateau ahead.

A haze of gnats swarmed over Père Philippe. Mindlessly, quite mindlessly, he swatted at them and murmured in a childish voice, "Kill the pests . . . just like I'll kill young Fabreville . . . when the time is ripe."

In the upper reaches above the swamp, the Red River was energetic and somewhat boisterous, flowing from one point to another in a no-nonsense manner. In the swamp, however, it turned lazy and slothful, sprawling out in a drunken stupor of aimlessly meandering channels. Most of these channels ended in bogs that could have slurped down a yoke of oxen. The trick was to find the single channel that didn't end with a bog.

The old man and the girl poled in the shadows, feeling their way through the low-hanging branches, the dead moss hair brushing their faces. The moss reminded her of Père Philippe's long, scraggly beard.

Perfectly attuned to the swamp, Reinette detected some current in the water and identified it as the main channel. The main channel led to the river—and towns, towns filled with people. Her curiosity ached to visit these places, but Père Philippe's warning that the people were as dangerous as alligators dampened her interest for a while, anyway.

Soon moonlight began filtering into the swamp. Strange protuberances called cypress knees reached up for the bateau from the watery depths. Mist rose from the water, and the swamp came alive with eerie sounds—screeches, hoots, howls—and something else.

She canted her head, listening for the sound that was out of place. Men's voices. Just ahead, looming out of the mist, she saw it—a boat much bigger than the bateau. And men, perhaps a dozen, armed with long rifles.

"There he is!"

"That's the old coot!"

"The girl's with him—you think it's her, the Brissac child?"

Père Philippe shouted, "Paddle, Reinette!"

Over her shoulder, she saw the blue-coated soldiers, as noiseless and swift as bats, swooping down on them. Then her paddle flayed the water.

Père Philippe tried to turn the bateau around, but a shot reverberated against the swamp's tunneled wall of trees. The bent old man struggled to his feet and lurched sideways, unbalancing the bateau. His arms flailed the air with Gallic madness. Then both of them were toppled overboard, and Reinette felt the mire and ooze swallow her.

CHAPTER

26

New Orleans   *May 1758*

MOTHER MADELEINE-LOUISE raised her palms in an uncharacteristic gesture of fatalism, as if to say, "What else could one expect?"

Her gaze blistered the uncommonly short frame of twelve-year-old Reinette du Plessis, which the girl insisted was her name although it was drafts on a Brissac account that paid for her boarding and education at the Ursuline convent.

Beginning with the girl's wooden-soled shoes plated with iron and which were worn only by rustics, the Mother Superior's scrutinizing glance traveled upward to the woolen stockings, short trousers, and coarse osenbrig shirt that could be found on any seaman along the riverfront. Mother Madeleine-Louise's critical perusal faltered when it reached the girl's face.

Her habitual expression of impassivity turned in on itself like a wadded portrait. "Bootblack?" the nun croaked, her voice sounding to Reinette like a swamp bullfrog.

Reinette ducked her head, which was covered by a floppy felt hat, shifted from one foot to the other, and kept her black eyes riveted on the wide cypress-board floor that was deeply worn by the tread of nuns. "*Oui*, Reverend Mother."

For an uncomfortably long moment, the Mother Superior of New Orlean's Ursuline convent stared at her. This escapade, passing herself off as a Negro footman, was only one in a series of misadventures. Last month, Mother Madeleine-Louise had looked as if she would topple face-forward into the font when she saw the host of tadpoles darting through the holy water.

The beleaguered nun's thin, veined eyelids closed out the disreputable sight before her. "Why?"

Reinette tugged off her hat, and her thick, honey-colored braid tumbled out to swish against the small of her back. She twisted the floppy felt between her hands. "I wanted to see the voodoo dances again," she offered in a small voice.

She had seen more than that at the weekly bamboula dances held beneath the sycamores in Congo Square, just above rue de Rampart on the city outskirts. She had just seen the most beautiful man alive. Not that her expertise in judging men was vast. In fact, it was almost minimal. For nearly the first six years of her life she had seen only one man, Philippe du Plessis, whom she had believed was her father.

Well, that wasn't entirely true. Occasionally, she had seen others. Every so often, old Father Raphael had poled his bateau into the swamp to minister the faith to a few renegade Indians, runaways slaves, and occasional trappers who occupied the magical land. But these people, who had flitted in and out of her life, were like fireflies with no real substance.

It was only when the soldiers had found her and dragged her to Natchitoches that she learned from the woman she came to know as Tante Emanuella just who Père Philippe was, not that it made any sense.

Père Philippe's exciting stories of France—and of the villainous Fabreville family who had taken all of Reinette's inheritance and the palatial Maison Bellecour—had made more sense and had been a lot more entertaining. Poor Père Philippe. He had battled the soldiers for her and had lost. By now the swamp's mire and ooze must have reclaimed his bullet-ridden body.

"What am I to do with you, my child?" asked Mother Madeleine-Louise.

"I could take the veil," Reinette ventured tentatively.

Mother Madeleine-Louise rolled her eyes. "Oh, Heaven forbid!"

Having made that dutiful response, Reinette replied cheerfully, "Well, then, I could open a gaming palace."

The idea had just occurred to her at that moment—activated by the elegant establishment farther down the rue de Chartres. She had passed it in her headlong flight from the Ursuline convent to Congo Square. That was where she had seen the man. Lucifer, the angel of the dark, had never looked so beautiful.

The nun's seamless face blanched as white as her wimple. "A gaming palace!"

Reinette jumped.

"Is that an example of the totality of your learning experience here at the convent?" the starched-up woman demanded.

Reinette dug the toe of her shoe into the tapestried carpet in front of the oaken desk. As usual, her frankness had landed her in molasses.

"Stop it!" Mother Madeleine-Louise snapped. She was wringing her hands like rosary beads.

Reinette stilled her errant foot and looked up with her best imitation of meek obedience. She would rather face Lucifer than the Mother Superior.

Mother Madeleine-Louise said, "Do you realize that the Ursuline sisters are known as the teaching nuns? God forbid that you should ever be used as an example of what we turn out."

Reinette remembered trying to tell Tante Emanuella she'd never fit in at the convent. She belonged to the swamps and the wild, mystical land of the cypresses. "I'll die if I'm cooped up like a sitting hen, Tante!"

But the widow, bless her departed soul, had merely shook her head sadly, saying, "It is for the best. Your mother would have wanted you educated, *ma petite*."

Reinette had learned to read, more slowly than the others since she had begun late, but numbers fascinated her. They had a magic of their own, and Sister Raphaele had taught her far beyond the rudimentary mathematical education the other young women received.

As far as fitting in with the Creole girls, Reinette had been right. They never accepted her. Reinette du Plessis was considered fey at the Ursuline convent. All the girls knew the truth of her wild background, born the daughter of a half-breed and raised in the swamps by a crazy man. It was even whispered that she dabbled in the voodoo brought over by the African slaves. By the end of the first month, Reinette felt that the girls were treating her as if she were the anti-Christ let loose to corrupt the sacred convent.

"Well, it's just as well you're leaving," said the Mother Superior. "Your education here is finished, such as it is."

"Leaving?" Reinette asked. She couldn't think of where she would be going. The only place she could call home was forbidden to her, Maison Bellecour.

But one day . . .

"Your benefactor's daughter, Madame de Soto, has sent for you. A de Soto Negress is upstairs packing your belongings now. She'll accompany you back to Natchitoches. But, *s'il vous plaît*, wash your face first."

With great reluctance, Reinette climbed the gently curving staircase past the second floor to the attic. The Negress stood before one of the deeply recessed, arched windows. The minute Reinette saw Quin-Quin, a familiar feeling—a good feeling—settled over her. Reinette tilted her head, looking up at the tall, svelte woman, and asked, "We've met before?"

Quin-Quin closed the portmanteau and smiled gently. "My name is Quin-Quin. You're going to be as beautiful as your mother was, *petiote*, once we get you out of those clothes."

Acquiescing to the black woman's instruction to undress, she asked, "Did you know my mother, Quin-Quin?"

Quin-Quin tugged the cotton camisole down over her head, followed by petticoats and a white demi-eyelet dress. "Your mother gave me my manumission. I used to play with you when you were just a babe." The black woman sat on the narrow cot and pulled the girl over before her. "We've got to do something with that hair, *petiote*."

Relieved that none of her roommates were present, Reinette submitted to having the brush tugged fiercely at her scalp. "After your mother and father . . . died," Quin-Quin said, "the Mistress Emanuella took me in. I was there when you were rescued from the swamps."

Reinette gritted her teeth against the pulling of the brush through her thick hair. She remembered very little of that brief month. Everything had seemed so strange. Only Tante Emanuella's kind face stood out as reality from the blur of that month. "Do I know this de Soto woman?"

"She's Mistress Emanuella's youngest daughter, and she's seen to it that money from the Brissac estates has gone toward keeping you here."

Reinette wrinkled her button nose. "I wish she hadn't. I never did like it here."

Quin-Quin chuckled and wound the braid atop Reinette's head. "The education was good for you." She turned the girl around to face her. "The Brissac estates have no more money left, *petiote*. It's time you returned to Natchitoches."

"Are you going with me?"

"I'd go with you anywhere, *petiote*. Your mother was good to me. No matter that my papers say *femme de gens de couleur libre*, I belong to you."

The beat of the oars thrust the half-galley against the mighty current of the Mississippi. Reinette stood at the ship's railing, delighting in the river wind that whipped at her hair and whispered in her ears. She watched the dingy wharves of New Orleans slip behind her, and then the encroaching forests blotted out everything except the strip of blue sky overhead. It was as if civilization had never reached Louisiana until, twenty-five miles upriver, the sloop passed by the neat, whitewashed houses of the Côtes des Allemands, where refugee Germans had settled a quarter of a century earlier.

When at last the half-galley veered up the Rivière Rouge, Reinette began to watch expectantly for the outskirts of Natchitoches. The wrought-iron-ornamented houses and business establishments disappointed her. She hadn't expected much of the settlement, just—just something more familiar. True, she had last seen the place when she was not quite six, and she had spent less than a month at Tante Emanuella's before being sent to New Orleans. Still, she was hoping to find something of her parents here. They were both such nebulous images in her mind. Philippe's wild, gray hair and his gentle, child's eyes had made a much more definitive imprint.

Tante Emanuella's daughter, Marie des Neiges de St. Denis de Soto, met them at the landing. Reinette had mixed feelings about the plump woman with a hooked nose above a discontented mouth. She was nice enough, but there was about her a cheerless aura at odds with Reinette's natural effervescence.

The woman seated Reinette in the chaise next to herself, with Quin-Quin riding up front beside a grizzled-haired black man who was driving. "Please call me Tante Marie," Madame de Soto said. "Your mother and mine were close friends, and I want you to be happy here in Natchitoches."

Reinette nodded cheerfully, feeling anywhere was better than the forbidding gray-stone convent.

The woman took her hand in hers and said gravely, "I think you're old enough to understand about estates."

Keeping with the serious vein, Reinette nodded again, this time more soberly.

"Your parents owned a highly profitable business, Reinette. With their deaths, there was no one to run the Louisiana Import-Export business. My father had already died, and my mother died soon afterward. I'm afraid little remains other than the property itself and odds and ends of inventory. My husband has managed to keep your parents' house from falling into utter shambles. When you reach eighteen, these two pieces of property, along with a trading post in Fort Rosalie, will be yours to do with what you want, though, I'm afraid, neglected as they have been, they won't be worth much."

Reinette squeezed the woman's pudgy hand. "Oh, that's all right, Tante Marie. I'm not planning on staying in Louisiana forever. I'm going back to France one day. That's where my home really is."

The woman's brow met over her humped nose in a frown of confusion. "If that's what you want, Reinette."

It was. She had vowed that one day Maison Bellecour would be her own, and when she made a vow, not even the Archangel Gabriel or Jesus Christ or Mother Madeleine-Louise could change her mind.

Reinette was installed in an empty bedroom at the old St. Denis house, a stately stuccoed home whose age half frayed it at the seams. Quin-Quin told her that the bedroom belonged to Tante Marie's eight-year-old son, who had been sent to France for an education. It wasn't long before Reinette learned the reason for Tante Marie's grim nature. From overheard bits and pieces of the house servants' gossip, she found out that Tante Marie had borne her son out of wedlock, an evil state lectured against by the Mother Superior.

As much as Reinette was in conflict with Mother Madeleine-Louise, she was totally steadfast in her faith. Like the catechism

ingrained in her brain, her religion was ingrained in her soul.
While Tante Marie bearing a child out of wedlock might be evil,
Reinette could find nothing evil about the man Tante Marie later
married.

Don Manuel de Soto was a robust and rotund Spaniard who,
accused of some treasonous crime against the Spanish government, had fled Texas for the refuge of French Louisiana. The
fatuous Don Manuel trailed after Tante Marie like a playful puppy.

The days passed pleasantly enough for Reinette. She didn't
feel quite the outcast there at Natchitoches, yet she kept hidden
a deep hurt that came from never really belonging behind a façade
of quick smiles and bright replies. Tante Marie taught her to play
the harpsichord, and occasionally Reinette would read a book lent
to her by Tante Marie—but only out of politeness. Books bored
her; they were stories of someone else's adventures. She wanted
her own.

Don Manuel tried to teach her to ride, and she was about as
good at that as she was at reading. However, one afternoon, she
rode with the jovial Spaniard over to her parents' house, a mere
log cabin that had had rooms and a wing added on over the years.
Brambles and briars had grown up around it as if to isolate it in
time.

She spent half an hour or so wandering through the rooms with
Don Manuel strolling after her in his red-heeled shoes. His ubiquitous clay pipe left a trail of smoke wherever they went. Her
fingers ran over the dusty bannister and banished the cobwebs
from a window shutter.

"*Pues*, what do you think?" asked Don Manuel.

She turned from the window and said, "I think this was my
parent's house, but it could never be mine. There's something
sort of sad here, don't you think, Tío Manuel?"

The good humor ebbed from his florid face. "*Sí*, I'm afraid so.
The children of Natchitoches claim it's haunted."

Reinette never went back.

One evening, after she had been a part of the household for
over three months, she was told that a visitor would be coming
from New Orleans the next day on business. "Our factor," Tante
Marie told her.

"What's a factor?"

Don Manuel puffed on his clay pipe, exhaled, then explained

patiently, "The factor acts as a commissioned agent in selling a plantation's products and in turn purchasing needed supplies out of the price received. Our factor, Aaron Simon, operates out of New Orleans."

"If he's coming so far, why isn't he staying for dinner?"

Don Manuel shot a helpless glance at his wife. Tante Marie put down her needlepoint and said, in what Reinette now recognized as her tactful voice, "Well, he's a Jew, my dear."

The word was vaguely familiar. "What's a Jew?"

The look of uncertainty passed between the two spouses again. "A Jew is a heretic," Tante Marie said. "One who doesn't accept the faith."

"Oh," said Reinette. A heretic she understood. Mother Madeleine-Louise said that heretics were the lost and the damned. In thinking about those lectures, Reinette recalled now how the Reverend Mother pictured the devil as walking the earth in the guise of a Jew in order to tempt good Christians.

From the gallery, Reinette watched for Aaron Simon's arrival. She was eager to see a real heretic. At twelve, she didn't expect him to sprout horns, but certainly he had to look terribly wicked.

When at last he rode up on a swayback nag, she caught a glimpse of his profile first. Later, she would remember it as the hard, intelligent profile of a Jew. She played the child's game, closing one eye and then the other so that his russet head hopped back and forth.

Suddenly, he swung off his horse and was facing her. He tilted his head to one side, watching her squint at him. His hands on his hips flipped back his coat panels. "Is there something wrong?" His voice was deep and confident and bore a faint trace of an accent.

She was too stunned to answer immediately. He was the incredibly beautiful man she had seen outside the gambling establishment on the rue de Chartres the day Quin-Quin had come for her. "So you're the terribly wicked heretic," she blurted.

His mouth, with a contemptuous tilt at the corners, strained mightily. When at last he gave in and grinned, she felt as she had the day before when her horse had balked at taking a fence and tossed her headlong into a briar bush—with a force that knocked the breath from her.

"What a *gamine* you are," he said, still chuckling under his breath.

An urchin. She supposed she did resemble an urchin with her hair a riotous mass of recalcitrant curls and her mouth smeared with fresh cream Quin-Quin had whipped for the occasion. "My name is Reinette du Plessis. I didn't mean you were terribly wicked. I meant—well, really, you're wickedly handsome."

"Well, thank you," he replied gravely, but a twitch lurked suspiciously about the ends of his mouth.

He tapped her chin with his knuckle and reached up to ruffle her hair, then paused. Thoughtfully, he fingered one of the untamed honey-streaked curls. His restless, intelligent eyes wandered gently over her slender, just budding body and then returned to her delicate face. "How old are you?"

"Twelve." She studied him as openly as he had studied her. "Your face is too young to look so—so—" She groped for the word.

"Cynical?" he offered.

"Yes, that's it."

"I see. Is there anything else that catches your notice?"

Her rapt gaze left his face to peruse the rest of him. He was only a little above average height, she noted, and extremely slender but for the two massive ridges that marked the muscles of his shoulders. His clothes were immaculate and of impeccable taste, though not of the most recent style. "Your cordovan boots," she said. "They've a lovely, deep shine."

"Thank you," he said, a sober note repressing the laughter she heard in his voice.

"Which means you haven't had a new pair in five or six years." She looked up at him. "Am I right?"

He caught her chin. "Reinette du Plessis, if you want to reach thirteen years of age, you must refrain from such honesty. Some people might not find your candor as refreshing as I do."

Provence, a vast strip of coun-
tryside along the southern coast of France was a semi-
independent feudatory of the French crown, yet a tide of Spanish
scholarship had swept over the French Pyrenees with the Se-
phardic, or Mediterranean, Jews, vigorously animating the intellectual life in Provence. The area had preserved this Jewish
community.

Initially, the great crusaders, and later the Dominican inquis-
itors with their cruel auto-da-fé and slaughterhouse efficiency,
mistook the Jews for heretics. Their motives, other than conversion, were simply envy of the Jewish merchant class, an occupation increasingly coveted by Christians, and an opportunity to
cancel debts owed to Jewish moneylenders.

Nevertheless, Provence remained a center of joint Jewish and
Christian scholarly activity in the transmittal of classical heritage
and Arabic learning to the West. Biblical and Talmudic scholarship flourished there, though the Jews were forced to wear a
yellow or crimson circle over their hearts, symbolic of the Dant-
esque circle of hell to which they were presumably condemned.
Later that pariah insignia made them victims of endless attacks,
especially during Passover.

Aaron Simon's direct lineage traced back to Ibn Simon, a family eminent in the twelfth century of France for its great prosperity, troubadour literature, and knowledge of astronomy, mathematics, medicine, and philosophy—all of which they had brought over from Moorish Spain, where they had labored side by side with the Moslems. For the medieval Jews, as for the Arabs, scientific knowledge was highly prized. Indeed, the Jewish physicians of Provence were famous throughout Europe.

The Simon family settled in Perpignan, a small town in southwest France, and became moneylenders, because by then other sources of livelihood had been closed to them. After the twelfth century, commerce had become progressively tolerable, respectable, even honorable, so the Jews were displaced from commerce by Christians, in part by sheer force and violence.

Like other Jews, the Simon family had become the most versatile element in trade and commerce because of, first, their detachment from the soil. Jews could not own real eastate, with the exception of small lots and houses in town, thus they were excluded from agriculture. Secondly, they had turned to trade because the dispersal of Jews had led to a network of contacts in urban centers throughout Europe.

Such circumstances also led other Jews and the Simon family from trade into banking and finance, where they had no Christian rivals.

Then came the sword-point baptisms. Those who refused conversion to Christianity were put to the death. In Portugal, King Manuel decreed that all children between the ages of four and fourteen were to be seized and led to the font to be baptized. The king had hoped the parents would follow, but instead many smothered their children and killed themselves. A great majority of the children were distributed across the country to be reared in Christian surroundings and were cut off forever from their parents.

Those Jews who did convert were called New Christians, or Marranos, and found all doors were open to them. In Spain, Aaron Simon's great-uncle converted and become the archbishop of Burgos, and on his great-grandmother's side, a Marrano Jew had intermarried with the royal house of Aragon, which later denied its tincture of Jewish blood.

Although the French Simons were coerced into becoming Marranos, they remained in surreptitious contact with those Jews who had managed to avoid the grim choice of apostasy or death. As Jews, they learned that it was safer to keep one's wealth in as liquid a form as possible so as to conceal or remove it as necessity dictated; for instance, in the event of expulsion.

Eventually, those unconverted Jews of Provence were reduced to degradation and poverty by the steady erosion of their freedom and autonomy. By 1507, the remnants of the Jewish colony of Provence were banished, along with Jews everywhere in Europe.

The expulsion deprived Europe of tens of thousands of dynamic elements in economic life and resulted in Europe's intellectual decline.

By 1750, the Jews who resettled in western Europe came to realize that to practice Judaism openly meant, among other things, that a father, if he had several sons, could keep only one with him; the others had to be sent away. His daughters remained with him only if they were lucky enough to marry Jews of their own city who had the right to stay there. Rarely was the Jewish father fortunate enough to live among his children and grand-children.

At the time Aaron was born, the practice of secret fidelity to Judaism had become an accepted way of life. Aaron's family kept the traditional Jewish ceremonies: his father ate only kosher meat, they had managed to marry for the most part among themselves, and they furtively attended synagogue.

Nonetheless, in other ways they were forced to conform to Christianity. The male babies weren't circumcised because, if discovered, the act was tantamount to a death sentence. The Jewish wedding for Aaron's sister had to be held privately after the compulsory Catholic ceremony. Like Christians, Aaron and his brothers learned to kneel and pray, and his prayers were no longer chanted but recited. His mother paid more regard to fasting than to feasting on holidays because fasting was private and could be concealed.

While Aaron was growing up, his mother often compared the story of Esther to the story of the Marranos. "You must never forget, my son, that the Jewess, Esther, never told of her race or religion, yet she remained faithful to her religion in an alien environment, just as we must do."

Despite the fact that Aaron's family were nominally accepted as Christians, they were still of the Jewish race and were secretly despised. Aaron was aware of this, but the fact did not impress him one way or another. Having been reared in the loving fold of his family and later sent to the Talmudic Academy at Troyes, the capital of Champagne in northern France, he basically went untouched by his prejudice.

Then, when he was barely sixteen, he returned one spring from the far-off academy, feeling very much worldly-wise. With the pride of a boy reaching manhood, he insisted on taking his mother to the *opéra-comique* in Toulouse. The affair was to celebrate her birthday and had been one of much planning and saving on his part.

At the opera house, a nobleman recognized his mother, having borrowed from her husband. He righteously demanded that she, a Marrano Jew, give her seat up to him, a "gentleman of quality."

Aaron could still remember the look of humiliation in his mother's eyes and the hot flush of her cheeks as she stood in the aisle, being berated by the pompous little man.

Something snapped in Aaron. He grabbed the comte's wrist from his mother's arm and gritted, "You pontifical ass!"

Those nearest the three gasped at the effrontery of the Jew. The opera-goers toward the rear began whispering and asking questions.

Aaron's choice of insults was bad enough, but when the aristocrat responded with, "You dirty Jews shouldn't be allowed to mix with people," Aaron ran amok. By the time three elegantly dressed men had pried him off the nobleman, he had pummeled the man's face to a mass of raw flesh with no discernible skin.

Unfortunately, the man lived and brought charges against him that made Aaron wish many times over that he had been condemned to execution rather than sentenced to the galleys. One poetic observer shudderingly said that a galley would cast a shadow in the blackest midnight.

It was during the many months Aaron awaited transportation to the chain assembly point at Marseilles that he implemented his reversion to a complete Jew. One night he bartered for a small, dull knife from the man in the cell next to his and circumcised himself. His immense anger with both his family and his own obeisance to Christian conformity acted as an opiate to the searing pain.

His anger failed to abate the pain of a *galérien*.

The 150-foot-long galleys were slave ships. All of the Mediterranean powers possessed galleys. The navies had to depend on two propellants—wind and oar; in consequence, the galley with its perpetual mobility was the important, fast tactical unit of a navy. It was the whip, with the threat of worse brutalities in reserve, that sent the long, lean, cranky craft into action at the requisite speed.

For five endless years, Aaron was chained, naked but for a pair of coarse canvas drawers, to the malodorous benches along with other bent, sick men. The convicts' heads were all shaven close. To the thud of a drum, their backs rose and fell with the swish of the oars beating against the water. Always there was the noise of their chains clanking with their limited movements.

Aaron learned that the society of the bench fell into five distinct classes: Turks, bought by the French government for the service; deserters; salt smugglers; genuine criminals; and the Huguenots— the first category being definitely the least badly treated and the last on the whole the worst.

The man chained on Aaron's left, Etienne Guirard, was unlucky enough to be a Huguenot.

The Huguenots were French Protestants against whom Louis XIV had applied forced conversions and dragonnades, along with financial persecution and the closure of religious schools. The heretical Huguenots were barred from working as midwives, jewelers, printers, lawyers, tailors—anything unless specifically sanctioned by the Edict of Nantes. Their pastors and teachers were restricted in number; mixed marriages were declared null and void, the offspring, bastards. To Louis's astonishment, two hundred thousand Huguenots fled France, risking the galleys rather than abjure their faith.

Over the months, and then years, Aaron learned all there was to know about the thirty-year-old, flat-nosed little Huguenot with the cold smile. The two of them, with three others, formed the gang of five assigned to bench thirty-two.

Arbitrarily selected for physical reasons, they were now entered into the closest of life partnerships, *la vogue*: rarely again ever to eat, sleep, or work apart; to be literally in close contact with each other until the end of their days. They ceased to be men; they became "an oar," one of fifty such oars carried by a galley.

"I was a silk maker in Poitou," volunteered the flat-nosed man one day during a lull when biscuits soaked in wine were thrust into their mouths. The only other meal was served at ten in the morning, a soup made of beans or peas with olive oil, with two-thirds of a pint of wine, morning and evening.

At each oar, all five men had to rise as one at each stroke, push the eighteen-foot oar forward, dip it in the water, and pull with all their force, dropping into a sitting position with every stroke. A Turk at each bench was appointed headman and set the tempo.

At first, Aaron didn't think it was possible to keep rowing for half an hour without pausing for a single moment. He learned differently.

Conversation occurred in hoarse whispers when the *comite*, or boatswain, was at the other end of the gangway, which ran beneath the half-deck the complete length of the ship. The *comite* was the chief slavedriver, the man with the *nerf de boeuf*, the bull-sinew whip, used on the rowers' backs for full speed ahead and the cane for half-speed. The first and only qualification for a *comite* was brutality.

"After the revocation of the Nantes edict," Etienne murmured at another time, "the commandant of Poitou installed his own reign of terror. He billeted his dragoons in our household. My family was at their beck and whim."

Those rowers who died or fainted at their posts were cut adrift from the bench and flung overboard without further ceremony. From below deck came the constant clank of chains, cracks of whips on bare flesh, screams of pain, and savage growls.

Such peaks of suffering usually occurred only in the heat of action. In normal cruising, sail was set whenever possible, or, if there was no wind, only the alternate oar was pulled so that each bench rested for one and a half hours in every three.

"They raped my daughter. She was nine years old." This was uttered by the taciturn Etienne maybe a week later, or a month; Aaron had lost all track of time.

Cooking facilities were primitive, and, as no one ever washed, the ship crawled with vermin from stem to stern. For the convicts, there was, of course, no question of sleep.

Life did become almost bearable after the galleys came into port in the winter. The petty officers, sailors, and marines were billeted ashore, and the *galériens* were allowed elbow room; beds were improvised in the bottom of the ship.

"The dragoons impaled my wife on a bayonet thrust upward into her womb." Etienne's voice was toneless. "One night I cornered the commandant and in the darkness hacked off his testicles with my silk shears."

Aaron made no sympathetic overtures. He suspected that if Etienne ever let the pain creep into his voice, it might be the beginning of insanity.

The winter was also a time during which the *galériens* earned money. Every *galérien* had a trade; if he had no manual dexterity, he knitted stockings—or else. Tailors, wigmakers, clock-menders—almost every trade was represented in the average galley. Aaron gave lessons in algebra. Etienne taught the tedious process of silk making.

Little by little, piece by piece, over that first year, Aaron told his own story to the little man on his left. In that first year, three men chained to the right of Aaron died.

Surprisingly, by an ordinance of 1630, a week ashore was allowed in the winter to the convicts of each galley in rotation. During this time, they were permitted to peddle their wares and services through the town and along the quay—naturally, under heavy guard.

"Don't think about escape," Etienne warned him as the galley hoved into Dunkirk. "With your hair as short as it is and dressed as you are, every citizen will recognize you as a *galérien*. Besides, your stink will give you away if your fetters don't. You'll be flogged until your flesh hangs in ribbons from your bones."

Aaron picked up the fat roach that crawled across his thigh and crushed it between his fingers. "Maybe not this year. But one year." One year, when he knew and understood more.

He was learning patience. He meant to survive—and to escape.

Still, that first time, when he stepped ashore after more than a year afloat, an exhilaration gripped him that he didn't think he could possibly experience again in his lifetime. Only lightweight fetters bound the *galériens'* thickly scarred wrists and ankles.

Aaron's leg muscles were weak from disuse. Etienne's were worse. After so many years, the little man's leg muscles had atrophied so that he was bandy-legged. To compensate, due to the constant rowing, his shoulders had developed immense and powerful muscles.

Returning to the galley and the heavy chains at the end of the week was more than mental torture. As Aaron approached the gangplank, he began to shake, great, agonizing tremors. Etienne dug his fingers into Aaron's arm. "Don't think about bolting. You're fish bait if you do."

A little over two years later, Aaron reached the haven of secretary to de Langeron, captain of the galley, and for the first time in three years found himself freed from his chains, newly clothed, and allowed to grow his hair. He was even given a corner of the storeroom to sleep in.

The first time he saw himself in a looking glass, he was shocked. The naive schoolboy of sixteen was gone. A hardened derelict looked back at him. He became meticulous with himself after that. His shabby clothing was mended; his auburn locks neatly combed. The half-moons of dirt that wedged beneath his pared nails were constantly scrubbed out. The dull looking glass reflected a rakishly handsome man, albeit a man who looked much older than his true age of twenty.

Occasionally, he saw Etienne and dropped a few cryptic remarks, but he didn't make the mistake of trying to make his former benchmate's life any easier with favors or food. A slipup and it would be over for both of them. There would be one chance for them—and one chance only.

Instead, he built up the trust the captain had given him. Stealthily, he began to acquire the captain's cast-off clothing. He let two years pass in the captain's service before he decided the time had come for escape. It was now or never. That winter, when the galley put into port, this time at Marseilles where he had started out as a *galérien*, he was ready but for one item.

The key to bench thirty-two's fetters.

Even for this, Aaron was prepared. Five years' close association with the criminal element of France had enabled him to learn, among other things, the art of light-fingered gentlemen. Unfortunately, these gentlemen of the underworld had no ready access to the key ring. Aaron did. He waited until the night before the galley was due to put into port. Just before dawn, when all slept deeply, he noiselessly purloined the ring from the snoring, burly *comite*.

As he moved among the *galériens*, several of them stirred, shifting in their constricted space. A slight click was the only sound in the midst of the grunts and snores. Etienne cocked one eye at him but said nothing. Aaron slipped out of the hold, returned the key ring, and resumed sleeping.

At daylight, the convicts were released from their chains about their ankles and waist and, fettered only at the wrists, were marshaled out onto the Marseilles quay. When Aaron submitted his wrists to the shackles, the soldier, armed with the standard bullwhip, never noticed that the clasp had been filed. Nor did he notice that the deep pockets in Aaron's frayed coat were puffy.

The Quai des Belges was crowded with hawkers, soldiers, merchants, and seamen of every nationality, all pressing to get somewhere. When the sergeant in charge of Etienne's file saw the little, flat-nosed man bolt from the line, he sent up a cry, but a jostle from behind sent the soldier sprawling.

Within ten minutes, Aaron and Etienne met in one of the subterranean passages that ran below a famed house of ill repute off the Canebière. Forgoing any kind of greeting, they rapidly changed by the flaming light of a wax torch into the clothing Aaron had smuggled in his pockets. For Etienne, Aaron had even provided a red woolen stocking cap to cover the cropped hair.

A vendor's cart served as their means of escape from the port city. Hidden beneath burlap sacks of citrus fruit, Aaron and Etienne discovered with disgust that they also shared the cart with carcasses of sheep and hogs.

"Where now?" asked Etienne.

Aaron had had a great deal of time to give thought to his future. He had considered Amsterdam. The Maranno Jews there controlled a large part of the Dutch maritime commerce and constitute one-half of the capital of the East India Company. Perhaps it was the rotting fruit and carcasses that made him decide at that moment against the idea. Europe was decaying.

"The New World, Etienne."

The first European to set foot in the new land had been Luis de Torres, who was of Jewish blood. Columbus's enterprise had been largely a Marrano one, both of inspiration and financing. The expedition had been made possible by a loan raised by Luis de Santangel, a financier of Marrano extraction, and Gabriel Sanchez, High Treasurer of Aragon and of full Jewish descent, was the expedition's patron.

Rumor even had it that Columbus himself was of a New Christian family.

Perhaps that was why Aaron Simon felt he had come home when his ship berthed at New Orleans's fog-bound docks. The fact that a quarter of a century before the colony of Louisiana had passed the *Code Noir*, or Black Code, which in addition to regulating slavery forbade Jews to settle in the colony, bothered Aaron little. He had been an outcast for almost seven years; it had become a way of life for him.

Both Aaron and Etienne were quick to note that New Orleans owed its bustling activity to the fact that it was located on the mouth of a mighty river that divided a continent, the extent of which no one was certain. Shipping was the key factor.

Aaron's keen mathematical sense spurred him into capitalistic activity—one far different from Etienne's choice, but one that meshed well with Etienne's enterprise, which was, surprising for the religious man, that of smuggling or pirating. "Merchant adventuring," as Etienne termed it. But, then, Etienne had grown bitter chained to a bench for eight years.

It took no time for the little man to make the necessary connections and set up a route from the Gulf, up through the bayous and waterways and marshlands to one of the cane-hidden islets that served as his headquarters. With Etienne's experience on the high seas, he had no trouble convincing a smuggler to give him ten percent of the take in exchange for his labor and, more important, his expertise. A charming little cottage in the rue de Bourbon, a silk shop, served as cover for his illegal activities within the city.

Aaron opted for something more than mercantilism. Opportunities were offered by the factorage system to men of little or no capital, usually of the overseer class, to embark in business for themselves. Aaron knew he was much shrewder than the typical overseer and saw that the opportunities to grow wealthy as a factor were boundless.

The factorage system was not of Southern origin but had its beginnings in the West Indies, dealing with the home agents of England. The factor was to the individual planter what the chartered companies had been to the whole body of colonists. He was at once merchant and banker. He acted as a commission merchant in the purchase of plantation supplies, and he discharged the functions of an agent in selling the plantation harvest.

Aaron rented a small establishment on the rue de Royale, wedged between an apothecary's shop and a hatmaker, and hung out his placard: AARON SIMON, FACTOR. He set up the second floor as his living quarters.

He took no precautions against concealing his Jewish background; in fact, he seemed to flaunt it at the gambling palaces and taverns. Jews did live in Louisiana, but they necessarily kept a low profile. Not Aaron.

It didn't take long for him to garner his first clients. Whatever the prejudice against Jews, most men recognized that Jews were the shrewdest of businessmen with contacts all over the world. Before six months was out, Aaron was negotiating the best of deals for his clients, few in number though they were at that point.

Although the French government forbade trading with any nation other than France or its colonies, Aaron, through his contact with Etienne's smuggling activities, was able to purchase otherwise unobtainable supplies or supplies at far better prices.

Aaron should have been happy with the niche he was carving in New Orleans, but he was lonely. As a Jew, he was forbidden from polite society; and Etienne, who traveled between his main base of operations in the delta and his silk shop on the rue de Bourbon, could not alone furnish the companionship Aaron sought.

At night, as he lay naked, accustomed after seven years to this natural state of sleepwear, it was no wonder that his thoughts should stray to the delightful sprite of a child he had met at the de Soto home in Natchitoches. Her eyes, too large for her face, were as black as a Hassidic Jew's beaver hat, and her hair was the color of the flowing honey promised by God to Moses.

Her innocence eased the loss of his own youth; her candor enchanted him. He looked forward to the business that occasionally took him to the Natchitoches outpost, and it wasn't coincidence that the de Soto plantation prospered.

CHAPTER

28

New Orleans   *September 1760*

W HILE IT WASN'T EXACTLY A
gaming palace, the coffeehouse at the corner of rues St. Anne
and Chartres, across from the Governor's House and the stocks,
was the closest Reinette knew she would come to entering a
gaming palace, at least for some time.

That September, Tío Manuel had to come to New Orleans to
transact business with his factor, and she convinced Tante Marie
and him to let her accompany him as a gift for her fourteenth
birthday. For the occasion, she donned a muslin gown with cobwebs of laces, all in white—that most becoming of all colors for
the young. Beneath the cool muslin, she wore wide panniers that
were abominably uncomfortable.

In place of *café au lait*, she was served chocolate in a demitasse
cup, along with crisp beignets. Eyes wide, she observed everything while Tío Manuel and Aaron Simon talked, from the jagged
leaves of the yucca growing in the squat wine jars that flanked
the doorway to the little black boy who pulled the rope of the
cypress punkah hung from the ceiling, moving it back and forth
to keep flies away.

"I'd advise you to shift from growing indigo to sugarcane,"
Aaron said. "The Jesuits have been very successful with their
sugar plantation." He drank *café noir*, and she didn't know how

he could stand it. His factorage business must be prospering, she thought. He wore froths of lace at his neck and wrists, and a black satin bagwig over his auburn queue.

Tío Manuel puffed on his pipe a moment, then shook his head. "I'm not so certain. With the war raging in Canada, Aaron, won't France need our cakes more than ever to dye their uniforms?"

"The English have taken Quebec and Montreal," Aaron pointed out, "leaving Louisiana completely cut off and orphaned from the French world of its forefathers. Two years without a French ship in port could conceivably stretch into four years."

"If that damned Madame Pompadour hadn't encouraged this war!" Tío Manuel muttered, then recalled himself as Reinette's face perked up with interest.

"The king's mistress?" she asked.

"Now what do you know of mistresses?" Aaron asked. His narrowed lids failed to shield the glitter of amusement that lurked in his warm blue eyes.

She dimpled. "With a name like Reinette, I should know a lot." Her smile fell. "But not that much, really."

"Ah, yes," Aaron replied, nodding his auburn head matter-of-factly. "Little queen, used to describe a king's mistresses. The point had escaped me."

Tío Manuel's clay pipe puffed like a chimney.

She canted her head, suspecting that Aaron was teasing her. Her little chin lifted, the same way her mother's used to, and she asked, "Have you done any speculation in sugar futures, Aaron? I would think cotton would be a better crop."

"*Vraiment?*" he asked mildly. "Please tell me more."

She blushed. "I confess I know nothing about business. Suddenly, her black eyes brightened. "But I do—or will—own two businesses, one in Natchitoches and the other at Fort Rosalie. Well, they used to be businesses."

Aaron hooked his arm over the chair's back. "I've traveled past Fort Rosalie with Etienne Guirard, a business associate. Whatever was there once is gone, swallowed up by vines and creepers. Most settlers avoid the empty place like it was a curse. I would think of another form of an enterprise, *gamine*, for the time being, anyway."

She liked the way Aaron Simon talked to her. Despite the use of his nickname for her, he treated her as if she were grown up.

She was amazed by his knowledge of planetary movements and geography and navigation and a hundred other encyclopedic interests. A man of culture, obviously; he was a complex, many-sided person.

"It all comes from Arabic scholars," he had once told her modestly when she commented on his vast wealth of knowledge.

He was an interesting man, intelligent, undeniably charming, and, she suspected, very subtle.

And he was a Jew.

The word drummed up forgotten images and phrases from her memories of the convent. The gentle clack and clatter of wooden rosary beads passing through her childish fingers . . . Sister Thérèse saying, "Jews are dirty!" . . . Softly flickering votive candles . . . Reverend Mother's pronouncement, "Jews are the murderers of Jesus!"

Reinette shuddered, barely restraining herself from genuflecting.

Tante Marie outdid herself for Reinette's seventeenth birthday: bisques of pigeons with steaming golden platters of shellfish and her specialty, *gâteau d'anis*. By six that evening, all that was left of the aniseed cake was crumbs, but still the birthday guests stayed to talk of the astounding news.

"Impossible!" said Raoul, the most handsome of Natchitoches's eligible young men. Twenty years old, he possessed velvet-brown eyes and a rakish smile that snared every feminine heart for miles around. "I don't believe it. France would never give up Louisiana!"

Aaron, who had come up on business, remained where he stood, lounging against the parlor doorway. "Nevertheless, it's true," he said coolly. "The war with England is over, and you all are now subjects of Spain."

"I notice you didn't include yourself as a subject," Reinette said, her chin propped on one fist in what Tante Marie lectured was a most unladylike manner.

Aaron raised a cynical brow. "Ah, but, *gamine*, no country wants to claim the Jews."

None of the guests were prepared for his bluntness, and Tío Manuel broke the stunned silence with a jovial laugh and said, "Right now I think we'd all rather be Jews than Spanish subjects.

Madame de Soto, are the brandied pears ready to be served?"

When the last of the dessert was finished, Tío Manuel and Aaron closeted themselves in the study, and the guests began to drift toward home. With relief, Reinette bid the guests *bonsoir* and watched them leave from the gallery. The night was cool, and she wore a gown of lavender-blue lawn that bared her shoulders, but she wasn't ready to go in. The party had been a strain on her, for she knew that Tante Marie was hoping to interest one of the settlement's young bachelors in her ward.

Reinette recognized the bald fact was that she had little to recommend her to families of good standing. She was practically dowerless and, what's more, was tainted by Indian blood. Having been raised in the swamp by a crazy man only added to her reputation as a strange little creature.

With a tiny sigh, she leaned her head against the wrought-iron post. She supposed she *was* strange, especially since she had no romantic thoughts about Raoul de Chassin. If anything, she was somewhat contemptuous of him. He was overly attentive to her, yet she knew he would never have the courage to defy either Natchitoches society or his parents and ask for her hand.

"Stargazing?" Aaron asked behind her.

She turned and smiled. "Aaron! I was glad when I saw you ride up today. I believe you're the only one in Louisiana who speaks his mind truly."

Hands in the deep pockets of his frock coat skirt, he moved to the other side of the post. "The propensity for saying what one thinks doesn't win friends, I'm afraid." From his pocket, he produced an ivory cameo pin of a long-legged bird. "Happy birthday, *gamine*."

"How lovely!" she exclaimed. "A heron, isn't it?"

He nodded. "The elusive blue heron. When I saw it, I was reminded of you."

Her lips pouted mutinously. "Now you sound like Tante Marie. 'Always off somewhere in the forest bogs, Reinette, I swear you're as elusive as a debtor.' " she mimicked, but with a mischievous grin. "Oh, I do love the cameo, Aaron!" She pinned it at her breast, declaring solemnly, "I shall never take it off!"

He laughed. "Well, I do think that there are occasions when—"

"Look!" she cried, and leaned out over the gallery's balustrade to point at the glowing light that flitted through the trees down along the river. "A *feu follet!*"

Aaron braced his palms on the railing, watching the phenomenon. "A ball of marsh gas. It's caused by decaying vegetation."

"*Mais non!*" she chided him. "It is a mysterious fire that haunts the lonely wanderer." Her voice dropped a level. "The Indians say if the *feu follet* appears near a house, it portends death. Others say it is the restless spirit of an unbaptized child lost in the swamp. What do you think?"

From his side of the post, he smiled at her, the cynicism temporarily absent from his lips. "I think you are a *feu follet*, a restless spirit—and absolutely enchanting."

Marie de Soto appeared at the door and said, "Time to retire, Reinette." The woman nodded at Aaron with a tight smile and retreated inside again.

Reinette sighed. She would rather have asked Aaron more about this secretive Treaty of Paris that supposedly ceded all of the French territory west of the Mississippi, including the Isle of Orleans, to Spain and . . . What was it he had said, something about all of the French territory west of the Mississippi going to England? If the treaty became official, how would that affect her trading post at Fort Rosalie, if the land was now claimed by the British?

She shook her head, stood on tiptoe, and kissed Aaron on the cheek. "Good night, Aaron. The cameo pin is the best birthday gift I've ever received!"

Aaron watched the sprite depart. She seemed unbelievably young, and smoother than whipped egg white. At seventeen, she still possessed all the ingenuousness of a child—and the body of a Botticelli Venus, softly, exquisitely shaped. Her whole person breathed an incredible mixture of innocence and seduction.

He was hopelessly infatuated.

He knew that Marie de Soto did not approve of the presence of a Jew in her home, but he had to give her credit, she did treat him with polite civility.

And what did Reinette think about him?

A self-deprecating smile squeezed wry lines into either side of his mouth. If she considered him at all, he imagined it was with pleasantly platonic thoughts. He doubted if she even suspected he had made the long trip to Natchitoches, not because of business negotiations, but because he remembered it was her birthday.

It surely never occurred to either Madame de Soto or Reinette that he was a man in addition to being a Jew. He thrust his hands in his pockets again and strolled on down the gallery. Tomorrow he would visit every whorehouse between Natchitoches and Baton Rouge, which was not very many. In fact, there were none.

"I expected to see webbed toes and watermarks around your knees."

With a gasp, Reinette whirled from her reflection in the bayou's blue waters. Surprised, she released her bunched voile skirts to swish over the exposed length of naked calves. Her blue satin pumps, garters, and silk stockings were mounded in the corner of a bald cypress a good ten yards away.

Between her and her footwear stood Aaron Simon, hands on his hips, his gray satin frock coat folded over the loop made by his left arm. July sunlight glinted against the deep red tints of his auburn hair. His mouth wore that same contemptuous curl that she had eventually come to realize had nothing to do with her. He was handsome, and she sensed that handsomeness was the last thing in the world that mattered to him.

"What does that remark mean?" she asked, laughing. Her bare feet waded through the tall marsh grass. The ground was still muddy from the last overflow of the river. She went easily to Aaron's side.

"You spend so much time wandering among the bayous and backwater places that I've started to think of you as the marsh maiden—web feet and all."

Grinning, she looked up at him. Despite her advanced age of seventeen years, the intrinsic sprite in her was delighted with the fanciful statement. "I'm hiding out from Jules Michaux."

"Your latest suitor?"

Her fingers adjusted the woven garlands of purple water hyacinths in her hair. "Mmm. He's a draper and terribly boring, Aaron. I confess, I'd much rather listen to the tales of New Orleans's pirates and priests and prostitutes that you so carefully edit."

He smiled. "You're so certain that I do?" The breeze spooled her unbound hair toward him. He caught the whipping strands and tucked them behind her ear.

"Of course." She grinned. "Everyone knows that the pirate always takes advantage of the nun's virtue. You don't come often enough," she complained, "and when you do, you're usually closeted with Tío Manuel so that I never hear the end of your stories."

She picked up her stockings, saying, "Now turn around."

He did as she bid. Somewhere far away someone was burning cane, and the snapping noise sounded like firing guns.

"Well, I won't be telling you any diverting tales for a while. I'm going to England on business for one of my clients."

Balanced on one leg like a flamingo, she said, "I'll miss you, Aaron." She concentrated on tugging the garter up about her thigh, adding sadly, "I wish I were going with you. I don't think I belong here. I suppose the Ursuline convent and education changed me. Now I'm neither fish nor fowl. Do you know what I mean?"

"If you mean that you're not really acceptable anywhere, if you don't feel at home anywhere, yes."

The razor edge in his voice prompted her to look up, but his back, ridged with muscles beneath the frock coat, was toward her. "I'm sorry," she said. "I forget that . . ." Her voice trailed off.

"Ah, yes, that I am a Jew." He turned around and picked up her slippers. His jaw was set like a hatchet in a log. "So were Abraham and Isaac and Moses and Christ and his apostles."

She touched his sleeve, saying softly, "Please, don't go looking so black."

He looked down at her with a grim smile and muttered, "I suppose I wear my Jewish insignia on my shoulder, instead of over my heart, as in the old days. Forgive me, *gamine*."

Her lips compressed. "Don't call me that—urchin."

"You didn't use to mind it."

She grasped his arm for balance. "I was a child then," she replied, distracted by the effort of fitting her damp foot into the little slipper. Her mouth was screwed up and her forehead knitted. "I'm a woman now."

"And how do you know that?" he asked, laughter dancing in his voice.

Still holding on to his arm, she looked up, lips parted in an anticipated answer. His eyes were as blue and hot as the July sky, and for the first time, she felt a stirring that she associated with danger warnings of her innate primitive instincts. Beneath the whisper of her blood was another whisper. The moment stretched like a dangerously fraying thread between them.

"By the way I'm feeling now," she replied at last in a soft, breathless voice, a look of bewilderment on her face.

His eyes scrutinized her face, and she wondered what he was looking for. "How *are* you feeling now?"

"Like my blood's galloping."

Her artless reply brought a smile to his well-defined lips, a smile that faded as she continued to stare at him, fascinated. For a fraction of a second, the muscles knitted in his jaw, then his hands circled her waist. Eyes wide, she watched his head bend over her. His face blurred as his mouth covered hers.

She went absolutely still and allowed her senses to evaluate the novel feeling. As far as she could recall, she had never been kissed, not even by a parent. Contrasted with the hardness in his arms, his lips were soft. She felt as if he were exploring her, as she explored and tested back channels of a bayou for bogs.

Her eyes closed. Her arms felt as heavy as cast iron. Her mouth went pliant. He opened his lips, and she liked the feeling of his breath, warm against her mouth. But when his teeth gnashed against her lips, the good feeling started sliding away. She squeezed her lids tighter, anxious to recall the feeling before it evaporated altogether.

"Reinette," he murmured huskily, "open your mouth."

She did as he bade, hesitantly and only partially parting her lips. His tongue split them farther. The invasion came as a shock, and she jerked as far from him as his grip on her arms permitted. She stared, a stunned look bright in her pained eyes. "I didn't like that."

"I think you are still a child," he said, and abruptly released her. She wondered how the heat in his blue eyes could vanish so quickly, as if a cloud had suddenly blotted out the sun. "Let's go back to the house before I compromise you further."

The kiss marked a change in their hitherto easy, informal relationship. Reinette missed the friendship she had taken for granted—and she resented Aaron for bringing about that loss. Worse, she was uncomfortable in his presence and made every effort to be absent whenever he called on the de Sotos after that. It was to be the loneliest year she could remember.

CHAPTER

29

An October wind banged the shutters back and forth. The first large drops of tropical rain pelted the window shutters. A blast of thunder brought Reinette bolt upright in her bed. Her first thought was that the remnant of an offshore hurricane, from the Indian word *hurakán*, was blowing through. The immense wind always unnerved her. It was one thing you couldn't fight or run from.

A surging flash of lightning silhouetted Quin-Quin in the doorway. Her short muslin shift gaped at the neck, revealing her sweat-sheened cocoa flesh. "Run, girl! It's the slaves, they've rebeled!"

Dazed with sleep, Reinette scrambled from her bed. The black woman was quicker. She grabbed Reinette's arm. "Scoot, girl, or you'll be running 'round like a chicken with its head chopped off." She pushed her toward the window.

From somewhere in the house, a scream pierced the wind. Reinette's blood curdled. She turned toward Quin-Quin. "Tante Marie? Tío Manuel? What about—"

"Go on, I said!" When Reinette hesitated, the black woman slapped her face. "There's nothing we can do for them. Now get!"

What sounded like thunder exploded again, and this time Rei-

nette realized that what she was hearing were pistol shots. Outside
the window, fingers of flame curled from Natchitoches rooftops.
For once, the brunt of the rain couldn't come too soon.

Quin-Quin threw up the sash and shoved the stunned young
woman through the window onto the gallery. Reinette tumbled
to her knees. Behind her, Quin-Quin grunted as she stumbled
against Reinette. Both women struggled to their feet. Blue-white
lightning scissored the sky and illuminated three black men loping
from the far corner of the gallery toward them. One carried a
cane torch. Machetes flashed in its blazing orange light.

Reinette yanked her nightrail up around her knees and sprinted
down the steps. Quin-Quin raced with her across the sloping
lawn. The wind tore off her nightcap and whipped her hair loose
from her braid. Lightning flashed all about them. A savage African yell rent through the storm's turmoil. The men were close
on their heels.

"The cattails!" Reinette gasped. She ran as she never had before. Her labored breathing pounded against her eardrums. The
wind lashed her hair against her face.

She swerved toward the tall reeds and bushes that banked the
river. Quin-Quin panted behind her. Reinette waded into the
river. The cold water slapped at her thighs. Hoping Quin-Quin
was following, she thrashed into the reeds and cattails. The undercurrent nudged hungrily at her legs.

Immediately, she stripped off her bright white nightrail and
tossed it toward the center of the river. The strong current there
carried it away. Naked, she submerged herself to her shoulders.
Over her shoulder, she saw Quin-Quin follow her example. The
older woman's black skin blended even better with the Stygian
river.

Above the roar of the wind, Reinette could hear the men's
voices arguing in the slave patois of French and African. Fingers
of light poked through the cattails. Her hair—its light color would
give her away! Childhood memories of the swamp returned and
prompted her to snap off a hollow reed. The torchlight swept
nearer to her hiding place. She stuck the reed between her lips
and sank below the water's scummy surface. Her betraying hair
floated upward. She grabbed a handful and yanked it down. The
cold water pressed in on her, demanding her breath. Her flesh

wrinkled. The long minutes crawled by like the span of an entire night.

The current, eddying through the base of the reeds, made its own sound, a swishing noise that filled her ears so that she couldn't hear anything else. Was Quin-Quin safe? She hated to think what the slaves would do to her if they found her because Quin-Quin, one of their own, had sided with their masters. The insurgents would want to make an example of her.

When Reinette felt her waterlogged limbs going numb, she surfaced cautiously. Her hair plastered her cheeks and neck and back like swamp morass. She peered through wet lashes but saw nothing but the ferns. The absence of torchlights lent her courage. "Quin-Quin?" she managed in a loud, raspy whisper.

"Here!" Half a dozen yards away, Quin-Quin rose from the water like a black Venus and waded toward Reinette. "You have to get away before daylight, girl. Those slaves aren't gonna give up till they find me."

Reinette stood up. The water sluiced off her, and she felt the mud squish between her toes. "I'm not going without you, Quin-Quin."

"And where can we go that they can't find us? Nowhere, I tell you! They know the land like the white man never will."

"They don't know the swamp like I do."

Intimations of daylight revealed a land laid low by the passage of the tail end of a Gulf hurricane. The marsh grass and towering cane were bent almost horizontal. Wet with the rain, they shimmered in the early-morning light.

The two fleeing women, both naked, slushed along a finger of the river overgrown with tupelo gums and cypress. Reinette was careful to wade never less than knee-deep, lest their footprints be spotted from the bank.

For a while, the subterfuge worked. Then the sluggish branch meandered into a marshland where one misstep could plunge a person abruptly into a nightmarish ooze that slithered about the thighs. A lonely and treacherous landscape, animals and people sometimes became stranded in the muck and died there. The pungent odor of marsh gas larded the air.

Reinette had to show Quin-Quin how to walk over the terrain. "You move with your knees loose, like this." She stepped from one gaseous clump of peat and roots to another. The few inches of saturated earth above the swampy ooze wouldn't support much weight.

Suddenly, the grassy clump gave way. Immediately, Reinette bent her knees to slump to the mud, braking her downward passage with the added resistance. Carefully, she jumped from one hummock to another. Had it been dark, her magnolia white body might have been mistaken for a *feu follet*.

Quin-Quin's attempt wasn't as successful, and several times Reinette had to turn back to help yank the woman loose from the marsh's sucking grip.

The terrain shifted by degrees from marsh into swamp, where they waded through mud abounding with snakes. Gradually, though, a beauty intruded into the swamp. Here cypresses and tupelo gums and crayfish abounded. Here was life, flowering in exotic languor, and food and shade and protection. Here, too, was the miasma, or malaria, that left a person with periodic but intense chills, fever, sweat, and a great weakness for the rest of his or her life.

By noon, Reinette felt it was safe to halt their headlong flight at the banks of a torpid bayou. On a ghostly *chênière*, a small sand ridge in a seemingly bottomless channel, they collapsed, conquered by utter fatigue, beneath the evergreen oaks.

Filtered sunlight penciled the two naked women, claimed by the sleep of exhaustion and fear, for the young, bearded fur trapper in the eighteen-foot skiff to find.

CHAPTER

30

Nova Scotia   *September 1755*

LA CADIE, OR ACADIA, WAS A vague region said to extend from Montreal south to the area of the Pennsylvania colony. Paul la Ronde figured the word La Cadie was probably a corruption of a Micmac Indian word, "quoddy" or "caddy," simply meaning a place or a piece of land.

The twenty-year-old cocked his ham-hock hands on his hips and turned his head upward to watch the long string of snow geese, looking like a crest of waves, wend their way southward. Though the Gulf Stream blessed Acadia's Bay of Fundy with a more gentle climate and fertile soil, the winters still weren't warm enough to prevent the migration of wildlife.

The winters could be worse, he reflected, going back to the tilling of his father's diked fields. Just across the Bay of Fundy, in Canada, cider and wine froze in casks and had to be served by the pound.

Paul's French forefathers had settled the fertile Annapolis Valley as far back as 1613, and the nearby Le Pré Ronde, a village of fifty or so small wooden houses with their own garden plots, had taken the family name. In those day, the settlers had gone out in the morning to tend their crops or livestock, uncertain of whether they would see their families again at the end of the day. In the field, behind any stump, tree, stone, or hill, an Indian

could conceal himself, waiting patiently for hours until the settler
came within range of his tomahawk.

Little by little, the stubborn immigrants had conquered their
uncooperative environment. The Acadians had become masters
of the marshland; they had learned how to build dikes, how to
control water levels, and how to maintain a drainage system to
ensure the growth of food, upon which all survival depended.
Now the English hungrily eyed the land the Acadians had reclaimed from the sea.

On the slope between the sea and the orchards, which wore
the autumn red and gold colors of ripening apples, were the
family's cabin—only its front porch painted white—and the out-
buildings. In the largest barn, Paul's father was preparing for the
night's sally.

Though Acadia abounded in timber, furs, fish, and flour, it
badly lacked manufactured goods, metals, implements, guns, and
ammunition. For years, Paul and his father and three brothers
had carried on an illegal, and therefore clandestine, trade with
New England for some of those necessities.

Lately, their outings had been converted to another purpose.
Paul's wife, pregnant with their first child, had wept tearfully
early that morning before daybreak. She had begged him not to
go out that evening.

"You worry over nothing," he had reassured her, speaking in
a hushed voice so as not to awaken his parents or his other siblings.
Soon his youngest brother, Lucien, would awaken to go out to
the mud flats in the bay, where he drove stakes before the massive
tide came in. The log stakes caught the sand and mud and silt
that the tide drew out into the bay and gradually built up the
land into salt marsh.

Tenderly, Paul touched her mounded stomach. His finger, the
size of a wine bottle's neck, circled the protruding navel. Everything about his wife was warm and soft, like her large breasts—
except for her stomach, taut now with the movements of the
babe. Her skin was smooth, unlike his, which was matted all over
with dark curls.

Brunette Emilie la Ronde, née Broussard, was the prettiest girl
in Le Pré Ronde, with the dark eyes of the Celts of Brittany and
the other poor French provinces of Normandy and Touraine,
from whom the Acadians descended. Like Paul himself, they were

all unsophisticated peasants, hardworking and conservative. And they were very stubborn and very Catholic.

He counted himself lucky that Emilie had selected him over the scores of foreign fishermen who visited the Acadian coves every spring and summer and often stayed to winter there.

"I'm not a fool, Paul. I know what you're about!" She clutched at his hair-spangled wrist. "The redcoats will kill you—if not this time, then the next."

"I am just going into Le Pré Ronde to reclaim some cattle and hogs the lobsterbacks stole."

The English would declare that the livestock had been confiscated, but terminology mattered little to hungry people; terminology mattered little to a man of Paul la Ronde's stolid temperament.

Ever since France had ceded the whole of the Acadian Peninsula to England by the 1713 Treaty of Utrecht, the English soldiers had made life miserable for the Acadians. Acadia was now called Nova Scotia, Latin for New Scotland. No priests were allowed to officiate, and all means possible were used to have Acadian children instructed in Protestant religion.

All this despite the terms of the Utrecht treaty, which gave the Acadians the right to practice their religion, the right to keep arms, and the right to retain their possessions. In addition, the Acadians were assured they would not be required to bear arms against their French brothers.

Then, the month before, Le Pré Ronde had received a contingent of twenty-five British soldiers. The redcoats had marched geometrically into the village square to the sound of a bagpipe and drum. In the houses, in the shops, out in the marshes—men, children, and women had heard the banshee wail of the pipe and the ominous thud of the drum and had come to investigate.

In atrocious French, the spindly, mealy-mouthed lieutenant had announced, "His Majesty, King George, intends to drive out the French soldiers who are illegally on what is now English soil. In ten days we will attack the French fort at Beauséjour. The men of Le Pré Ronde will be required to assist in the attack."

It was Paul's father, as big and white-haired as a polar bear, who had stepped forward and said, "Lieutenant Peters, by the provisions of the Utrecht treaty, we aren't required to bear arms against our former countrymen."

The officer hadn't been able to keep the triumph from his smile. "In that case, since you will not help us, I have no recourse but to demand you surrender all your arms—in order to protect my rear, you understand. I want every pike, musket, pistol, and saber here in the village square by nightfall."

Mutterings of astonishment had broken out among the townspeople. Paul's brother André had pushed to the forefront of the crowd and demanded, "Just how do you expect us to protect ourselves from the Indians—and our livestock from the wolves?"

"That is your problem. But I will warn you that if a realistic number of weapons is not piled in the square, then I will order my men to do a house-by-house search—and I can't guarantee how carefully they'll make the search. Do you understand me?"

Shock and angry murmurs had rippled through the assembled townspeople. Paul's father had held up a restraining hand. Though he wasn't the town's mayor, he was nonetheless respected and listened to, not only because he was a descendant of the founding family but also because the people had come to depend on his sound judgment. "We will comply with your demand in order to keep our neutrality, as specified by the treaty."

That night, the British soldiers had collected the mounded weapons from the square and boxed them for shipment the next day on their anchored vessel. The soldiers had remained, quartered in the tavern and the town's two largest houses, commandeered by the English lieutenant. For a while, the people had grumbled, but eventually things seemed to return to normal—except for what amounted to a neglible underground resistance by the la Ronde males, the recovery of the stolen swine.

The town buzzed the next morning with the news of the death of one of the lobsterbacks. The sensation of the soldier's grisly demise overshadowed the puzzle of the missing swine that the British soldiers had kept under guard.

Just after dawn, a farm boy, on his way to the bay for fresh fish, had spotted a portion of red material stuck in quicksand. Closer inspection had revealed a rigid claw of fingers. The unearthed soldier had last been seen leaving the town's taproom in a highly drunken state just after midnight. Apparently, in his inebriated stupor, he had wandered off in the direction of the hazardous marsh terrain.

Not everyone accepted that explanation.

Lieutenant Peters had a suspicion that the gin-sodden private had been abducted to the area of the quicksand and left to his hideous fate. The English lieutenant also had a good idea who the perpetrators were, but he was in no rush to arrest the culprits.

The people of Le Pré Ronde outnumbered the soldiers of his troop, and, though they now had no weapons, they still had pitchforks and scythes and other implements just as lethal.

Besides, within the week the belligerent Acadians would no longer be a pain in the ass. Preparations for dealing with them were to be kept carefully secret, on orders of Parliament.

He tossed down the mug of rum and left the tavern's taproom with such a pleased expression that an old fisherman, entering the tavern, thought his fellow townsmen could have been wrong about the lieutenant.

Lucien's mallet halted in its downward plunge against the stake. His eyes narrowed, uncertain in the morning fog of what they saw. Ships. The same ships, he was sure, that had been wallowing in the trough of sea yesterday and the day before that. By the time the bright sunlight burned off the fog, the ships would be farther out to sea, beyond the horizon.

He went to tell Paul. He found his oldest brother in the tunnel-like foyer of their house, bending over to adjust his points fashioned from leather thongs. Paul listened to Lucien's excited recounting, finished trussing up his leggings and trousers with the leather thongs, then asked, "You're certain that they're British ships? You could make out their flag?"

"No, but . . . "

"I'll talk to Father."

When their father heard the report, he said gravely, "Get out the word for the town's leaders to gather this evening at our house."

Paul, Charles, André, and Lucien spread the word, but as it turned out, the leaders, along with the rest of the town's males, were instead ordered to assemble that afternoon at the church to hear an important proclamation from the English government.

By the time the appointed hour came, three ships had sailed into the bay and landed more troops. Lucien counted over a hundred armed soldiers marching into the town. His mother, her skin weathered by the elements, caught at his father's hand in a gesture of panicky beseechment. Her husband shook his head and went on into the church.

Emilie stood beside Paul's mother and watched in bewilderment, along with most of the town's women, as their menfolk shuffled nervously into the little white church. One mother had to shush her pugnacious son, who stuck his tongue out at the nearest redcoat and called him a pig, fortunately in French.

Paul squeezed Emilie's shoulder, hoping to ease the fear in her tight, little face, then filed in behind his father and brothers.

In back of the women and children, the newly arrived soldiers took position, their muskets ready at their sides.

Inside the church, Lieutenant Peters stood before the altar and looked out over the pews crowded with more than a hundred and fifty Acadian peasants. His lips curled unpleasantly, and Paul wondered what kind of harassment the lobsterbacks now planned. Could they possibly demand that the families turn over a portion of their earnings?

When a moment later the lieutenant's troop entered, their muskets slanted against their shoulders, Paul shifted on the hard, smoothly worn bench that was the la Ronde's family pew. It seemed sacrilegious to him to bring weapons into the church. A muttering of indignant protests passed along the pews like a ripple that grew into a wave.

"Quiet!" snapped Lieutenant Peters. The soldiers who now lined the walls brought their gun barrels down from their shoulders into their palms with a smart, resounding slap, and the furious hum of voices was immediately silenced.

In a stentorian voice, Peters read from the proclamation unscrolled between his dainty hands. "As of the past August one, seventeen fifty-five, all Acadian lands, tenements, cattle and livestock are to be forfeited with all other effects."

From outside came muted shouting, indicating some kind of commotion going on simultaneously, but within the church, the Acadian men were utterly stunned by the proclamation. None of them seemed capable of speech.

With a self-satisfied smirk, Peters continued, "All French inhabitants of Nova Scotia are to be removed, and they are prohibited from carrying any of their possessions, except as much of their household goods as they might carry in their hands."

Paul's father bolted to his feet, a large, veined fist raised. "We won't do it!"

A single shot silenced any further outburst from the older man. Before he could topple over the pew, Paul caught him. Lucien screamed. Everyone froze. Then a babble of shouts erupted. In an instant, Paul assessed the situation. Even though the peasants were unarmed, they outnumbered the soldiers surrounding them. A successful revolt might be possible, but the women and children who had gathered outside faced certain execution by the newly arrived troops.

What was happening did not seem possible—except when the men were prodded from the church under armed guard and saw that some of their wives and children were being rowed out in the bay toward one of the three waiting ships.

"No!" Paul said under his breath. They were taking away his wife and his mother—and his unborn child! He shifted his father's sagging weight onto André's brawny shoulders and charged through the line of soldiers in front of him.

A musket butt crashed into his forehead, and he collapsed face forward in the dirt. The lobsterback responsible stared in disbelief. The big man's skull should have cracked like an egg from the force of the blow. Already the man was stirring groggily, shaking his shaggy, blood-matted head. The soldier swung his musket butt again, and this time Paul went out cold.

The story was the same in every major Acadian village. In Beaubassin, some four hundred Acadians had gathered to hear the proclamation. As at Le Pré Ronde, they were all imprisoned in ships, some of which had been brought from as far away as Boston. Military detachments were sent throughout the countryside to bring in all other peasants. A few had enough advance notice to flee into the forests, but the English governor, Lawrence, set a bounty of thirty pounds sterling for each male scalp over sixteen, and twenty-five pounds for younger males or women and children. Although this was ostensibly limited to Indians, in practice the English paid the bounties without inquiring into the race of the original owners of the scalps.

The majority of the Acadians were driven aboard transports

to be taken into exile. No attempt was made to keep families together, and for the most part, husbands were separated from wives, and children from their parents.

On October twenty-seven of 1755, fourteen ships carrying 2,900 Acadians joined ten transports in the Bay of Fundy with 1,900 more prisoners. This was only the first wave of imprisonment and transportation that was to continue for years to come.

Paul sat deep in the foul-smelling cargo hold of a cockleshell of a ship. He had little more than elbow room. He longed for the luxury of stretching his big frame out lengthwise. For the past three weeks, while the ships waited in the bay, he had received only rations of water and biscuits, as had the other two hundred prisoners. The hatch, the one source of light and air, was rarely opened except to lower food in buckets, which were then used for the more embarrassing bodily functions and once filled, hoisted back up again.

The mortality rate was high, especially among the old and the young. Sometimes their rotting carcasses lay in the unbearable hot hold for several days until the sailors arranged for the bodies to be lifted out.

Lucien had been separated from him, but André and Charles were in the hold with Paul. The three brothers discussed where the transports would possibly take them. Privately, Paul worried that Emilie might not survive the voyage to be reunited with him—to wherever it was the English planned to reunite the families. His mother was stronger and unhampered by pregnancy. At least she'd be able to care for Emilie . . . if the two were even on the same ship.

Their first week on the Atlantic, smallpox swept through the hold. Paul watched first André, then Charles die the horrible death. Then, he, too, succumbed. For days, he lay delirious, but somehow his big body escaped death.

At last, the ship put into Chesapeake Bay. Paul and the others emerged into the intensely bright sunlight and weakly but anxiously made their way down the gangplank to the warehouse-banked wharf. Only then did they learn that there was to be no reunion with loved ones.

The men wept openly when they heard the full story of what was happening. Nova Scotia's Governor Lawrence had decided to scatter the exiles among the British colonies on the Atlantic seaboard, only he had neglected to inform the authorities of those colonies that the Acadians were coming.

As a result, no preparations were made for them. Most were dumped ashore with no friends, no money, no food, and only the clothing they wore. The British colonists, hostile to everything French and/or Catholic, made no effort to help them.

Most of the Acadians were forced to become indentured slaves. In the southern colonies, they were put to work in the cotton and indigo fields. Children who were still with their families were taken away and distributed to Protestant homes, where they were to grow up English.

Since Maryland had been settled by English Catholics, Acadians who landed there were not considered aliens and instead were quartered in private homes until they could fend for themselves. Those Acadian expatriots were the lucky ones.

The family of a shipbuilder in a suburb of Baltimore took Paul in. For days, he lay apathetically in a bed that was too short for him. He paid little heed to the comings and goings of the matronly woman or her short, stout husband, Roger Moreland. Their attempts to converse fell short because they spoke only a few words of French.

Their daughter, a homely, soft-spoken woman of twenty-five, occasionally came up to the guest room to feed Paul or to check on him. Her French was better, though badly fractured.

"You need to be shaved,"she said one day. "Would you like me to do it for you?"

He looked at her then, really looked at her. She had mouse-colored hair and a thin but kind face. "No, thank you. If you'll get me a razor and mug and brush, I can perform the task."

She stood uncertainly in the doorway. "You are sure you're strong enough?"

Despite his melancholy, a grin found its way to his bushy face. He thought it droll that his strength could ever be questioned. "*Oui.*"

Her skepticism had been well placed, for he was so weak he barely finished shaving. When his beard and moustache were neatly trimmed, he felt a little better and managed to converse in a more civilized manner with the daughter. He learned that her given name was Edna. He talked desultorily to her—of everything but the devastation of the Acadians. Gradually, she came to his room, more often on little pretexts. It wasn't long before he realized that she looked upon him as more than a mere patient.

She must have sensed his impatience to be up and gone because, one night, after he had been in the Moreland household for almost a week, she entered his room wearing only a plain muslin gown. Her braid was over one shoulder, and she didn't look quite so stringy a maiden. The candle she held revealed that she had knobby, little breasts.

"You'll be leaving soon, won't you," she whispered from the doorway.

He nodded.

Her mouth opened and closed several times, and he thought she resembled a fresh-caught fish. "I want you to take me into your bed."

He propped himself up on one arm and stared a long moment at her. "Edna, I'm married."

"You don't know that. You don't know that your wife survived the transporting."

He wanted to strike the woman for her callous remark except that he knew she was right—Emilie, being pregnant, would have to have been very lucky to have lived through the deportation.

"I know what you're thinking," she said, moving to stand next to his bed. She set the candle holder on the lowboy, and the candle's light wavered across the walls. "I know you love your wife. If—if she is alive somewhere, would you want to know she is being well cared for?"

"Of course."

"Even if it meant another man was caring for her, loving her— as I have cared for you?"

"I can't answer that," he growled. "Listen, I'm tired and—"

"Then you don't love her."

He kicked back the covering and sprang to his feet, catching Edna by her narrow shoulders. He shook her so roughly that her head bobbled on her body. "What would you know of love, you dried-up, scrawny old maid?"

The candlelight diamonded the tears in her eyes. "That's just it. I don't know anything!" Unable to help herself, her eyes slid downward over his huge, naked body. A shudder of desire rippled visibly through her. Her fingers crept out to comb through the springy hair that tufted his entire torso.

He closed his eyes. His immense frame shuddered with the need to spill his seed, a need he had repressed since his Emilie had grown large with their child. Six long months.

When Edna's fingers closed hungrily around his jutting organ, he groaned and released her shoulders. She knelt before him like some primitive worshipping an idol. Soft sounds of her adoration mixed with the little, slurping noises of what she was doing to him. He braced his hands on her shoulders to keep from sagging with the sudden relief that flowed out of him.

As she used the hem of her nightrail to clean him, he watched with something akin to melancholy mingled with regret. When she finished, she looked up at him, waiting. He bent down and scooped her up, taking her over to his bed. Wordlessly, she pulled the nightrail over her head.

Her exposed body looked bony and hard and unyielding. Gingerly, he lay down atop her, just lay there until he felt his strong, young body responding, growing hard again.

"The first three transports," Roger Moreland said at breakfast three days later. "I've been able to trace them." His knife crunched the bacon on a plate painted with violets and buttercups, and he didn't look up.

Edna translated for her father, and Paul felt a heavy sinking in his stomach. *"Oui?"*

"Two of the transports were bound for South Carolina but were hit by a storm and forced into Boston for repairs. Do you know a man by the name of Le Blanc?"

"Honoré Le Blanc, a neighbor," Paul replied.

Roger Moreland's bald pate broke out in a shiny sweat. Edna's voice was a raspy whisper when she translated her father's next statement into French. "Le Blanc said your mother died of smallpox."

Paul set down his utensils. He closed his eyes, then opened them. "And my wife?"

Moreland seemed to understand the question. He glanced at his wife. Her lacy mobcap dipped with her head as she fastened her eyes on the untouched egg and tomatoes on her plate.

"Childbirth," Moreland got out. "Your wife died aboard ship of childbirth. A son—the infant lived two days, Le Blanc told me."

After Edna haltingly translated, Paul swallowed hard. His hands clenched and unclenched. He rose and went to his room. Later that day, Edna came up with a tray of food. "I know you're not hungry," she said, "but you must eat if you are to be strong enough to carry out your plans."

He lay on his back, hands clasped behind his head. Without stirring or looking up at Edna, he asked, "And what are my plans?"

"The way I see it, you could go back to Canada. You could sail to the French colonies in the West Indies, to the Sugar Islands such as Saint-Domingue, Martinique, and Guadeloupe. You could go to France. Or you could stay here, Paul. Father could give you a job in the shipyards. He could use someone like you."

With a sigh, he swung his feet to the floor and sat up. "I'm going to the colony of Louisiana."

"Louisiana?" she said. "Why, that's a wilderness, if ever there was one. What could you hope to find there?"

"The wilderness." He knew he wasn't good at expressing himself. It had been hard for him to verbalize his deep feelings of love for Emilie, but she had understood, anyway. He hoped Edna would understand why he couldn't stay permanently.

He worked in the shipyards for three years, long enough to repay the Morelands for their kindness and to save a portion of his wages for the trek he would be making. Throughout those years, Edna continued to come to his bed, and they took solace in each other.

If her parents expected or hoped for a marriage between him and their daughter, they never said, though her father indicated several times that he valued Paul's work at the shipyards and hoped he would stay on.

When Paul felt the day had come for him to leave, Edna made no ugly scenes—she only kissed him on his bearded cheek and said, "God go with you, Paul."

He set out on foot for the Ohio River the following spring and built a raft that floated him down the Ohio into the Mississippi River and French territory. To his surprise, he found several Acadian families at Poste des Attakapas. The curé had rechristened the post Nouvelle Acadie des Attakapas, but some of the settlers had begun to call it the Village of St. Martin, in honor of a French bishop of Tours.

The village, built along the luxuriant Bayou Teche, was a scattering of austere homes. The whitewashed front porches supported staircases that led to attics for the storing of grain or for use as extra bedrooms. Paul was invited by several of the Acadian settlers to occupy that extra attic room. But he wasn't ready for society yet. He didn't know if he ever would be. The isolation of the impenetrable swamps called to his pain-wracked soul.

CHAPTER

*Colony of
Louisiana*　　　31　　　*October 1763*

THE LITTLE HOUSE PERCHED ON
stilts over the muddy bayou. The Acadian had laid out a log road
that half floated on the surface of the marsh, and built behind the
house a stone bridge that arched across a lagoon, whose opaque
turquoise water reflected the moss-draped oaks surrounding it.

Trying to absorb the dim heat of the sun, Reinette sat on the
porch on a wooden-slab bench, her head resting against a rough
cedar post. From between her dense black lashes, she watched a
brown pelican on the far side of the bayou scoop fish and water
into the large pouch of its lower bill.

The past five days had been spent helping to obliterate the
horror of the night of the slave rebellion. That morning, restless,
she had talked to Quin-Quin about making their way back to
Natchitoches. "Tante Marie and Tío Manuel might need our
help."

"And they might be dead, girl," Quin-Quin countered. "Uh-
uh, we're not going back to that place until the danger is over."

Reinette chafed at the inactivity. Through slitted eyes, she
watched the big Acadian as he worked over at the shed, which
was connected to the cabin by a boardwalk on stilts. The remains
of steel traps lay everywhere: rusting jaws, broken springs, and
chains. Some hoop nets for catfish hung from the wall.

Paul la Ronde seemed old to her, though she knew he and Aaron Simon were about the same age, nearing thirty. He stood before a bench and wielded a knife that made quick cuts around the paws of the dead muskrat he held. The movements of the knife were no more traceable than flashes of sunlight. With the pelt suddenly loosened from the body, the muskrat appeared to be draped in a luxurious fur coat.

For such a gentle man, his method of earning a living seemed almost cruel and brutal. He lashed the bedraggled pelt back and forth with a rhythmic motion so that droplets of water showered in a fine mist around him. He tossed the skin into a bucket already overflowing with others like it. Animal corpses were every-where—on the benches, on the floor, along the wharf, and in the skiff tied to it.

The muskrats' huge incisors were a shining orange, and their ratlike tails splayed out from piled-up skins like seaweed from rock. A heap of skinned and gutted carcasses lay bunched up near the door to the shed, their gunmetal-blue entrails in a wooden tub next to him, while the pelts soaked in a washbasin. More pelts hung on racks, swinging to and fro as they dried in the cool wind.

Quin-Quin opened the cabin door. The tall woman wore a threadbare shirt of Paul's and heavy gingham trousers that were far too large around her slender middle. A rope held them in place. Reinette had had to make do with Paul's huge leather tunic. Her bare arms and legs poked out, making her feel terribly ex-posed. But then Paul had seen both Quin-Quin and herself birth-day-suit naked. More than once over the past week, she had sensed his brown eyes following her.

"Frogs' legs are simmering, girl. Just about ready."

After nearly a week of isolation with only Quin-Quin and Paul, Reinette had regained her finely tuned senses, honed sharp by her childhood years spent in the swamp. Her ear picked up the slight, subtle differences of speech between Quin-Quin, Paul, and herself.

She spoke Creole French, the lingua franca of the descendants of pure European Frenchmen. Her pronunciations were clear and precise, and her diction was selective with no slang or word substitutes. Paul's Acadian French was a two-century-old patois. His clipped, staccato phrasing was less pure and intermixed with

English word substitutions and expressions. Quin-Quin's Gumbo French was a patois of French and African with many word improvisations.

Reinette lifted her head, alert, listening. Down the boardwalk, Paul did the same. They both detected the swish of paddle against water. Quin-Quin came to stand beside Reinette's bench and shielded her eyes with her hand.

Soon, a boat came into view around the bend. It was one of the itinerant merchants who paddled their bateaux along the swamp's back canals. Madras and calico materials lay heaped in the bateau's prowl.

Paul tossed aside the pelt he held and walked out on the wharf to talk to the man. Reinette could hear enough to know they were discussing the slave uprising. A few more words were exchanged, and then the man shoved off, paddling into the bayou's sluggish current.

Paul shambled toward the two women. By the look on his face, she was afraid the news wasn't good. He knelt on one knee in front of her. The odor of blood was strong on him, reminding her of the smell of rust and earth.

"The mercer"—he jerked his thumb over his shoulder toward the boat dwindling in the distance—"he says that soldiers up from Poste des Opelousas have finally quelled the uprising."

She swallowed hard and asked, "Did he say anything about the de Sotos?"

"I asked. They're both all right. But their house, along with several other homes in the area, has been burned to the ground."

The breath eased out of Reinette.

"*Grâce à Dieu*, they're alive," Quin-Quin said.

Paul rubbed at his bearded jaw. "I suppose I can take you two back to Natchitoches tomorrow morning."

Reinette wrapped her small arms around her legs and propped her chin on her knees. "Paul, I don't think I can ever thank you for rescuing Quin-Quin and me—and taking care of us like you have this past week."

"But . . . ?"

She looked up at Quin-Quin. "But I won't be going back to Natchitoches. I don't really belong there."

"Where we going, girl?"

"As a child, I used to think there was nowhere else I wanted to be than here in the swamp. In the swamp was safety. But I don't belong in the swamp, either. I'm restless even here. There must be somewhere for me," she finished a little forlornly.

Paul rose from his kneeling position to prop a booted foot on the bench. "Where's the rest of your family?"

"I'm all there is. But there is a place . . . "

"She means to go back to France," Quin-Quin said. "Am I right, girl?"

"One day. One day, I'll get back what is rightfully mine."

Paul's thick brows bunched down over his eyes in puzzlement. "What is yours?"

"My inheritance. Estates, vast estates. A château on the Loire, a Paris town house, investments that stretch all the way from France to Canada. They were inveigled from my family by a man named Fabreville. I've been thinking. I'll need money, lots of money—and connections. It'll take time to acquire all of this. I might be an old lady by the time I do, Paul, but it doesn't matter. One day the Marchesseau estates will be mine."

"And until then—what?"

"I've been thinking about that, too."

"You've been doing a lot of thinking for one so young," he said solemnly.

"I'm nearing eighteen."

"You're not much taller than a musket."

She grinned up at him. "I've been thinking that I'd like to own a café. An establishment patronized by the *haut monde* of New Orleans."

She recalled the high-class gaming palace she had seen in New Orleans. The Palais Royal. She had never forgotten the plush, red-velvet interior—nor her first sight of the rakish Aaron Simon. His devil-may-care attitude at once fascinated her and made her uneasy.

Quin-Quin rolled her eyes. "What do you know about owning a café?"

"Not a thing." Reinette spread her hands, palms up. "But what do I have to lose? The clothes on my back?" She laughed. "They're not even mine."

"I suppose you have a plan for financing such a place?" the black woman asked.

"My parents' property in Natchitoches and Fort Rosalie."

"That tumbled-down place won't bring that much, girl."

"Whatever you own at Fort Rosalie," Paul said, his brown eyes grim, "has been confiscated by the English. They rebuilt the place and renamed it Fort Panmure. Good King George is doling out huge land grants to retired soldiers and favored civilians. The fourteenth colony, it's called. A small version of Tory England."

For a moment, she sat thinking—of what she faced back at Natchitoches. Marriage to a tradesman, no doubt. Someone like that tedious draper. Somehow, she wanted more from life than that, though most young women would probably be delighted at the security of such a marriage.

No, she wouldn't go back, only forward. "There's still the property at Natchitoches, the house and the land occupied by the trading post." Enthusiasm sparkled in her black eyes. "I could put the property up as collateral for a larger loan."

Paul rubbed his bearded chin. "Who would want to risk backing an inexperienced girl—"

"Convent-reared, at that!" Quin-Quin interjected.

"Aaron Simon."

Quin-Quin stared at her, speechless.

"At least I think I can convince him to do it," she added.

"Now I know you're out of your mind, girl."

"I've heard of him," Paul mused. "A Jew. He's making a name for himself as a factor in New Orleans."

"Aaron Simon is the de Soto's factor," Reinette said. "And he's an outcast. Like myself. That's why I think he'll help me."

She leaned back on her palms and looked up at the black woman and the Acadian. "I'll need help in other ways, too. Quin-Quin, you once told me that, being a free woman of color, you weren't accepted by your people—but neither have you been accepted by the white race."

Quin-Quin's smile was white against her *café au lait* skin. "I see your point, girl. I guess that makes me an outcast, too."

Reinette looked up at Paul, her brows raised in question.

His smile came more slowly than Quin-Quin's, but it was just as firm. "If an exile is the same as an outcast, then I suppose you can count me in."

The tangy, brisk breeze off the Mississippi tumbled the refuse along New Orleans's long wharves, which were banked with every size of vessel flying flags from a dozen different nations. The only sight missing was the cassocked Jesuits, who had been vanquished by the French parliament when Father La Valette went bankrupt.

Spain might now own the vast Louisiana colony, but one would never know it. Everything still bore the French imprint. The French fleur-de-lis still waved from the Place d'Armes, which was crowded with seamen, slaves, soldiers, and farmers from the German coast there to sell their produce to the market on the levee.

Reinette had forgotten the strong odors New Orleans emitted. The stench of unwashed bodies was overpowering—as was the offal that mixed with the mud in the drainage ditches. At the marketplace, the smell of lobster and butchered pork and singed chickens vied with roasted coffee from an open café and fresh flowers from a nearby stall.

In the intervening years, since she left the convent, the city had tripled in population. Reinette, dressed in a simple blue muslin Paul had procured for her, noticed that shops jostled each other for room alongside private homes. From the tunnel-shaded *porte cochères* that led to secluded courtyards wafted the scent of gardenia bushes, magnolia blossoms, and orange trees.

"Watch out!" Paul warned, thrusting her hard against a wood and stucco wall. From the second-story window, an empty chamberpot added its contents to the filthy street below.

Laughing uneasily at her near escape, Reinette saw that Paul's face held no hint of laughter. Looking up into his eyes, she saw the ardor betrayed in their chestnut depths. From a few terse statements he had made, she knew that he had lost a wife years before, but it had never dawned on her that the big man might be falling in love with her. Perhaps she should be afraid of him, but she wasn't—and she was of Aaron. That wasn't entirely true, she thought. She was afraid of the feelings Aaron engendered in her.

"*Merci bien*, Paul," she said, managing a friendly, offhanded smile. Obviously, the death of Paul's wife and infant son had hurt him deeply, and she didn't want to hurt him more. When she sidestepped out of his grasp, he hastily rearranged his clothing to conceal his sudden arousal from her and Quin-Quin.

To Reinette's disappointment, the establishment that bore the sign of AARON SIMON, FACTOR was closed. Aaron could be anywhere—in the colony with one of his clients, in England or Spain or the Sugar Islands purchasing plantation supplies, or he could simply be in one of the numerous taverns.

"Now where?" Quin-Quin asked.

"The Palais Royal," she replied, trying to infuse some assurance into her voice.

To her adult eyes, the Palais Royal looked gaudy instead of plush, slightly seedy and time-worn. She paused just inside the doorway, uneasy at the glances aimed her way by the male customers.

"Do you see him?" Paul asked.

Her gaze swept the tables where men diced or played five-card trump and French whist. More men stood at the bar. She started to shake her head, then she spotted his handsome face at a corner table, a pewter mug in one hand. A little man with a flat nose sat across from him.

"That's Aaron Simon," she said, "over in the corner."

As they wove their way among the tables, Paul walked before her like a bodyguard and Quin-Quin followed behind as if she were Reinette's maid.

When Reinette halted before Aaron, he stared up at her with eyes that looked like broken glass with red ink spilled in the cracks. Either he had gone without sleep for several days or he had been on one long drinking binge—or maybe both.

"*Bonjour*, monsieur."

Carefully, he set down the mug and fixed her with those glazed eyes. "You're supposed to be dead, you know." His voice had the gravelly rasp that came from downing a great deal of gin in one sitting.

"Am I? I suppose I should try to contact Tante Marie and Tío Manuel. I know they'll be worried."

He rose, surprisingly quite steadily, and bowed. "Please be seated, *gamine*."

She grimaced at the sobriquet. The gin on his breath was as heavy as a bayou fog. "Not here. Is there somewhere we can talk business?"

He nodded toward his companion. "This is my business partner I told you about. Etienne Guirard."

She gestured at Paul and Quin-Quin at either side of her and smiled. "And these are *my* business partners."

Aaron raised a cynical brow. "Not only do you do a disappearing act, but suddenly you're a businesswoman. My office?"

She grinned. "That will be fine, monsieur."

Aaron studied Reinette from across a heavy trestle desk. Etienne had found the exquisite scroll-worked piece of furniture on an English ship that had had the misfortune to be blown off course into the Spanish Main. The high-beamed office was crowded with the articles of Aaron's profession.

Rolled maps of recent properties he had acquired, mostly cotton and sugar plantations, were propped in one corner. Invoices and correspondence, the latest a letter from the recently established outpost of St. Louis in the Illinois territory, were strewn over a round, leatherhide table. Books he had not had time to categorize were haphazardly tucked into crates scooted against the rear wall. The striking *femme de couleur*, Quin-Quin, sat there in a chair wedged between the crates, watching Reinette and Aaron like a forbidding duenna.

Aaron had sent Etienne with the big Acadian to find two rooms at a reputable inn for the night. Etienne could have arranged some sort of accommodations on his own for the three, but Aaron wanted Paul la Ronde out of the way for the moment. Just what was the Acadian to Reinette?

"You've been busy," Reinette said. She sat on the edge of the tapestried chair, her back broom-straight, no doubt as the nuns had instructed her. He noted her fingers abstractedly traced the threads of gold brocade on the armrest. "You've done well in New Orleans."

"Despite the fact that I'm a Jew?" he asked, his intelligent eyes watching, waiting to weigh her answer.

"Because you're a Jew, I think."

He was pleased with her candor. She had not lost that, though she had changed in other ways. Over the years, she had filled out, become a woman, but the changes seemed more pronounced since last July. Her black-lagoon eyes and raven-wing brows contrasted attractively with her tawny-gold hair. Anyone would stop to look twice at the arrestingly beautiful young lady. But her mouth reminded him of a child's, it seemed so vulnerable.

He steepled his fingertips. Her breasts, small but defiant against

the blue muslin dress, distracted him. "You spoke earlier of discussing some sort of business?"

She leaned forward. "Yes, I've nowhere to go, Aaron."

"What happened to 'monsieur'?"

She blushed. "Please, don't make this more difficult for me than
it already is."

Her voice and eyes coaxed him, like a summer rain, he thought.
It was too much to hope that she at last wanted him as a woman
does a man. His lips curled sardonically. "You could marry."

She made a flicking motion with her hand. "With my wild
background—a half-breed father, raised in the swamps by a crazy
man? I don't think many eligible bachelors are going to seek me
out." She glanced around and added, her voice lowered, "And
I'm afraid my pride won't permit me to consort with the riffraff,
Kentucks, and pirates in gambling dens like the Palais Royal."

Just where did she classify him? "If marriage isn't the answer,
surely you aren't planning to take the veil?"

She grinned, one of those crooked smiles leftover from childhood. He had forgotten the way the delightful dimples formed
just below her full cheekbones. "Mother Madeleine-Louise ruled
that out a long time ago."

"Then what are your plans?"

"I want to open a café—an establishment that females won't
be reluctant to patronize. A place that the *beau monde* of New
Orleans will seek out."

He directed a probing squint at her. "You once mentioned
returning to France and a place you called Maison Bellecour."

"I still plan to. When the time is right."

"I see. So, what is it you want from me?"

"I want you to capitalize the venture." She hurried on. "I've
my parents' Natchitoches properties that I could deed over to
you as collateral."

Cold calculation told him that if he helped her, he would, in
effect, ultimately lose her; that she would build enough savings
eventually to go to France. But if he didn't help her, someone
else might.

"I am a businessman, Reinette. What do I stand to gain by
financing this?"

"Ten percent, as a silent partner." She gestured over her shoulder to Quin-Quin. "She and Paul each will have ten percent also. As the proprietor and manager of Café du Monde, the remaining percentage is mine."

She sat watching him, apprehension straining her expressive mouth. After a moment of feigned consideration, he said bluntly, "All right. But on my terms."

A faint line creased the bridge of her small nose. "What terms are those?"

"That I am more than a silent partner. I want to be a working partner. You are to report to me personally all daily transactions."

She hesitated. If he hadn't been so certain of her strong desire to reacquire her French holdings, he would have been worried that she might back out. "In this way, I can advise you so that your Café du Monde profits handsomely."

"All right," she conceded reluctantly, then, with a pleased grin, held out her hand to consolidate the agreement. Instead of shaking her hand, he lifted it to his lips and kissed her fingertips.

She withdrew her hand, as fleetingly as a startled sparrow.

Reinette put her hand through the leafy pattern of the black wrought-iron gate and swung it open. The derelict L-shaped building was at the corner of Bourgogne and St. Philippe. Paul had located it. Beyond lay only the ramparts and, after them, the swamps.

She entered the small courtyard. Creepers and trees and bushes had run riot, reclaiming the space. Across the length of the courtyard ran a gallery reached by wrought-iron stairs built into the wall. The tavern had obviously done double duty as a brothel. Five or six doorways led to private rooms off the gallery. Some rooms had doors, others didn't. Outside one of them, a door swung crazily in the afternoon breeze.

Below the gallery was a taproom with heavy wooden doors opening onto the courtyard. Paul pushed open the double doors. Smoke-blackened walls and low cypress beams made the room seem dark and oppressive. Wooden tables and benches in various states of disintegration filled three-quarters of the room; the remaining space was stacked with staved and spigoted empty barrels linked by cobwebs. The stale, pungent odor of West Indian rum still pervaded the room.

Quin-Quin trailed her fingers over the thick dust on one table. "Hmmph. A miracle and a lot of elbow work going to be needed before this place going to look like an exclusive café."

The rooms off the gallery would be perfect for living quarters. Reinette looked up at Paul. "Are you any good with a hammer?"

Amidst the thicket of his beard, his lips curled genially. "I'm better with a mallet, but I could make do with a hammer."

She smiled winningly. "Now I have to convince Aaron to purchase a former brothel."

"Don't bother trying to convince me, Reinette." Aaron tilted back on the scrolled rear legs of his chair. "You've got to convince your damned New Orleans aristocracy that a café in the wrong part of town would be worth frequenting."

She halted her pacing and paused before his desk. "Whatever is taboo always entices."

"Does it?" he asked quietly.

She placed her palms on the highly varnished desk. "Doesn't it?" she countered. "As a Jew, you're taboo to every woman in New Orleans. But in the past three days, several Creole women have called on you, ostensibly for business advice."

A slow smile pleated either side of his mouth. "Are you suggesting that they came for other purposes?"

She straightened upright. *Mais, oui!* One, a delicious-looking, young widow; another, a matron who couldn't keep her hands off you."

His smile lost its amusement. "Only in private, my dear Reinette. In public, I'm a leper—dirty, you know. Your nobility doesn't realize that we Jews practice a stringent law of cleanliness and hygiene, whereas you Christians used to think that cleanliness was a form of pagan pride and opposed to godliness."

She threw up her hands in resignation. "Then why in the world did you choose to settle in a place that has such a thing as the *Code Noir*?"

His eyes narrowed over high, flat cheekbones. "Precisely because of that reason."

CHAPTER

32

THE COURTYARD OF THE CAFE DU
Monde was transformed by Reinette's loving handiwork. Perfumed shrubs and flowers bordered the flagstones: magnolias, honeysuckle, hibiscus, oleander, and her favorite, as it had been her mother's, the cloyingly sweet cape jasmine, or gardenia as it was called there in the New World.

Etienne had managed to waylay a Spanish galleon with a load of wrought-iron tables and chairs bound for the sugar stronghold of Hispaniola. Paul repainted the wrought iron a bright white and placed the furniture in the courtyard randomly.

In the evenings, the Creole ladies and their escorts, only a few couples those first weeks, sat beneath romantic stained-glass lanterns. These patrons were the crème de la crème of New Orleans—the well-to-do merchants and indigo planters from the city's outskirts.

They came dressed in the latest styles from Paris or the more sober fashions of Madrid and ordered little cakes flavored with honey. The ladies drank *café noir* or *café au lait* from dainty, porcelain demitasses, and the gentlemen sipped refreshing concoctions from the taproom, which was presided over by Quin-Quin: mint leaves mixed with bourbon and sugar; gin mixed with

cream, orange-flower water, lemon and lime juice, sugar, and the
white of an egg.

The taproom's mud-and-moss limestone walls had been whitewashed, and a crystal chandelier was now suspended from one
of the heavy, smoke-blackened beams. Its forty candles shimmered over the crowded taproom, where only males were allowed. Games of whist and dice were underway at the rebuilt
wooden tables. Five black boys carried trays of mugs filled with
the pungent West Indian rum dispensed from the spigots of the
repaired casks.

However, the main attraction at Café du Monde was music.
Paul surprised Reinette and Quin-Quin with his proficiency on
the fiddle. He mixed the Acadian, or Cajun, music of the fais-
do-do with the more rhythmic African zydeco. Moving among
the customers, Paul's melancholy smile would flash through his
wiry beard, and he would strum a few strings of a traditional
Acadian tune on his fiddle. Then, with fast chopping motions,
his bow would sing out a rapid-tempo song, much to the audience's delight.

With a flourish, he would finish his nightly entertainment with
his habitual Cajun benediction: *"Laissez les bons temps rouler!"* Let
the good times roll!

His music drew the patronage of some of the more well-off
Acadians who were flocking into New Orleans and the surrounding countryside. The first New Orleans settlers had been mainly
bourgeois city people, steadfastly opposed to any kind of physical
toil: nobles, tradesmen, and artisans. These Creoles derided the
Acadians, or Cajun French, for their rural, unsophisticated manner and their lusty attachment to outdoor life, hunting, fishing,
and manual labor.

Nonetheless, Creoles and Cajuns alike mixed congenially enough
at the Café du Monde. The festive atmosphere pervading the café
even drew patrons from as far away as Mobile and San Antonio.

Reinette presided over her establishment with both style and
discretion. She usually wore gowns of rich silk or satin in the
latest fashion, with the overskirt hitched up and shoes with two-
inch wooden heels. Normally, she left her honey-streaked hair
unpowdered and dressed in side curls and a chignon, a wide loop
of hair that hung from her crown to the nape of her neck. The
laciest of butterfly caps perched modestly atop her coiffure. Some-

times, she affected a velvet ribbon around her neck or a small, black-patch beauty spot on her cheek.

If any of the gentlemen patrons became too attentive to the beautiful proprietress, the physically imposing Paul was always nearby to act as her bodyguard.

Month by month, her profits accrued in the Royal Bank of New Orleans. She felt a certain sense of satisfaction and elation at her success, tempered only by her visits to Aaron each week. She didn't dare let Aaron come to the café, for he and Paul barely managed to tolerate each other and then only for her sake.

In the course of managing her establishment, she met many outstandingly handsome men. She soon discovered they were either monumentally stupid or unbearably dull. Aaron was neither. He was intelligent and amusing.

The combination was irresistible.

One torpid June afternoon, she made her customary call on Aaron. For their business rendezvous, she normally selected something sedate such as a pet-en-lair, a thigh-length jacket shaped to her small waist and flared below over deep-flounced overskirts. She felt that a practical, tailored mode of dress put her visits with Aaron on a more businesslike footing.

Regardless of what she wore as armor, she always felt that little tremor of excitement when she was in his presence, for all that he accorded her polite, respectful but amused attention. Lean and philosophic, his intensity barely masked an ironic awareness of life's absurdities.

That afternoon, she chose to dress *à l'anglaise* in a salmon-pink jaconet waistcoat and a gray-striped, box-pleated florentine skirt. Etienne had smuggled it in with a waylaid shipment to Puerto Rico. A smart, feathered hat completed her costume. When she entered Aaron's office, his sharp gaze traveled over her.

"Do you approve?" she asked, spinning full circle before him.

He narrowed his eyes in critical inspection. She was tailored and smooth and neat. "A veritable peacock, Reinette," he told her at last.

She wrinkled her nose at him and began removing her long eyelet gloves in preparation for reviewing and updating the week's financial status. Her glance strayed to the paper-strewn desk. "Where are the café ledgers?"

He came around the desk and took the gloves draped in her

hand. She observed that he wore a fustian frock coat with sparkling paste buttons. The frock coat couldn't conceal the mass of
knotted shoulder muscles. "Not this afternoon. Don't you know
what today is?" He grasped her elbow and propelled her out the
door. "It's the first anniversary of our venture."

"Why, so it is! I had forgotten."

"That's why"—he steered her around to the wooden stairs set
into the side of the building—"we are going to have a drink to
toast an even more profitable second year before we apply ourselves to business."

Cautiously, her hand gripped the wooden railing as if it were
a wisteria vine she was testing for climbing. She felt as if everyone
on the rue de Royale was observing her from behind the wooden
jalousies in the street.

When he opened the door for her, she stepped just inside and
looked around a sunny, rectangular room divided by a black and
gold silk screen. On the near side, two heavy Marchesseau silk
sofas faced each other before a fireplace like opposing armies. A
sideboard and small cherry-wood secretary were the only pieces
of furniture in the main portion of the room, but she could make
out the corner of a purple taffeta canopied bed just beyond the
screen.

"Your place is. . . lovely." She felt awkward, tongue-tied, in
the masculine-furnished room. "Where did you find the screen?"

"Etienne, *naturellement*." He went over to the sideboard and
removed the glass stopper from a crystal flagon. "He intercepted
a merchantman returning from China."

"I don't drink spirits."

He turned to face her, a stemmed glass in one hand. Sunlight
streaming through the French doors opening onto the narrow
balcony dusted his auburn hair. "I'm not planning on seducing
you, Reinette."

Nettled, she left her defensive position just inside the doorway
and crossed to him. She looked up into brilliant blue eyes. "What
do you want of me, Aaron?"

He set the glass on the sideboard. "I want you as more than a
business partner or a friend."

"Why?" she asked.

"Perhaps I find something in you that you don't. Perhaps someday you'll see some quality in me that I don't even realize is there."

She felt she had been stripped to the bone, her soul seemed so exposed to him.

"For a long time now," he continued relentlessly, "you've hid all the hurt in your life. When anyone draws too close, you conceal your feelings with a pert reply. I think people rarely suspect the storeroom of feeling in you. I know you, Reinette. I know you like I know my own reflection."

His speech shook her profoundly, frightening her as nothing ever had—not the soldiers coming to take her away from the swamp; not the cold, austere convent; not the lonely years at Natchitoches; not the blood-crazed slave rebels.

"I also know that nothing means as much to you as this nebulous Maison Bellecour. But I'm willing to wager my love for you against the lure of your French estates."

She backed away. "I really don't feel like celebrating."

"Do you mean you don't feel like celebrating—or celebrating with a Jew?"

Her hands bunched up in front of her mouth. Her lids squeezed shut. "Aaron, " she whispered in a little girl's voice, "I can't help what I feel. Intellectually, I understand and accept you as a Jew. Yet for so much of my life the convent condemned your people and their religion. I can change my thoughts, but I can't change my feelings!"

His lips pressed together, as grim and narrow as the slash mark of a razor. He didn't try to stop her from leaving, though if he hadn't wanted to let her go, she never could have escaped the muscled arms of the former *galérien*.

She lay awake that night in her comfortable tester bed. She had drawn the *baire* about the bed to keep out the mosquitoes— and perhaps as a barrier to thoughts of Aaron, too. But he was always in her mind; he was there when she awoke at night, every night. He was always there.

CHAPTER

33

E TIENNE ENTERED THE TAPROOM by the rear door. The howling wind banged the door back and forth against the mud wall. By the next morning, the building Gulf squall would sluice the streets with rain.

On his powerful shoulders, he bore a cask of the finest French wine, ostensibly prohibited in the province now occupied by Spanish troops, small though they were in number. It was late, nearing two in the morning, and all of the customers had at last cleared out, including the three Spanish officers, who had nervously fingered the gold hilts of their swords while they drank.

They were part of the tiny, one-hundred-odd contingent of the newly arrived Spanish governor, Antonio de Ulloa. To the astonishment of the few colonists who had turned out for his disembarkation earlier that year, the unimpressive little man had refrained from proclaiming the formal possession of the province for the Spanish crown. Nor had he ordered the French flag to be lowered and the red and yellow standard of Bourbon Spain to be hoisted in its place.

Still, there was no denying that Louisiana officially belonged to Spain now, not with Spanish soldiers demanding Catalonian wine instead of Bordeaux!

Quin-Quin looked up from the table she was cleaning. Beer

rings dotted the taproom's tabletops. "Have you had anything to eat?" she asked Etienne in her slow, husky drawl.

Etienne set the cask down and shook his head. "No."

She refolded the damp, smelly rag and smiled. "Let me fix you something then."

He eyed her, and she knew he was trying to figure her out.

The Huguenot was like a porcupine, all bristly if one approached too close. She saw the loneliness behind those nondescript hazel eyes. She was lonely, too. But her race and his race never found comfort with each other—they only spent shared lust. That she could have anywhere, anytime. Sometimes she did, with some Creole gentleman who took her fancy. In the stranger's frenzied embrace, she would pretend he was whispering words of tenderness—not instructions on what tricks excited him.

The few times she had taken one of the Creole customers up to her room, Reinette must have been aware of what was occurring, yet the girl had never mentioned a word about it. Reinette was going on twenty-three, and Quin-Quin knew the young woman had never known a man.

Quin-Quin put her fists on her hips and narrowed her eyes on the little man with the bowlegs and muscle-bound shoulders. "I'm taller than you are—and darker-skinned. I'm a woman, and you're a man. I'm not educated, and you seem to be. Otherwise, Monsieur Pirate, I see little difference between you and me. We're both lonely. The way I make it, we can ignore each other, like we've been doing for the past three years, or we can be friends."

Etienne nodded slowly as if he were reluctantly coming to terms with her proposal. "I think I'd like to eat."

Quin-Quin chuckled. "Well, that's a start."

She took the flat-nosed man into the separate kitchen at the rear of the tavern. While he sat silently at the long trestle table, she prattled away, carrying on a steady monologue as she moved around the small kitchen.

"Paul is the only one who ever eats around here." She diced a variety of peppers and turned them into a pan to simmer over the fire in the hearth. "That big Cajun's idea of food is to stay just this side of the line between pleasure and pain."

She paused to wipe her brow on her stained apron. The night was hot and humid, and the kitchen was even hotter. "Paul claims if you cross that line, people won't enjoy the food." She sprinkled cayenne powder on the sauce base and added a hearty dash of garlic powder and white pepper. "Says if you stay just this side of it, each bite leaves an aftertaste, and you keep wanting one more."

She greased the skillet, then set it at the front of the fireplace on the ash-covered coals. At one side of the hearth, where the iron crane swung out from the fireplace, rushes were laid to catch the meat drippings.

"For my way of thinking, I think the food is too spicy. More pain than pleasure. Curls my tongue like it was crisp bacon."

The wind had risen, slapping the shutters against the wall and playing havoc with the guttering candles in the sconces. She thought about closing the window, but Etienne spoke then, surprising her.

"It's been a long time since I've had anyone offer to cook for me," he said haltingly.

She wanted him to open up to her, but she knew she couldn't rush him. He would have to find his way of purging his tortured soul on his own. In some ways, he and Paul were alike, both of them taciturn. But where Paul was open, Etienne had turned inward, where no human emotions could touch him.

She returned to the worktable and began to dice crayfish and crabmeat into small pieces, saying easily, "Some people don't like to cook. For themselves, leastways."

"Babette liked to cook."

"Babette. That's a pretty name." She dumped chicken livers into the steaming rice, careful to keep her back to him. "I always wanted a different name. Now who do you know named Quin-Quin?"

"Babette didn't like her name, either. That was about the only thing she didn't like."

Two sentences back to back out of the man. Amazing. He was acting quite out of the ordinary. An old, West African Mandingo word for such behavior came to her unbidden: *jasi*, though she had heard it corrupted to jazz here in New Orleans.

"I wager your wife wouldn't like this Cajun étouffée."

"She liked everything and everyone. She even liked one of the dragoons quartered in our cottage. Called him a nice boy."

Quin-Quin heard the crack in his voice. She set down the saucepan and turned. Etienne was weeping. Silent tears coursed down either side of his flattened nose. He drew deep, gulping breaths as if there were no air in the room. "The dragoon . . . he was the one . . ." Etienne buried his face in his hands. His bunched shoulders heaved. Great sobs wracked his body.

She removed her apron, draping it over the back of a chair, and crossed to the weeping man. Her *café au lait* hands cradled his head against her stomach. "Go ahead and cry, *mon cher*. It'll do you good."

A torrent of words poured from the man, a broken recounting of the loss of his family. The wind had increased and sometimes drowned out his low, harsh words.

She held him against her and listened. Her fingers combed through his hair in soothing motions. "It's all right, it's all right," she murmured softly, interjecting her consoling words intermittently with the fragmented sentences of his nightmarish tale of the years as a prisoner in one of the infamous French galleys.

In comforting the man, she didn't notice the wind whipping her apron's ties about or the candle flame that licked at the material. One tie caught fire. The wind flapped the tie against the rushing on the floor. The greasy rushes *whoosh*ed up in flame.

Quin-Quin spun at the crackling noise. That side of the wall was a torch. She grabbed the broom to beat out the blaze, but the wind fanned it out of control. Before she or Etienne could stamp out the fire, it had leaped to the low thatched roof. In seconds, the kitchen was wrapped in a lurid sheet of devouring flames.

Resentful of the disturbing noise, Reinette buried deeper into the goose-down mattress. To awaken before daylight was sinful, she thought sleepily. Especially if you didn't get to sleep until one o'clock in the morning.

From her open window came the faint cracking of planks tortured by a blaze, and then more loudly the crash of falling roofs. Groggily, she tumbled from her bed and ran to the window. Flames, enveloping not only the kitchen now but a portion of the taproom, shot up to an immense height with the hissing and soughing of a hurricane.

Neighbors, clad only in their nightcaps and nightclothes, fled their burning homes. One woman ran, shrieking, down the street nude. Some stood paralyzed with shock, unable to decide what to do. A man hurried past, his arms loaded with wine bottles, booty from the wine shop next door. The street was chaos. The flames leaped from roof to roof. Red cinders fluttered and flared across the night sky.

Reinette dashed for the door. Outside, a tremendous blast of heat struck her face. She held up her arms to shield it. Fire engulfed the taproom and sucked up into the gallery. Smaller flames licked at the hem of her dressing sack and scorched her feet. She tore off her nightclothes and caught her wind-whipped hair close against her throat.

At the rear staircase, she picked her way down through the flames. A portion of the stairs buckled, crumbled, and gave way. She grabbed and hung on to the railing. Hot wood blistered her palms. Billowing smoke stung her eyes and burned her lungs. She felt dizziness spiraling through her head. She choked and coughed and gasped for air.

Air! Blinded by smoke, she followed turbulent currents of blessed cool air. Halfway down the stairs, she stumbled into someone's arms—Aaron's.

"Reinette! Blessed Jehovah!"

He scooped her up and tossed her over his shoulder, and the breath *whoosh*ed from her. At the base of the stairs, away from the flames' searing heat, he deposited her on her feet. She winced at the blisters already forming there. He yanked off his fine cambric shirt and jerked it down over her head, covering her nudity.

Behind them, Etienne and Quin-Quin broke through the barrier of spectators. The black woman yelled over the babble of hysterical voices, "Paul—he just went up to get you, girl! By the front stairs!"

"*Palsambleu*, no!" The words rasped from her sore throat.

She struggled to loose herself from Aaron's grip, but he thrust her at Quin-Quin. "Watch her!"

With dazed eyes, she watched Aaron ascend the crumbling staircase into the inferno. She lost sight of him behind a wall of licking flame and black smoke that funneled upward to lose itself in the dark heavens. She waited in agonizing expectancy, almost holding her breath. Her fingernails dug crescents into her palms. Nothing could walk out of that blazing oven and live.

Aaron didn't walk out. Through a rift in the smoke, she saw him half crawl, half pull himself out onto the gallery. The staircase at that end of the gallery collapsed in a shower of sparks, and she screamed.

Sudden droplets pelted her upturned face. Through rain-soaked lashes, she watched Aaron roll Paul off the gallery and then saw the crumpled body thud against the ground below. Then, and only then, did she faint.

CHAPTER

34

"**H**ERE, SEE FOR YOURSELF,
Paul." Reinette held up the silver-backed hand mirror. Paul propped
himself up in bed and stared at his reflection.

His glorious beard was gone. That morning, now that he was
feeling somewhat better—and she knew that he was going to
survive the usual complications of smoke inhalation—she shaved
off his badly singed beard. He looked so totally different without
it, younger certainly, and not so fierce. Singed, too, were his
brows, lashes, and patches of hair bordering his forehead.

His lips crimped in a rueful smile. "I look like a shorn sheep."

"You look quite handsome," she corrected, and took the hand
mirror from him and replaced it on the lacy doily next to a silver
brush and comb on the bureau. The bedroom was elegant. Aaron
had rented the town house of an absentee sugar planter for the
three displaced people.

"Half the women in New Orleans will be throwing themselves
at your feet," she teased the big Acadian. It was all she could do
to smile, she felt so utterly exhausted.

"If that were so," he said so solemnly that she glanced around
at him, "then I wouldn't hesitate to ask you to marry me, Reinette."

Her tongue couldn't seem to work properly. Of course she

knew he cared for her. She cared for him. Those last five years, he had watched over her like some guardian angel. "Paul, I love you, but not—not in the way that—in that way."

Paul would be kind to her, but how could she think of being true to him as a wife when her thoughts would be unfaithfully turning to Aaron?

She had seen Paul naked and cared for his bodily needs, but it was the mere sight of Aaron's hands that could cause her to go all trembly.

Even now, she could close her eyes and recall those supple, brown hands. Holding them in hers, she had rubbed salve onto the blisters that bubbled the skin of Aaron's palms. An exciting sensation had coursed through her, and when she had looked up into the brush fire of his gaze, she had felt as if the tropical sun were melting her into creamy, little puddles. He still treated her politely, respectfully, but that affectionate teasing was gone, replaced by a cool, distant manner.

She crossed the room to Paul and said crisply, "Besides, I don't plan on remaining here in Louisiana forever. One day, I have to go back to France." She glanced down at him, her eyes pleading with him to understand.

He was silent, but it wasn't a confused or baffled or apologetic silence. There was utter tranquillity in him.

She bent over and placed her hands on either side of his smooth jaw and kissed his forehead. A look of childish contrition appeared in her coal-black eyes. "Rest, Paul. I'll be back later with something for you to eat."

She shut the door behind her and leaned against it. She no longer had to conceal her exhaustion. The past two weeks' vigil over Paul had taken its toll. Then, too, her preoccupation with rebuilding the Café du Monde from its ruins sapped her normal vitality, her *joie de vivre*, as Paul called it. It seemed that the heat of the fire still burned in her blood.

Her footsteps dragged down the hallway toward her bedroom. She stopped twice to regain her strength. Her bedroom doorway seemed terribly far away. She thought about calling Quin-Quin for help but remembered that she had sent her to the market for fresh fruits, thinking that their juices would be good for Paul.

She longed for one of the woman's healing African tisanes or maybe one of her cooling mint cloths, laid over her burning

forehead. She pushed off the wall and tottered two more steps
before a silver spike of pain drove itself deeply into her brain.

Ten days before the fire, a Congo slave called Khyber had
staggered from the hold of a Havana slave ship and fallen onto
his knees on the New Orleans's wharf. The other slaves, linked
with him by a chain, were bound for the outlying Parlange plantation and would bypass the capital in their journey on foot.

The overseer cracked the whip, just pinking the black man's
flesh. Then, bending low so that the slave could see his face, he
smiled genially and said, "You don't get your black carcass back
in line with the rest of your people, you're a dead man!"

Khyber was already a dying man. He gave his sickness to the
overseer. The overseer was a man of little intelligence but a great
deal of conscientiousness. Usually. The opportunity to partake
of New Orleans's fleshpots, which came rarely, was one he couldn't
pass up. He had all the black ass he wanted . . . but thoughts of
a pink-skinned little thing straight out from Paris were just too
much. With instructions to his eldest son to start the slaves on
their way, he left the wharves with the intention of catching up
later—after he had visited the nearest whorehouse.

The overseer passed the disease on to Louise, a thirty-one-year-
old who looked fifty, who, in turn, gave it to René, a young and
wealthy Creole gentleman. The next evening, René took his young
wife to the Café du Monde for their first anniversary. That night,
the night of the fire, they infected thirty other people there,
including Reinette.

Two weeks following the fire, a large pile of corpses without
coffins lay in the graveyard in horizontal layers, one above the
other, like corded wood.

The blacks did not seem to succumb as often to the yellow
jack, which struck every third year on the average. Those citizens
of New Orleans, unaffected yet by the disease and who had not
run away from the city, dug trenches and threw the putrid corpses
into the ditches indiscriminately. When the next seasonal rains
came, the decayed bodies would be found floating in the streets.

The plague, called yellow fever, or, more commonly, "swamp
miasma," because doctors believe that the fumes escaping from
the swamp gases were the agent, ravaged its victims. To watch

the epidemic run its course, in most cases, to the victim's inevitable death, was unbearable to the family.

In the last stages, profuse hemorrhaging occurred from the mouth, nose, ears, eyes, and even toes; the eyes became prominent, glistening, yellow, and staring; the face was discolored with orange and dusky red. The skin was mottled, livid, swollen, and stained with blood and black vomit. The veins of the face and body were distended as if trying to burst free from the diseased body.

In those first two weeks, the disease took nearly four hundred lives, but Aaron was determined that one of those lives would not be Reinette's. Quin-Quin had given him the horrible news when he came round to see how the Acadian was doing.

"You can't come in, Monsieur Aaron," Quin-Quin said, her lips trembling. Fatigue had dug craters under her eyes. "The mistress has swamp miasma!"

"I don't give a damn, I'm going in!"

He entered Reinette's bedroom to find her comatose with a raging fever. He shrugged out of his frock coat and, before Quin-Quin's startled eyes, began to strip Reinette of her layers of clothing.

"You going to bleed her?"

"*Merde*, no! That'll kill her if the yellow jack doesn't."

He sounded more self-assured than he felt. He rolled up his sleeves and set to work. He allowed no one admittance. For the next three days, he went without sleep. He tried purging the fever from Reinette by literally turning the bedroom into a sweat room, furnished with bricks that Quin-Quin heated in the kitchen. The Creole owner was going to have a miasma of his own when he returned to see the bedroom's warped wood.

When sweating didn't seem to work, he turned to deluging her with bucket after bucket of cold water. Hour after hour, he massaged her pain-wracked limbs, oblivious to her womanly curves. He resorted to camphor, calomel, and Quin-Quin's peppermint. Then he vainly tried to make her vomit by forcing her to drink copious amounts of water. Her fever abated, but her pulse rate fell.

He knew from his experience aboard the galley that this was the second stage. He was stricken. There was no recovery from the third stage, when the skin turns yellow and the victim vomits black blood or black vomit.

Throughout the fourth night, he sat with his elbows braced on his knees, his face in his hands. Outside, he could hear the church bells tolling for the increasing number of dead. The streets were jammed with makeshift hearses, their drivers yelling: "Bring out your dead." Each time Aaron heard this, he shuddered. He couldn't imagine heaving Reinette's lovely body onto those putrefying corpses.

All night long, the creaking wheels of the death wagons rattled through the streets. Tar was set on fire in the streets, and lime was thrown profusely on the recent, shallow graves that were dug by torchlight.

The tar pots blazed so intensely that the downtown streets seemed as bright as daylight. Great clouds of smoke hung suspended over the beleaguered city like a funeral pall, disputing darkness itself. Artillery fire shook the city every other hour, because of the belief that the combustion of tar and gunpowder was supposed to clarify the atmosphere and disperse the miasma. Bedding and clothes were burned, adding to the awful pall of smoke. Sulphuric acid was sloshed over the homes visited by death.

Toward dawn, Aaron reached the pit of despair. He could tell that Reinette kept sliding back and forth from pain to sleep. Her labored breath had the odor of death on it. Her face was the color of bone and seemed to have shrunk from her skull. Throwing back the sweat-soaked sheet, he saw that her naked body had the dry, crinkling appearance of old newspaper.

He had no faith in the remedies left to him: either dosing her with mercury to the point of salivation, which was usually the fatal dose, or applying eighty to a hundred leeches to her throat, although he had seen the bloodletting done once with a lancet.

Silently, he cursed the Almighty God that could let this happen, cursed the Hebrew Yahweh as he never had all those years he had been chained to the galley bench.

Paul barged his way into the room. Behind him, Quin-Quin stood looking helpless and like she had been on a four-day crying binge. The Acadian looked as huge and unsmiling as Jehovah. "Is she worse?"

Aaron nodded. Veins made a pulsing road map of his forehead.

Paul made his way to the foot of the bed, and Aaron could tell the Acadian was still in a great deal of pain. In a possessive gesture, Aaron pulled the sheet over her body. The big man looked down at the plague-wracked face. Then he surprised Aaron by dropping to his knees and bowing his head over his interlocked hands.

Why, he believes in all this, Aaron thought incredulously. The fool believes God is listening!

When Paul finished, he sought out one of the hard-back chairs and sat through the passing of dawn with the silent Aaron. With the light of another day, Aaron's rage at the nebulous Creator passed, leaving a feeling of utter finality, a feeling of unaccustomed peace, because there was no hope whatsoever left in him.

For two days, the two men faced each other like old opponents who have finally called a truce. Each had beard-stubbled faces and eyes like red coals. Then toward dusk of the second day of their joint bedside vigil, Reinette broke into a flood of sweating. Aaron suspected it was the beginning of the end and tried to prepare himself emotionally. At midnight, however, the fever broke; she opened her eyes and smiled wanly. "Have I been a nuisance?" she asked of Aaron in a lung-rattling rasp, then immediately fell into a sleep that had none of the symptoms of her previous coma.

In utter relief, Aaron's eyes stung from the sudden rush of tears that poured down his smiling cheeks.

CHAPTER

35

NEW ORLEANS'S LEVEE WAS UP-
wards of four miles long now, but, as Aaron had once predicted,
few vessels were moored along its length. Reinette walked on the
levee beside Aaron, humoring him, for he was adamant that she
get daily exercise to restrengthen her body, wasted by the yellow
fever six weeks earlier.

The streets, filled with their "night soil," a euphemistic term
for human excrement, might not be a safe place to walk, but
neither were the rat-ridden warehouses and docks. In fact, nowhere in New Orleans seemed to be safe. Only that morning
there had been a riot in the Place d'Armes with shouts of "Liberty!" from landowners who had flocked in from every nearby
village and plantation to join with the upper-class merchants in
the city. The tradesmen and merchants opposed the strict mercantile restrictions imposed by Ulloa that tightened the control
over importation of goods by them.

On every Creole tongue, there was talk of a republic. Under
the indifferent Spanish administration, an independent spirit had
taken root. A dozen or so of New Orleans's leading Creoles, a
number of them members of the governing Superior Council, had
gathered to plot rebellion several times at Reinette's café before
it burned. Most of them were full of noble ideals; young and

handsome men like Jean Milhet, Rouget de Villeré, and La Freniere. Their zealous words and phrases, "Tyrants!" . . . "Oppressors!" . . . "Freedom and liberty!," spread like a contagion.

Aaron had warned her of the danger of being linked with the ringleaders of this cabal, but she had replied peevishly, "Just because you and the Superior Council don't get along . . ." and said no more.

Although Aaron as a Jew was in violation of the *Code Noir*, no one, not even the Superior Council, had the courage actually to order him from Louisiana since they depended on him as a source of their borrowing to sustain their high style of living. In that time of monetary crisis, when Louisiana's treasury was experiencing a dearth of funds, Aaron alone in the colony had reserves of gold and silver coin via his network that stretched all the way to Persia and the Far East.

For this reason, Reinette had sought him out on that particular day. She had chosen a dress of mauve tiffany with a matching parasol. The color set off her fair hair and skin. Though she was almost skeletally thin and her hair was drab and still brittle from fever, she had wanted to look her best. She had even tucked a gardenia into a bosom bottle she wore.

She persuaded him to stroll over to the market, just in front of the levee, for coffee. "I tire more easily than I used to," she cajoled, smiling up at his aquiline, Mediterranean countenance.

The market's open café was packed with couples, mostly Spanish soldiers courting young ladies of the middle-class Creole families, which oddly the French soldiers had not done to any great degree. The upper-class Creole families refused to allow their daughters to associate with the Spanish interlopers.

"Well, at least, here there is no talk of revolution," she said.

"If Louisiana does revolt, it'll be the first European colony in America to proclaim its independence," Aaron said thinly.

"You're against revolution, aren't you?"

"You must admit the Spanish regime has been far less corrupt than your French one."

"Why do you say 'my' French one? You're French." At that, she could have bitten her tongue, remembering the last discussion they had had on the subject of his nationality.

He didn't refer to it but said instead, "I became a man without a country when I was sentenced to the galleys. I will give my allegiance only to a country that answers solely to itself. And I don't think that will happen in our lifetimes."

She flicked her fan open and waved it restlessly before her face. The subject of revolution and rebellion was not one she had planned to broach.

Aaron ordered *café au lait* for her and *café noir* for himself along with the market specialty, warm, crusty rolls. After the little waiter departed, Aaron crooked an arm on the back of his bamboo chair and said, "You have something you want to say, Reinette, so let's get it over with. You've always been forthright with your unbearably candid statements. What is it that's prowling through your mind now?"

Unprepared for his direct attack, she was at a loss for words. He knew her better than she realized. Had he not seen her as naked as the day she was born? She blushed and, hands braced atop her parasol's ivory handle, blurted, "I can't afford to live in the town house you rented for us without some means of support. I have almost enough savings to completely rebuild the Café du Monde, but I'll need, in addition, further capital to get it back into operation."

The waiter interrupted at the most inappropriate time, with their order, and she silently cursed. Aaron took his own sweet time to reply, first taking a sip of the steaming, thick coffee, then a bite of a roll. The feminine laughter and attentive male voices of the other customers were infuriatingly distracting.

"Aaron! *Ciel! S'il te plaît*, say something!"

He leaned back in his chair and fixed her with a scrutinizing stare. "You haven't completely repaid my first loan," he said at last.

She looked at him, stunned. "But you know that the café will be a success again. We never had a slow night the first time. Why, just look at the crowd here. I can easily repay you within six months."

"The first time I made a stipulation that you make me a working partner. This time I have another stipulation."

The way he said it . . . She frowned. "What sort of stipulation?"

"You have to marry me, Reinette."

Her coffee sloshed onto her lovely lace fichu. Trembling, she set down the delicate cup of Limoges porcelain. A network of blue veins pulsed at her temples. "You know I can't," she whispered. "That—that would mean staying in Louisiana forever."

"You're not being totally candid," he reproved, and casually took another sip of his coffee.

"You know why!" she gasped, tears in her throat. "You—you're a Jew, Aaron!"

He shrugged. "Then I won't advance you the money."

Her rage was like a bell jar clamped down around them blotting out the laughter and ringing glasses. "My love for you would—"

"Then you do love me?" he asked almost idly, pausing with his cup in the air in front of his twinkling eyes.

"No. Yes. I don't know. Oh!" She hit the table with her small fist, and her cup rattled in its saucer. "Can't you understand that whatever feelings we share now would be jeopardized if I married you?"

He leaned forward and cupped his hands around her trembling fist. "No, Reinette, I can't. Because I believe that I love you enough to overcome any obstacles that you try to put in our way, even my race and religion."

What could she say?

A wedding date was set for six months later, in October, after the restoration of the Café du Monde. More than that, Reinette needed the time to prepare herself emotionally for the event. She was frightened of committing herself to Aaron and giving up her old goal of reclaiming the du Plessis estates, which had been all that had kept her going during those lonely, difficult years. More than that, she was frightened of compromising her faith.

Because she was Catholic and Aaron was Jewish, she consented to forgo a religious ceremony in lieu of having the Spanish governor perform a civil one. But the night before the ceremony was to take place, Don Antonio de Ulloa and his wife had withdrawn to his ship at anchor in the river after the inhabitants of New Orleans took up arms, along with Acadians from the surrounding countryside—many of whom had been celebrating the approaching wedding with Paul only that morning. The Superior Council had actually demanded in a petition with five hundred and sixty signatures that the Spanish governor leave the colony.

In a way, Ulloa was as much of an outcast as Reinette and Aaron, for he had left New Orleans not too long after he first arrived to acquire a bride from Peru, a great heiress, it was said. She had brought with her a retinue of servants and a group of friends.

The New Orleans Creole women were incensed that Ulloa had passed them over and, worse, that the heiress refused to see them, preferring to remain shut up with her own friends. Her suppers and balls were for her friends alone.

Thus it was that the acting governor, the pompous, little Frenchman, Charles Philippe Aubry, pronounced Aaron and Reinette man and wife. He did so only because he owed Aaron a fortune in notes that Aaron could call in on a moment's whim and thus ruin the ugly, little man.

For the brief civil ceremony, Reinette had chosen a gown of champagne satin with rich brown embroidery on the stomacher and heavily flounced lace sleeves, and a pale ivory lace mantilla. The wedding was staged simultaneously with the café's reopening. Reinette had planned a simple affair, but a great number of the café's patrons showed up for the festivities afterward.

Aaron took charge of the reception. Wine flowed from a fountain built in the courtyard's center. Paul, reconciled to the wedding, serenaded the two with romantic ballads. When he finished, she kissed him on the cheek and said, "I love you, Paul."

Quin-Quin, of course, wept, but Etienne, the flat-nosed Huguenot, was there to comfort her in her joy.

Aaron arranged for Chinese fireworks, smuggled in by his old *galérien* partner. Along with the enthralled guests, she and Aaron watched the showering of fireworks from the balcony outside their bridal room. "Happy?" he asked, and laid his hand over hers on the wrought-iron balustrade.

She nodded, barely able to breathe. She felt the need to escape the press of people, to flee to her beloved marshes and swamps.

He took her fluted glass from her other hand. His blue eyes smoldered like the blue-hot center of a flame. "It's late, and I've waited too long for you, gamine."

Blood thundered in her ears. Facing him across the width of the four-poster, she tried to recall the gentle man who had cared for her in her illness, but all she could think of was that in surrendering herself to Aaron, she was also surrendering her identity, betraying her faith.

Outside, a host of Acadian gallants beat pans and pots and

played raucous music in the time-honored shivaree. She was ready to invite them inside, anything to postpone the inevitable.

Aaron blew out one of the myrtle-wax candles, leaving the room in soft light and shadows. Then he didn't give her any more time to think. Coming to her, he put his arms around her and pressed her head against his chest. "I'm frightened, too, Reinette. Listen. Don't you hear my heart pounding like a frenzied voodoo drum?"

Some of the stiffness eased out her spine and muscles. "Let's get this over with, then," she mumbled against the lace fall of his stock.

He laughed and set her from him to capture her stubborn chin. "I sincerely hope that I make this more pleasant for you than one of your 'duties.' "

His hand deserted her chin to circle behind and remove the wooden pins and ivory comb that bound her hair. When the heavy mass of golden-brown hair hung loose around her waist, he unfastened the tiny buttons that followed her backbone. She closed her eyes, unable to watch the building bonfire of his gaze. When her clothes lay crumpled around her, he knelt before her. Terribly embarrassed, she crossed her hands before the mound of wiry golden curls.

"Put your hands on my shoulders," he said softly.

With great reluctance, she did as he instructed. She was cold and uncomfortable standing nude before him. Almost tenderly, he removed first her right satin slipper and then her left. Next, he took off her garters and hose.

She understood now. This was Aaron's gesture of humbling himself before her. That one act endeared him to her and made what she did next easier.

She knelt down also, directly in front of him. With his fevered gaze on her pale face, she loosened his stock, then, with a little more difficulty, drew his silk shirt up over his head. At once, her eyes were drawn to the ugly purple welts that corduroyed his shoulders. The fingertips of her hand ran wonderingly over one weal. He winced at her touch, but she sensed it wasn't from the scars' sensitivity.

"The galleys did this to you?" she rasped.

He caught her wrists. "Don't. It's not pity I want from you, Reinette."

Haltingly, her gaze lowered to lock on his male nipples, nested with hair. She forced her gaze lower, to his doeskin britches. Her fingers fumbled with their fly buttons.

His strong, warm hands closed over her trembling fingers, stilling them. "I love you, Reinette. Don't be afraid of me—ever."

She swallowed hard and nodded.

Outside, the gallants finally departed, bent on making merry mischief elsewhere.

Aaron slid his hands under her armpits and lifted her to her feet, then scooped her up against his chest and carried her to the bed. She lay there, shivering with a different kind of cold, and waited for him to come to her. She tried separating her mind from what was happening, tried to tell herself that she had seen Paul naked and that all men were the same.

When Aaron stood naked before her, she was startled by the sight of his male organ—not by its size or his erection, but by its scarred, ravaged flesh.

He must have seen the astonishment on her face, for he came to her and leaned over her, saying, "I'm sorry . . . I should have prepared you."

She shook her head. "Keep me warm, Aaron."

He stretched out alongside her, enfolding her in his arms. "I want you to know and understand." Absently, he stroked her bare shoulder while he talked of the grisly past, of how he had initiated his final reversion to being a Jew on himself.

"Several times I passed out at the pain. At one point, I thought I was going to bleed to death. And then, lying there in my blood, I thought that death would undoubtedly be preferable to the galleys, anyway. Many times in the five years after that I had reason to wish—"

She rolled toward him, half covering him, and slid lower on him. Tears streamed off her face and fell on the mutilated flesh. Before he could stop her, she wiped the tears away with a handful of her hair. What began as an act of infinite tenderness grew into one of passion for her, as she nuzzled him with her cheek and her hair.

However, her growing excitement was tempered by her reluctance to commit herself fully. Later, when he took her, she tried to keep the old distance between him and herself. But he was there when she awoke at night.

Every night.

Gradually, the beaming sunlight of his love eroded the convent's dark teachings against the Jews. At first, she was bewildered by the warm and gentle wind of Aaron's abiding devotion sweeping over her. She tried not to trust its warmth, but little by little she surrendered herself, until the day came when she found herself blessing both her Holy Father and his Yahweh for giving Aaron to her.

CHAPTER

36

THE IMMEDIATE RESULT OF THE merry mischief of the shivaree resulted in Ulloa's ship being set adrift down the Mississippi. Infuriated, he set sail for Havana the next day. For ten months, the citizens of Louisiana reveled in their easily won freedom from Spain.

Then, on the afternoon of August 17, 1769, 2100 soldiers debarked from a large Spanish armada of twenty-four ships commanded by Lt. Gen. Alejandro O'Reilly. Tall and suave, the Irish mercenary had come to put down the Louisiana rebellion. Spain saw Louisiana as a strategic buffer against England and viewed the revolt as one likely to provoke other rebellions in Spanish colonies unless it were subdued.

At five o'clock the next day, his batteries of artillery and companies of infantry moved with military precision into the Place d'Armes to the sound of bugles and drums and cannon salvos. They arranged themselves about the square in front of the cathedral. Then the guns of the Spanish ships roared out a salute, which was answered by the fifty cannon of the batteries.

Next, Lieutenant General O'Reilly and his staff came ashore clad in brilliant red uniforms and, with great pomp, marched to the square, where the sycophantish Aubry, acting as interim governor, awaited them at the flagpole from which fluttered the French Bourbon flag of white lilies on a golden background.

The dashing Irishman nodded his head, and down came the French flag. Up went the Spanish Bourbon one with lions and ramparts, to a two-thousand-strong cheer of "*Viva el Rey!*"

Few Frenchmen were at the Place d'Armes, or Plaza de Armas, as it would now be called, and even fewer cheered. Some wept.

The new governor-general permitted himself a slight smile of satisfaction. So far, he was pleased with the steps he had taken to establish Spanish authority. The pageantry of his dramatic entry would inspire at least the respect of the colonists. But he wanted more than their respect. He demanded their absolute obedience. For this reason alone, if for no other, he was the favorite troubleshooter of King Carlos III of Spain.

That evening, he summoned Aubry to the office he had set up in the governor's house. "In the name of King Carlos, I am giving a reception to be held three days hence in recognition of the transference of French *Louisiane* to Spanish *Luisiana*. I want the conspirators of the rebellion to be invited."

"But . . . I thought . . . I understood that there would be no reprisals," Aubry stuttered.

"Not against the participants in the rebellion. I will grant them amnesty. But the dozen or so conspirators—I want them present at the reception. Do you understand?"

Aubry, who was without nobility or dignity or even proper bearing, swallowed and nodded. For too long, he had been walking lightly across quicksand, trying simultaneously to please the powerful Superior Council and to appease the ineffectual Spanish governor, Ulloa. Now he had to deal with this formidable soldier, who was confident to the point of arrogance.

"In the meantime," O'Reilly said, taking a pinch of snuff from a jade-lidded box, "I want every citizen to take the Oath of Loyalty to Spain."

Reinette fingered the poster Paul had ripped from one of the plaza's chestnut trees. She pushed back her hair and looked up at Aaron, who was buttoning his stock. "Surely every good Frenchman will refuse to attend the governor-general's reception," she said.

"Just as they all refused to take the Oath of Loyalty?"

"You shouldn't have refused yesterday," she whispered, as if afraid O'Reilly had spies listening at the door.

Aaron shrugged. "According to the *Code Noir*, I am not legally a citizen of Louisiana, so how could I take an oath of loyalty?"

"Then let's not go tonight, Aaron!" She sat up in bed, and the sheet fell away to expose a small, pert breast. "Please, I feel uneasy about the reception."

He left his stock dangling and bent to kiss her upturned breast. "You tempt me mightily." He spread his hand on the little mound of her stomach; his voice sank to a husky whisper. "I long to make your belly grow big with our child."

She wrapped her arms around his neck. "Then let's stay home tonight, please, Aaron?"

A shadow darkened his face. "We can't. Earlier today, I received a personal invitation from the general himself, delivered by Aubry's manservant. I have reason to believe Aubry may have implicated me as one of the ringleaders. If we don't go, we'll look even more guilty."

Reinette's face blanched as white as the rumpled muslin sheet. "Impossible!"

"Why? Everyone in town knows that it was the revelers from our wedding reception who set Ulloa's ship adrift. That was considered the final straw by Madrid. A coincidence, a piece of bad luck, perhaps, but it has to be set straight."

"But most of the leaders are members of the Superior Council," she said, rising from the bed to go to him, "and everyone in town also knows the council and you are at odds."

"Are we?"

Her heart stopped at the inflection in his voice and the deadly serious gleam in his eyes. "What are you saying?"

"That for too long now people like Paul, myself, Etienne, and others have lived under suppressed freedom. That with the rebellion the colony of Louisiana has become the first in America to voice the principle of self-determination of nations."

He sighed then and clasped her upper arms, drawing her gently against him. "I'm saying that I financed the revolution."

"You can't have done something foolish like that!" she whispered, aghast. "I thought you didn't uphold with the idealism of—"

"I didn't want to tell you because I didn't want you to get

involved." He pressed her head to his chest and stroked her un-
pinned hair, saying, "But perhaps it's better you're prepared for
whatever happens." He set her from him, adding, "Now go ready
yourself for the reception."

Panicky, Reinette went to her dressing room on boneless legs.
She washed in perfume, but her trembling fingers refused to help
her dress. Finally, she sent for Quin-Quin, who pulled tightly
on the stomacher's laces while Reinette held her breath.

"Don't go tonight," Quin-Quin whispered to her mistress.

Reinette looked over her shoulder at the black woman. "Why?"
she asked breathlessly.

"There may be trouble tonight."

"How do you know that?"

Quin-Quin shrugged. "The usual way. A cook in a kitchen
sings a Creole song while she rattles her pots and pans but tacks
on a few words at each verse's end intended as a message. Another
slave, working nearby, listens intently and passes it on. By the
end of the day, such news is carried from one end of the city to
the other."

With a sigh, Reinette slid into her patterns. "Aaron already
suspects foul play, but he insists we go. I'm frightened, Quin-
Quin."

She had reason to be even more frightened when she faced
Lieutenant General O'Reilly at the reception. She had only to
look into those implacable eyes to see that he was a true man of
iron.

O'Reilly had made the most of the situation by installing himself in a magnificently carved, gold-canopied chair on a dais.
Behind him, his officers were arrayed in splendid red uniforms
that were a counterpoint to his severely cut black one, which was
decorated only with gilded epaulettes and a paucity of golden
piping.

As the New Orleans citizens entered the oblong room, they
presented themselves before him. They all wore the same pinched
and worried expression. At O'Reilly's side stood Aubry, who,
Reinette was sure, whispered names and other identifying information.

Her gloved fingers clutching Aaron's hand, she managed to
drop a deep curtsy before the general, her yellow satin skirts
spreading about her like sunflower petals. When she looked up,

his hazel-gray eyes impaled her. His narrow face beneath the white club wig might be called handsome; certainly, it was arresting in its strength. His glance merely twitched over Aaron's curt bow, which she felt boded even worse.

Spanish wine flowed freely but not freely enough to ease the tension between the Spanish officers and the French citizens. All of the members of the Superior Council in attendance wore faces as yellow as her ball gown.

They were fervently banking on a technicality to save their necks. Since Ulloa had never presented his credentials or raised the Spanish flag, they argued that they were still French citizens at the time they were accused of rebellion against Spain. If that failed, they hoped O'Reilly would demonstrate the king's clemency.

Reinette had only to look into those hard eyes to know that he would demonstrate the king's strength and, in so doing, his own.

She and Aaron were politely ignored by the aristocratic Creole families. From the time of her marriage to him a year before, she had been ostracized by the socially pretentious Creoles. She cared about that not one whit. Recalling their slights, it pleased her no end to see the haughty Creole politicians sweating heavily under their periwigs.

Once all of the guests were officially received by the general, the dancing began. A violin maker and his three sons provided the music, opening with the Spanish court's stately pavane, which they played badly. No one moved to dance.

Behind his hand, Aaron whispered, "You can wager you café, my love, that before the night is out every Creole daughter will put aside her pride and dance with one of the Spanish officers on orders from Papa."

O'Reilly solved the problem by rising from the canopied chair and descending the dais. For the first time, Reinette saw that he limped. As he crossed the room, he seemed to exaggerate his infirmity purposely, almost as if he took pleasure in flaunting it.

She knew what was about to happen: He would request a dance from one of the Creole ladies and set the precedent for all time to come for the Spaniards in Louisiana; surely no one dared to refuse him. Sympathy stirred in her for whatever poor maiden he selected as an example.

He moved down the line of nervous citizens, and with mounting horror, she realized she was to be his victim. She darted a sidelong glance at Aaron. His intelligent face was closed over. What was he thinking? What in the name of God should she do?

"Madame," O'Reilly said, "will you dance?" It was a command, not a question.

"Monsieur, I don't know the steps of the pavane." Her voice was little more than a whisper.

"I will lead you through the figures," he said, making it a matter of little or no consequence.

She didn't dare look at Aaron, for fear of drawing him into her conundrum. Beneath the deadly silence of the room ran the nerve-wracked undercurrent of the guests' tension. Perspiration beaded between her breasts and on her temples. Surely that was the fault of the heat of the candles and the press of bodies in the packed room.

"I'm a married woman, monsieur. I respectfully request that you honor my status."

She had expected a rebuttal from the mercenary, for he was not the kind to give up, but she had not expected the one he chose. "No, mademoiselle, you are not a married woman. According to the *Code Noir*, your union is not recognized as legal. It violates the prohibition of the mixing of the races."

She recoiled from his cold, dispassionate statement. "But that applies to a marriage between a white and a black or the Indian races," she blurted.

"It includes Jews also." He held out his hand. "Mademoiselle?"

Aaron's hand tightened on the agate head of his cane. She saw the tendons bulge momentarily in his temples and knew he was reliving the night the nobleman had demanded that his mother give up her opera seat.

"No," she gasped, and stepped between Aaron and O'Reilly. "I am a quick learner, monsieur. Will you lead me through the figures?"

With every censorious eye upon her, she moved like a puppet through the posturing steps, her features frozen into an expression of polite boredom. She refused to meet O'Reilly's steely gaze, but once, when the steps brought them together beneath their upraised, clasped hands, he said, "You dance the pavane impeccably. You lied, madame. Do not do so again."

She lifted her chin. "Do not ask me what I cannot guarantee."

Fortunately, the pavane's steps parted them once more. Soon other couples joined them, but their expressions were stiff with resentment. She noted that O'Reilly's limp wasn't as pronounced when he moved through the pavane's gliding steps. When next they came together, their shoulders touching, he said, "I ask of you the same that I ask of all King Carlo's subjects: Submission."

The dance ended, and she dipped an elaborate, mocking curtsy. "Spain has our fealty, monsieur."

He took her hand and helped her to rise. "But do I? I shall soon see."

When she returned to Aaron, she saw that only his great intelligence was holding his anger in check. She touched his hand and whispered, "Aaron, I love you. Don't do anything that would make me lose you."

O'Reilly instructed the violinists to play an English minuet next, then a French contredanse. The gesture was not lost on the guests: the Spanish pavane would be the dance of the court of little Paris, but O'Reilly could be lenient enough once the citizens went through the motions of obeisance.

More of the Creole females were dancing with the Spanish officers, but with about as much enthusiasm as Reinette had with O'Reilly. She could still feel his watchful gaze on her and Aaron, and it made her extremely uncomfortable. Beneath her fingers, Aaron's muscled forearm was tense with barely restrained fury. She devoutly wished the reception would be over soon.

Toward the end of the evening, when it appeared to the guests that nothing untoward was going to happen, the tension eased somewhat. Laughter, albeit nervous, tittered on the tongues of the Superior Council's prominent members and their families. The Creole sons and daughters managed to converse in a somewhat stilted manner with the Spanish officers, whose French they found uniformly execrable.

"Perhaps it will not be so unbearable under these austere Spanish dogs," one of the council members, a man with his bagwig askew, whispered in an aside.

Whatever friendly thoughts other citizens may have entertained about the Spanish immediately evaporated when a few of the guests prepared for an early departure. Soldiers with muskets were posted at either side of the heavy double doors, which had been barred. At once, that news passed quickly among the other guests. Stark fear sent them scuttling toward the doors. A plump matron in a towering wig shoved against Reinette, and she nearly tripped beneath the trampling crush.

Aaron gripped her arm and propelled her away from the frenzied human wave. His lean body wedged her against one wall, protecting her. She closed her eyes, feeling his warm breath on her cheek and inhaling the subtle scent of his cologne. She thought, If I could only stay like this, pressed by his flesh on mine, and everything else would just go away . . .

"Ladies and gentlemen," O'Reilly announced in a pleasant but unmistakable tone that caused everyone to spin around to where he stood on the dais. Only then did the guests notice that the Spanish officers stationed strategically around the room had drawn their rapiers. Immediately, O'Reilly had their undivided attention.

"I regret this incovenience," he continued in an impatiently amused voice, "but I must interrupt your departure. I will require some of my guests to stay. The rest may go."

He nodded curtly toward the Director-General Aubry, who read a list of names in a shaky voice. Reinette listened in shock as Aaron's name was called. Her lungs ceased to work while the rest of the names were read. Those whose names were not called were too relieved to offer any resistance or defiance on behalf of the others. They fled through the now opened doors.

An officer approached her and Aaron, and she clung to her husband's arm. He laid his hand over hers and said, "Go on. There is nothing you can do for me here. I worry for you, though. Find Etienne. He and Paul will take care of you."

"You must leave, señora," the officer said, gesturing toward the door with his rapier.

She looked up at Aaron, and he nodded. As she parted from him, her fingertips clung to his until at last she had to release his hand. She was escorted to the door with the other women; some, like herself, were stunned, others weeping. The plump matron who had nearly run over her wailed loudly and struck at her own breasts like a deranged woman.

Somehow Reinette made her way home, though she couldn't remember just which streets she had taken or if she had passed anyone. She vaguely recalled tripping in one of the gutters, later confirmed by the brownish stain that splotched the hem of her skirt in front. Her palms were dirty and held the stench of sewage.

Etienne was upriver in British-held Manchac plying his smuggling trade, but Paul and Quin-Quin were still up when she walked into the taproom. The café had had few customers that night with most of the regulars attending the reception. Paul took one look at Reinette's ashen face and asked, "What has happened?"

Numbly, she slumped into the nearest chair. "It's Aaron. He's been arrested."

Quin-Quin knelt before Reinette and rubbed her malodorously clammy hands. "Were you . . . did the soldiers hurt you in any way?"

Dazed, Reinette shook her head.

"They can't do anything to Aaron without a trial first," Paul said.

Reinette looked at him, hope springing alive in her glazed eyes. "A lawyer." Her brows lifted with her excitement. "That's the answer! We'll hire the best lawyer we—"

"Reinette!" Paul's flat tone stopped her. "Reinette, who do you think would represent Aaron? Only another Jew, and you're not going to find a lawyer—at least one who admits to being a Jew—in all of the Louisiana territory."

Her shoulders slumped.

"Even if he does get a trial," Paul said, "he has about as much chance of it being a fair one as a bird's egg between an alligator's jaws."

"Etienne should be back tomorrow," Quin-Quin said, rising to her full six-foot height. Her stomach was large with Etienne's child. "He knows Aaron better than anyone. And he knows the back doors to bribes."

Reinette glanced up at her disconsolately. "I saw the governor-general's face, Quin-Quin. He is not a man to be bribed."

The black woman shrugged. "There are others besides the governor-general who might be bought. Now, let's get you upstairs to bed. You can't do anything to help Aaron in the state you're in now."

Listlessly, Reinette submitted to Quin-Quin's affectionate ministrations. Reinette was so bone-weary that she thought if she ever made it to bed, she'd sleep forever. Instead, she didn't sleep at all. After Quin-Quin snuffed the candles, Reinette lay there, frightened of what might happen to Aaron, terrified of a future without him.

Dawn, made grayer by a steady drizzle, found her pacing the floor, searching for and discarding escape plans one by one. By midmorning, Paul brought the news that Aaron had been interned in the barracks of the Lisbon regiment along with several of the other detainees.

"Do you know when the trial is to be held?" she asked.

"O'Reilly's promised that the leaders of the rebellion will be punished without delay, so I should think by the first of October."

She saw the pained expression in Paul's eyes mixed with the ubiquitous glow of love he always bore her. "What else is there that you're not telling me?"

He sighed and ran his fingers through his brown hair, tugging some strands loose from his clubbed queue. "The Irish mercenary has issued a proclamation stating that only the ringleaders would 'answer for their crimes—and be judged according to the laws.' "

"Which means?" she asked in a hoarse whisper.

Paul grimaced. "If I remember the broadside tacked outside the billiard hall this morning, the Spanish law reads something about whosoever persuades any people—or province—under the dominion of the king to rise against His Majesty is a traitor."

Reinette didn't have to ask to know what the punishment for treason was.

CHAPTER 37

Etienne sat on a bench and bent over the taproom's table. Before him was a crudely drawn map of New Orleans along with the Mississippi delta and its intertwining bayous. Behind him stood Quin-Quin, a loving hand on his permanently hunched shoulders. Reinette, sitting opposite him, knew that in addition to being worried about Aaron, Etienne was concerned for Quin-Quin. The bandy-legged little man felt that she was too old at forty-three to be having a baby.

Paul stood beside Reinette, his hands braced on the tabletop. "What have you been able to find out, Etienne?"

"A tailor whose daughter is being courted by one of those Spanish swine says the conspirators' trial is scheduled three weeks hence. During the trial, Aaron will have to be marched daily from the barracks to the governor's house and back. I can have a galley and crew ready at the levee if you"—he glanced up at Paul—"can find a way to disable the guards."

Paul rubbed his regrown beard. "We'll have to hope the trial isn't a speedy one. I'll need two or three days to see what sort of pattern is followed: how many guards accompany Aaron and the others at each outing; whether they take the same route each time; even if it's the same guards every day. Any change in any of those circumstances could make the difference between failure and success."

"With the Spanish such sticklers for details," Etienne said, "I don't think there'll be any problem with a quick trial."

The three weaks of waiting were unbearable. Reinette tried to visit the barracks to see Aaron several times but each time was turned away at the gate by the guards.

"Be thankful he isn't imprisoned with the others at the jail," Paul counseled her one night as she sat in the near empty taproom. Despair had driven her to drink a glass of the cognac she so reviled.

She understood all too well the implication of his words. Down through the years, there had been whispers that the jail, which was near the church, had secret rooms where iron instruments of torture were applied. It was said that private court meetings were held there and that an underground passage ran from the rear of the cathedral to somewhere under the *calabozo*, as the Spaniards called the jail.

Two days before the trial, word leaked out that one of the conspirators had died. Reinette was frantic. Quin-Quin tried to quiet her. "You're not helping Aaron at all by carrying on like this, weeping and cursing."

"If he's even alive!" Reinette cried.

The black woman deserted the distraught Reinette to go in search of Paul, who set out at once for the governor's house first, then the barracks, and lastly the jail.

That evening, he returned to the café with the news that Aaron was still alive. He told Quin-Quin, Etienne, and Reinette, "It appears that one of the conspirators has taken his life in his jail cell. But who knows if that's the truth," he added ominously.

All four of them thought of the legendary secret rooms beneath the cells.

Reinette dried tears of relief from her cheeks and said bitterly, "Next we'll have the Spaniards bringing in their Holy Inquisition."

Etienne shook his head. "I don't think so. This O'Reilly's a military man through and through. I've seen enough of them. He's not the kind to mix with those hair-shirts types, with their thumbscrews and torture racks. That's not his method of fighting."

Reinette tried to prepare herself to be calm on the day the trial

finally arrived, but sleepless nights, tension, fear, and too little
food and too much drink had made her a mere shadow of her
former self. Early that morning, Paul gently pried the near empty
mug of rum from her rigid hands. She had poured it to fortify
herself for the worst.

Unlike the British legal system, the accused was given no opportunity to face his accusers or to cross-examine witnesses, and
the judge's decision in each case was final. This procedure was
inherited largely from the precepts of ancient Roman jurispru-
dence.

With the rest of the conspirators' families and a few curious
spectators, she and Quin-Quin were at the governor's house when
the prisoners were marched in. With satisfaction, she noted that
they weren't chained, which would have made escape more difficult.

She spotted Aaron easily by the set of his shoulders. Although
he was only of medium height, he walked taller than the rest; he
held himself separate, aloof from the others. To her relief, he
didn't look as if he had been mistreated.

"Aaron!" she cried. Either he didn't hear her or he ignored her.

With Quin-Quin, she stationed herself outside the governor's
house throughout the day. It seemed there were soldiers everywhere; some of them strolled through the plaza with Creole ladies
on their arms. Enterprising merchants had set up stalls around
the Plaza de Armas, formerly the Place d'Armes, and were vo-
ciferously hawking fruits, lemon-flavored drinks, and little cakes.

Reinette didn't think she could ever eat again, at least not until
Aaron was free. Desultorily, she waved a fan before her and every
so often glanced around to look for Paul, who was scouting the
route taken by the guarded prisoners that morning.

Toward midafternoon, the townsfolks sought out whatever dim
patches of shade were afforded by the few trees bordering the
plaza parade ground. The late-autumn weather was hot and muggy,
but a dank breeze off the river made it just bearable. When court
was adjourned for the day, the people outside crowded close,
waiting to see if a verdict had been reached, but it had not.

"What did you expect," sneered one man, who dabbed his
sweating face with a lavishly scented handkerchief. "You know
Spanish bureaucracy and their fetish for trivialities."

Reinette posted herself close to an oak the prisoners had to walk past. As Aaron drew near, she stepped close and called his name. When he didn't respond, she knew for certain that he was ignoring her.

A heavyset guard slanted his musket in front of her. "Step back!" he ordered, and a fetid odor of garlic washed over her.

Defeated, she turned away. Quin-Quin braced her arm about Reinette's waist and said, "Aaron's doing this to save you. He doesn't want you implicated with him, don't you understand?"

'I *am* implicated!" Reinette said, fighting back tears. "I'm his wife!"

"No," Quin-Quin said softly, sadly, "in the eyes of the law, you are not. You can never be married to each other any more than Etienne and I can."

"But Aubry married us!"

"Aubry's not the law. O'Reilly is."

The same procedure—Reinette waiting outside the governor's house and Aaron staring through her as if she didn't exist—went on the next day and the next and the next. By then her nerves were completely frayed. Once she saw O'Reilly promenading across the dusty parade ground with a tall, striking brunette on his arm. Doña Merced Albanasta, rumored to be the widow of a Havana official, had followed him to New Orleans. A Negro dwarf trailed close behind her, the curiously designed, sharp-edged bolo he carried almost as big as he.

Paul reported that the guards were holding to no regularly established routine. Worse, soldiers were patroling the area around the governor's house, making any hope of overpowering the guards doubtful.

"Then find another way!" she snapped. "But set him free!"

Under the wiry beard he had regrown, Paul's mouth tightened into a flat line. "We can always challenge the whole damned Spanish army."

Fleetingly, as an apology, she threw her arms around the big man. "Oh, Paul, I don't know what's happening to me! I feel like I'm crumbling into little pieces. I'm falling apart. Without Aaron, my world *will* fall apart."

Closing his eyes, he held her against him, treasuring the rare opportunity, heedless of the events that brought her into his arms. "I'll find a way," he said roughly. "I'll find a way."

He designated the day beginning the third week of the trial for the break, and the night before it outlined his plans to Reinette, Etienne, and Quin-Quin. "The newly appointed *alcalde* precedes the prisoners into the governor's house. We'll have to take him as a hostage at that point, demand Aaron's release, make a dash to Etienne's ship waiting at the wharf, and outrun two thousand soldiers in the bargain. Ready to risk it?"

"No." Reinette rose from the bench and looked down at the other three across from her. "I cannot ask you to risk your lives for Aaron." She lifted her refilled mug, saying forlornly, "I've been incredibly selfish."

Quin-Quin rose then, dwarfing Reinette. "Look at us, *petiote*. Etienne and me, we've no chance of happiness here, anyway. We couldn't bring up our baby here. We're risking nothing."

"And you?" Reinette asked of Paul.

Paul wouldn't look at her. He got up and took the mug from her and set it on the bar. "If Aaron doesn't go free, you'll destroy yourself, Reinette."

She understood what he couldn't say: that either way she was lost to him, and so he could only choose to help her and Aaron.

He looked at her over his shoulder. "My effort to free Aaron: consider it lagniappe, extra, free, unlooked-for."

Reinette, Paul, and Quin-Quin positioned themselves close to the entrance of the governor's house. In Reinette's reticule was a small pistol. Paul had pleaded and scolded and cajoled Reinette to wait with Etienne's crew abroad the galley moored to the wharf, but she had been adamant about helping.

"You need every able-bodied man you can get." She had grinned, her spirits lifting as the time of the rescue neared. "I always thought I would have made a better man than woman."

"Aaron would dispute that," Paul had said drily.

Waiting for the prisoners' arrival, she wished more than once that she had a man's courage. Her blood was beating a thunderous tattoo in her eardrums. She glanced up at Quin-Quin. Perspiration glistened on her brown face.

When the time came and went for the prisoners to be marched to the governor's house, Reinette began to grow more and more nervous. Her palm, tucked covertly inside her reticule, was sweaty against the pistol's wooden grip. The townsfolk waiting in the

Plaza de Armas began to murmur agitatedly. Bewilderment was mixed with consternation in their faces.

At last a Spanish patrol approached. They halted before Reinette. "Señora," asked the stern-faced sergeant, "you are the one who alleges to be the wife of the Jew, Aaron Simon."

"I *am* his wife," she replied. Her mind was icy with a foreboding that made her shiver.

"Then I must arrest you in the name of His Majesty, King Carlos of Spain."

CHAPTER

38

Hands clasped behind his back, Alejandro O'Reilly took a turn about his female prisoner, who stood stonily in front of his desk, her chin tilted defiantly. A curious power lent a sort of grandeur to his uneven gait. For all his leisurely pacing, his limp was acutely pronounced. His wife would have known by that peculiarity that he was thinking hard.

When once again he faced Reinette, he said, "I remember requesting your submission, mademoiselle." His tone was casual, bantering. He had found that listening to lies was sometimes indicative of the truth.

She didn't lift her eyes to his but kept her gaze fastened on the silver military cross over his left breast. "I promised my fealty."

"Aiding traitors is not an act of fealty." His voice hardened. "In fact, it is tantamount to treason itself."

At last, she looked up at him. Gray sunlight from the slatted window fell in a slant over his face, which was narrow but had strong bone structure around deep-set, flinty eyes. He wore no wig that day but had clubbed his hair. Silver strands had invaded the deep red hair at his temples, yet his lean face looked to be no more than forty or so. In a room full of people, he would have been hard to ignore, so commanding a presence did he have.

"What difference does my reply make? If my husband is to die"—she hung her head—"I don't care what happens to me."

His fingers lifted her chin. She kept her lashes lowered, hiding the defeat in her eyes. He studied her face as he might a piece of merchandise. "Yes, I can see that. You haven't been taking good care of yourself. And you've started to drink, haven't you?"

Her lids snapped upward. "How do you know so much about me? Even at the reception, you already knew about my marriage to—"

"Not a marriage, madame, a farce." He released her chin and picked up his snuffbox, casually inhaling a pinch of tobacco.

"And you knew about the escape plan!" she charged. "Etienne and his crew were arrested aboard his ship before Paul ever had a chance to position himself for the guards."

"Agents, madame. In my native Ireland, the English government taught my parents the value of agents. A man planted as a crew member, say, picks up a great deal of valuable information. As for my *intimate* knowledge of yourself—suffice it to say that I laid eyes on you the day before the reception when you took the Oath of Loyalty. I make it a policy to familiarize myself in great depth with every aspect of the people I govern. Your newly acquired habit of drinking, which I intend to break, has become common knowledge among the late-night patrons of the Café du Monde."

The muscle ridges that flanked her spine from the small of her back to the base of her skull tightened into rigid columns. Inchoate thoughts screamed at her. "You speak as if . . . What is to happen to me?"

"That depends on you."

Suddenly, she felt so weary. Two days under house arrest with Quin-Quin, not knowing what were the fates of Paul, Etienne, or Aaron, had sapped what remained of her strength. She closed her eyes and shook her head. "I don't know what you mean."

He stepped back and settled his impaired leg on the edge of the desk. "By the laws of Spain, you could face death for your part in all of this. However, I'm reluctant to issue the order. The execution of a female would not cement good relations with the people I govern."

Somehow she found the strength to stand straighter, her shoulders back. "You don't have to say anymore, General. I think I understand. You take a *chère amie* from among the colonists and you become more acceptable to the Creoles as their ruler. But why me?"

"I don't really know," he said honestly. "You are undoubtedly beautiful, but I have seen other women your equal in beauty. The way you walk, the stubborn set of your chin . . . I really don't know. I just know that I want you."

She shot him a withering glance. "Then why not rape me? Why are you bargaining with me?"

"Rape is not my style, madame. I'm lonely. I suppose. My wife rarely travels to the outposts I govern."

"Lonely?" She raised a brow. "With Doña Merced Albanasta at your side?"

"I'm also tired," he said with a sigh that was half mirth. "The Spanish madonna is like a racehorse."

The wry smile that threatened the stern corners of his mouth took her by surprise. "I'm afraid you'll have to select someone else to replace your mistress, General. I really am not interested in bargaining for my life."

"Or that of your paramour, the Jew? And the two others—I believe their names are Etienne Guirard and Paul la Ronde."

"You would set them free?" she asked, afraid he was playing with her.

"No. I can't do that. Today the judge found the Jew guilty."

She sagged at that pronouncement. His hands caught her under her armpits, steadying her. "Are you all right?"

She smiled morbidly. "*Mais oui.* You've just told me that the one man I love has been condemned."

"Madame, I can only lighten his punishment, commute his sentence to death. The others, for them I could reduce the length of time they must serve."

She rubbed her forehead with the back of her hand. "I . . . you're asking that I become a—a whore, General."

He set her from him with a grunt of exasperation. "No. I don't want that." He limped to the window and looked out on the dusty plaza. A rising wind, promising rain, blew fine grit in small clouds along the street. "I've never had to resort to blackmail for female companionship."

Abruptly, he turned to face her. "Where will you go? Your belongings and property, even the velvet gown you're wearing

now, belongs to the state. Do you think there's a soul in New
Orleans who will lift a hand to help you? When you cast your
lot with the Jew—"

"I wish you'd stop calling my husband a Jew in—like that. It's
an aspersion."

"Indeed it is. At least here in New Orleans. I don't think the
convent would even take you in despite the years you spent there."
He crossed to her and cupped her face with splayed fingers. "Tell
me, is what I'm offering such an insult? I'm offering you a refuge,
Reinette . . . and commuting the death sentence of the—of Aaron
Simon. I'm only asking for your companionship until Spain posts
me somewhere else."

Her lips trembled. She twisted her wedding band. "Companionship?"

"I want more of you than that, but I won't demand it of you."

The measured cadence of the muffled drum signaled that the
hour of Spain's retribution against the conspirators, or traitors,
as O'Reilly had pronounced them, was at hand.

Reinette sat before the dresser mirror, a cold lump leaden in
the pit of her stomach. The six traitors chosen as the examples
to the people of the rebellious Louisiana colony would soon be
facing a firing squad.

Because she sat there in O'Reilly's house, because she had
carried on polite and neutral conversation with O'Reilly every
night for the last three nights at dinner, because she slept in a
large anteroom off his bedroom, Etienne, Paul, and Aaron would
not be executed that day.

Instead, that afternoon they were to sail for the Caribbean and
Havana's El Morro fortress, the Spanish counterpart of the Bastille. For ten minutes, ten precious minutes, she and Quin-Quin
would be allowed to visit them aboard ship. O'Reilly had conceded that much and no more.

From the shutters left ajar could be heard the babble of the
growing number of townsfolk who were on their way to the
Lisbon barracks adjoining the Ursuline Convent to watch the
execution.

"Close the shutters," Reinette said, her voice sounding like the
rustle of sand through the windswept street. "How can those
people be so morbid?" The men about to die were well known

in the close-knit community: neighbors, fathers, husbands, lovers.

With the shutters closed, the noise of the spectators was muted. Candles on either side of the mirror lit the now darkened room. In the mirror, she saw Quin-Quin's eyes flex, squeezing back further tears. The black woman moved slowly, encumbered by the approaching birth of her child. The ivory-backed brush in her hand trembled as she brushed out Reinette's hair. Static electricity crackled through the tawny strands like the lightning that had scissored the sky for the last three nights. The gloomy storm that had been threatening was sure to descend with a vengeance by evening.

"Do you want your hair powdered?" Quin-Quin asked in a voice husky with swallowed tears.

Reinette's bleak stare was a shimmering reflection in the mirror. "Twenty years! Oh, God, Quin-Quin, I don't think I can stand it." She covered her face, fighting back another onslaught of tears.

"Yes, you can, girl." With a sigh, the black woman set the brush down and began braiding the golden hair. "Twenty years in El Morro is better than life imprisonment."

"Twenty years *is* life!"

"But it's not death. Your husband may have been unjustly found guilty of financing the revolution, but at least he's not going to mount the gallows today."

Reinette's hands dropped nervelessly into her lap. Dispirited, she raised her head and said, "O'Reilly told me that a hangman couldn't be found, so the condemned are to face a firing squad."

At that moment, O'Reilly was no doubt at the Lisbon barracks presiding over the macabre ordeal. Since the day the judge had passed the sentences, several families had come to see him, to appeal for O'Reilly's clemency to commute the death sentences. He had been obdurate, betraying not a trace of compassion from those flinty eyes, as he listened to wives or sons beg that he spare the lives of their loved ones.

Reinette had not dared to go out during this time. The resentment toward her had grown into revilement. Just as she had expected. For her alone had O'Reilly relented. She didn't care what the citizens' attitude was toward her; Aaron was alive and that was all that mattered.

Quin-Quin's usually deft fingers fumbled with the plaits. "Well, a lot of things can happen. Your Aaron might be freed long before his term is completed."

Reinette reached over her shoulder and caught Quin-Quin's hand. "I'm being self-centered, not even thinking of what you're going through. Etienne, and Paul, may have been sentenced to only six years instead of twenty, but at least I'm not facing the burden of having and raising a child alone."

Quin-Quin squeezed the younger woman's hand. "Selfish, are you? Etienne and I both have you to thank that he won't be swinging by his scrawny chicken neck today."

"But will Aaron feel that way?" Reinette asked in a dull tone. "Or will he hate me, knowing what I've done . . . what I've become?"

"I can't see how he could hate you; after all, he owes his life to you."

"You know his fierce pride. I'm almost afraid to face him this—"

The crackle of musket fire rent the air. Both women went still. A tense silence seeped through the shutter slats. The terrible deed had been done.

Knees trembling, Reinette rose from the brocaded bench and said tonelessly, "Lay out the black taffeta for me."

At the appointed time, she donned her cloak and pulled on her gloves. A black lace mantilla, anchored by a tortoiseshell comb, covered her face. Still, a dozen or so citizens recognized her when she ventured out on the storm-darkened street an hour later, accompanied only by Quin-Quin.

"Irishman's whore!"

"Jew lover!"

A boy of perhaps twelve spit at her skirts. She turned to face her persecutors, her stare through the lacy gauze level and unyielding. One by one, they slunk off, and she turned her anxious steps toward the levee and Aaron. The wind whipped at her cloak and mantilla, and the first droplets of the deluging rainstorm pelted her face.

By the time she and Quin-Quin arrived at the wharves, the Mississippi was lapping at the levee with large breakers and churning its muddy, gray water against the moored and anchored vessels. Armed soldiers greeted the two women when they boarded the pitching brig.

"This way, madame," one of the red-coated soldiers said as he led her and Quin-Quin toward the aft cabin.

O'Reilly was there with the brig's captain, a stout, gray-haired man dressed in the Spanish navy uniform of blue wool. At her entrance, the Irishman turned, his hazel eyes raking over her. "You're certain you want to go through with this?"

She nodded, her heart thudding.

"I'll have the prisoners brought up." He snapped an order to the soldier who had escorted her and Quin-Quin.

With a respectful bow, the captain diplomatically left the cabin on the heels of the soldier—and left the two women with O'Reilly. Reinette folded the lacy mantilla back over her head and asked, "Will you leave us alone with the prisoners?"

He lifted a brow. "How do I know you won't try to help them escape?"

"Do you want to search us?"

"You wouldn't like that, I promise you."

Outside the cabin, they heard the clanking of irons. She spun toward the door. Aaron came in, followed by Paul and Etienne. All three were manacled at the wrists and ankles. Her hungry gaze went to Aaron. A scruffy beard covered his jaw but couldn't conceal the emaciated hollows beneath his flat cheekbones. His eyes burned in their sockets like campfires.

"Aaron!" She wrapped her arms about his neck. He smelled of sweat and bilge, but she didn't care. She wanted to lose herself in his musky, male scent. She wanted to feel his hands caressing her, to feel his weight pressing her down, to make love to him one last time. Her hands roamed his shoulders and face and chest, assuring her of his reality and that he was unharmed.

O'Reilly cleared his throat.

Quin-Quin was already enfolding Etienne against her great frame, murmuring words of endearment to him. Paul's eyes were fixed tactfully on his chained wrists.

"I'll leave you to make your farewells, Reinette," O'Reilly said. "But, remember, a guard is posted just outside this door."

Reinette! O'Reilly had never intimately addressed her so, using her given name before others. Feeling Aaron's stiffness beneath her hands, she stepped back. At the cold look in his eyes, she felt sick to her stomach.

"What does the general expect us to do?" Paul asked bitterly after O'Reilly left. "Jump overboard weighted with chains?"

No one said anything.

Etienne made an uncharacteristically jocular attempt to relieve the strained silence in the room. "We could always mutiny."

His attempt at humor fell flat. In the frayed stillness that followed, Reinette cried out, "It's not what you think!"

"The soldiers who guarded us talked of O'Reilly's new mistress," Aarson said. His face was sad and still.

She threw herself against him, drumming her fists against his chest. "I had to do it. Don't you understand? I'll do anything—whatever I have to do to save you! I love you, Aaron. I need you!"

He set her from him. "I don't think you understand, or ever understood, me." His voice was quiet, gravelly. "For you to barter our love is worse than any death sentence."

She recoiled from the sting of his words, the back of her hand pressed to her lips.

"Guard!" Aaron called out. The soldier poked his head inside the doorway, and Aaron said, "I'm ready to go below."

CHAPTER

39

O'REILLY SURPRISED REINETTE by gradually winning the good will of the populace those first months. Once the rebellion had been dealt with, he directed his tremendous energies to achieving stability and prosperity for the Louisiana province.

His first act was to abolish the Superior Council and replaced it with an *ayuntamiento* or *cabildo*, which was the Spanish equivalent of a town council. To house this town council, he ordered the construction of a *casa de cabildo*.

Next, he declared the French laws null and void, specifically the *Code Noir* and instituted instead the Code O'Reilly.

In addition, he permitted French officials to continue to hold their offices and even appointed two French Creoles as lieutenant governors of the Natchitoches and Illinois districts. In all of his reforms, he insisted that the old customs of French Louisiana be kept as much as possible. Lastly, he sent the sniveling Aubry packing off to France in retirement.

Slowly but steadily, to her irritation, the colony began to prosper under the Spanish administration, much more than it had under the inefficient French system. If the sobriquet of "Bloody O'Reilly" was bandied about on rebellious lips, it was done so in a whisper. The general had shown that he could slip off the velvet glove and hit with the iron hand.

Wherever she went with him that winter—to levees, soirees, *bals masqués*—she witnessed the undeniable fact that he had reconciled the French Creoles of Louisiana to the rule of Spain.

In the weeks she had lived under his protection, his treatment of her was most courteous and never demanding. He made it almost impossible for her to remain aloof, polite but distant. Worse, she didn't know how to go about telling him what she had only just discovered herself—that she was carrying Aaron's child. She had thought that the delay of her monthly bleeding was due to the traumatic past weeks. Now she knew the truth of her condition, but could she tell O'Reilly and risk the chance that he might take out his anger on Aaron—or on Aaron's child once it was born? She decided to keep what she knew to herself for the time being.

Having appointed the mild-natured Colonel Unzaga to succeed him as governor, O'Reilly spent more time in her company. One particular evening, they attended a soiree given by his cast-off mistress, no less. Doña Merced occupied a house formerly owned by one of the executed conspirators, which the government had confiscated. How she had managed to do that, Reinette could very well guess.

The seductive widow missed little opportunity to appear in O'Reilly's presence. He found the scathing looks she directed at Reinette amusing. "You have something Merced wants badly," he told Reinette as he handed his *chapeau bras* to the servant at the door, "so you can afford to be nice."

"I'd rather be disemboweled," she said, letting him remove her brown velvet cloak trimmed with sable. At his lingering touch on her bare shoulders, something deep in the pit of her stomach fluttered.

For the soiree, she had selected a crimson silk polonaise with a daring décolletage and matching silk pumps with gold buckles. An ivory fan dangled by a silken cord from her wrist. If he was going to parade her as his mistress, then she would certainly dress the part.

He grinned. "You know," he said, tilting her chin up, "I think I might be coming to care for you, Reinette."

"Why did you do it?" she whispered. "Why did you use my

given name in front of Aaron that day he sailed for El Morro?"

His reddish brows furrowed. "I thought you had forgotten that.
It was a kindness, *chérie.* He would have worried himself to death
over what would happen to you in his absence. Now he knows
you're well cared for."

"How thoughtful of you," she snapped.

He released her chin and said gravely, "I wanted you. When
you want something badly enough, you—"

"—you trample whatever hearts you have to in order to get it,"
Merced finished, appearing beside them. With her was her ever-
present Moro pygmy bearing his menacing bolo.

The tall, high-strung woman wore white silk with a black lace
overskirt. With her unpowdered mane of night-black hair and
pale blue eyes, the effect was powerfully dramatic. She stood
staring down at Reinette with a quiet, fastidious, and intimidating
inspection.

For once, Reinette wished devoutly that she was tall.

Merced was a finely boned, obviously self-possessed woman
who seemed accustomed to having what she wanted. Her features
had a sharp edge, which she disguised with pale ivory powdered
starch, and her thin lips were rouged carefully so that they looked
fuller.

At fourteen, Merced had wandered the dusty streets of Toledo
barefoot, the daughter of roaming gypsies. When the thin stick
of a mayor of the town had paused on his magnificent steed to
admire her wild beauty, she took advantage of the moment. An
hour later, she was instilled in his bedroom. She had given her
virginity to an uncle two years before, but the spindly Albanasta
never suspected.

He was so grateful for the erections he had managed to achieve
through her delightful manipulations that a month later he had
opposed the formidable opinion of Toledo society and took her
for a wife. That might have been the end of his political career,
but Merced was forceful, determined, and shrewd. Within six
years, he had risen, by dint of her efforts, through the diplomatic
ranks to viceroy of the Spanish Moluccas, or Spice Islands, of
Indonesia. She had acquired the Negro pygmy while there, a
Moro who pleasured her when old Albanasta could not, which
was quite often.

Then came the day Albanasta was posted to Havana, where

fate brought Merced face to face with Alejandro O'Reilly. His driving force matched hers in bed. She was desperate to hear him say the simple but necessary words, *"I love you."* He never did, and she assumed it was out of loyalty to that absentee wife of his, which was all right by Merced. She was in his bed; the wife wasn't.

Every day, Merced fell deeper and more wholly in love with him. He become the only thing she wanted. There was an insatiable, ruthless need to possess him despite everything she knew about him; all the difficulties he presented; all the faults clearly observed in him; the women he had had before she met him. They didn't matter because she knew they were nothing to him. Nothing mattered, except her avid, addictive obsession to keep him.

Now she faced his newest interest, the petite and lovely blonde, Reinette du Plessis, former mistress of the exiled Jew despite her claim of a marriage by civil ceremony. "You know, mademoiselle," she told Reinette with a cold smile, "you and I both seem to have something in common. We're both whores."

Reinette flushed angrily. But she would not give O'Reilly's former mistress the satisfaction of denying what everyone suspected, that she shared his bed.

O'Reilly's eyes flashed fiery salvos at the Spanish widow. "You forget yourself, Doña Merced," he warned.

"I find you a coarse woman, Madame Albanasta," Reinette said coolly, leaving the widow and O'Reilly to greet other arriving guests.

At the entrance to the enormous *salle* that served as a ballroom that evening, she halted, her gaze traveling over the assembled guests. She lifted a glass of wine from the silver salver a servant proffered and drained it in a single gulp.

"Do you need wine to fortify yourself to face the guests' animosity?" O'Reilly asked ruefully at her side. He took the glass from her hand and replaced it on the salver.

She shook her head slowly. "You don't need to hide the liquor decanters from me anymore," she said dully. "I'm beyond that."

He raised a skeptical eyebrow but placed her hand on his sleeve and led her into the *salle*. As they passed, the ladies dipped low curtsys and the gentlemen made sweeping bows of homage. She could imagine what was in their thoughts. They might respect

O'Reilly, but above their obsequious smiles their eyes couldn't hide their dislike for her.

She found it ironic that they could acquiesce to a Spanish woman in their midst but ostracize one of their own, a French-woman. Except O'Reilly wouldn't let them do so; he forced her upon them, and they resented that almost as much as they resented her.

She had compounded one insult on them after another. She had flouted public opinion and opened a coffeehouse, outraged them by marrying a Jew, and committed the final faux pas: escaping Spain's retribution for the rebellion by becoming a whore—or so they assumed.

Their erroneous assumption she found morbidly amusing, and above the gently fluttering fan, she eased her lips into a brittle smile that startled the guests nearest her.

The evening's entertainment was just one more ordeal she had to endure. Sometimes she thought of fleeing O'Reilly, but where would she go? Besides, she owed him Aaron's life and meant to live up to her part of the bargain—the gift of her companionship as long as he was posted to New Orleans.

Then, too, at the back of her mind lay the hope that Aaron might escape from El Morro, as he had the slave galley. If he did, and she had fled New Orleans, he wouldn't know where to find her.

On the heels of her hope for his escape, despondency usually followed. Even if he did escape, he would never return for her. His pride was too great.

She felt as if she were in mourning and it would be lifelong and private. Grief was still in her but shorn of its numbing softness—and now there was a secret hollow Aaron had once filled. The one thing that sustained her was the knowledge that she carried his child.

When the first pavane began, O'Reilly led her out to the center of the ballroom, flaunting his limp as he flaunted her. As they moved through the stately steps, the long skirts of his indigo-blue satin frock coat swung about his thighs. Naturally, attention was drawn to his infirmity, which she suspected pleased him immensely. Even if he'd had no eye-catching limp, he still would have been the center of attention, such was the power of his presence in any situation.

He inclined his head toward her and said, "Madame, I will be journeying up the Mississippi next month to inspect the farthest reaches of the colony. I would enjoy the honor of your company."

His request caught her unprepared. With everyone watching and the music distracting her, she stuttered, "Quin-Quin's child is due anytime. Please, I want to be here for the birthing."

It was true enough, but she didn't utter the major reason for her reluctance: She grew more uneasy in his presence daily and she feared he would discover the reason why, a reason that had little to do with the fact that she carried the child of his foe within her.

The fact was that his mere touch stirred sensual responses that had nothing to do with her love for Aaron. The way O'Reilly looked at her . . . It was foolish, she knew, but when he came close, her skin flushed with inexplicable heat, the very hair on her arm prickling in anticipation.

His eyes narrowed, but she saw their passionate glitter as they scanned her form. "My patience isn't infinite, Reinette."

Later that night, after they returned to his house, he insisted she stay and share a drink with him. Reluctantly, she took a seat in one of the two royal purple brocaded chairs. Either his lackey or Quin-Quin had left a single taper burning on the drop-leaf table. The *salle* was cast in soft shadows and pale, shimmering light.

"I have no one I can tallk with," he said. He limped to the sideboard and poured two glasses of brandy from the silver carafe. "The role of a commander demands a constant show of strength. No confessions of weaknesses to his subordinate, you understand." He passed her a glass, saying, "I find I grow weary in the role."

She took a sip of the brandy, noting that the hard lines of his soldier's body looked anything but weary. The ironlike plate of chest muscles offered her a refuge from her own weariness, from the months of putting on a show of bravado before the hostile New Orleans citizens, from facing down insults and innuendoes. She could feel a weakening in her defenses toward the man she habitually regarded as a stranger, an enemy, despite the months they had lived under the same roof, possibly because of his essential kindness toward her.

Feeling the need to reverse the lassitude beginning to suffuse her spirits, she asked tersely, "Then why do you do it?"

He took the chair opposite her, stretching his legs and crossing his highly polished cordovan boots at the ankles. "Soldiering is all I know. In County Meath, where I was born, the English were persecuting the Catholics . . . doing terrible things to our people." He paused and swallowed a quarter of the brandy in his glass. Whatever unpleasant memories he was recalling, he didn't elaborate upon them.

"Anyway," he continued, "my parents fled to Spain where at the age of ten I became a cadet in the Hibernia Regiment. From there I saw action in Austria and France."

"How did you injure your leg?" she asked bluntly.

A smile broadened his narrow face, making him very handsome at that moment. "Most people are afraid to bring up the subject of my infirmity. A grenade wound in the campaign against the Austrians in Italy is responsible for my uneven gait."

"You spoke of a wife once. How did you manage to fit courtship into your military career?" She felt that as long as the conversation continued, any encounter with intimacy would be forestalled.

He shrugged in a self-deprecating manner. "In sixty-five, I was fortunate enough to save King Carlos's life during a riot in Madrid. After that I was welcomed at court. There I met Rosa de las Casas, a member of an influential family. We have a son," he finished flatly.

"You miss your family? Your wife and son?"

He rose and took her glass of barely touched brandy from her. "Yes. But Rosa doesn't want our son to experience the danger and deprivation of military life, as I have. Perhaps she's right, perhaps what she is doing is best for the boy. I can't honestly say that my life as a soldier has been all that rewarding."

He set the glasses on the sideboard and said quite formally, "Thank you for your company tonight. *Bonsoir*, madame."

Once she retired, she lay in bed, unable to sleep. She felt as if one of Paul's iron traps were slowly closing its rusty jaws on her very being. She turned onto her stomach, seeking a more comfortable position; she fluffed the flattened pillow; she kicked off the clinging linen sheet. Outside, the breeze off the river rustled dead leaves along the street. She rolled back over. Sometime later, she heard the nightwatchman cry out the hour in his German accent: two o'clock.

When she finally drifted into a raveled, opiate sleep, nightmares assailed her. The dark dungeon of El Morro . . . torture chambers . . . the slave galley . . . Aaron, the flesh on his back ribboned by the cat-o'-nine-tails . . . herself, weeping over his broken body. Even in her dream, she knew she was actually crying, but she couldn't seem to stop.

Then she awoke instantly, tears streaming down her cheeks, her pillow damp. Although she had not heard the adjoining door open, she froze. She knew that O'Reilly was near . . . in the room. She rolled over onto her back. Her eyes focused on his silhouette at the foot of her bed. The white of his nightshirt shimmered against the dark. She tried to speak—and couldn't.

He parted the *baire* and looked down at her. "You were weeping."

She drew great drafts of air, trying to regain control of her shattered emotions.

"I'm lonely, Reinette," he said, "and you are, too."

Her throat worked soundlessly. She drew the linens up over her in a gesture of denial. Dear God, she silently begged, don't let me betray Aaron.

He came around to her side and whipped the covers back. Easily, his arms lifted her from the bed, but he moved slowly, his left leg dragging as he carried her into his bedroom. She knew she should resist him, but what was about to happen had seemed inevitable from that first moment at the reception when he had chosen her to dance the pavane with him.

She wanted to get this over with as quickly as possible. When he removed his nightshirt, she was surprised. She had been prepared to martyr herself, to endure the soldier's rough and clumsy lovemaking. But he was superbly built, like a Greek warrior, and that made the coming act that much worse. To actually enjoy making love with him would be the greatest betrayal of all to Aaron.

For a man who made his living by destruction, he was extremely gentle with her. His battle-scarred hands divested her of her nightrail. With infinite tenderness, they explored her body, lingering over her smooth nape, where wisps of hair feathered, then traced the curve of her hip and thigh. His lips nuzzled the furred hollow beneath her uplifted arm, and he inhaled deeply. "I love the smell of you," he whispered against the undercurve of her breast. "Your woman's body gives me great pleasure, *mi amor*."

She gasped at the sensations his fingertips generated. "You shame me," she whispered.

"*Mais non!*" He smiled faintly. "I glorify you!"

He pressed his lips against her navel and breathed gently, patiently, without a single, additional motion until her hands dropped to her sides. At last, white and trembling with barely contained passion, she whispered, her voice melancholy, "You've never kissed me, Alejandro."

"An error, one of the few I've made, but one which I will rectify immediately."

He kissed her closed mouth, concentrating his entire physical and mental energies on that one action. Gradually, her lips eased, warmed, and swelled with passion. Still, he confined himself to the erotic area of her mouth. She groaned, and her lips parted, but he held himself back, only his tongue tapping lightly about the inside of her lips.

"Alejandro . . ."

"*Non*, not yet."

His tongue resumed playing with her, pressing forward only a little each time until it filled her mouth, ravaging and ravishing. Then she was writhing beneath him, betraying unbearable excitement. Her hair was wet at the scalp with the sweat of lust. "Do it," she begged.

He laughed, the supreme chuckle of the triumphant male. "I, too, can wait no longer. I've waited too long as it is, Reinette."

He loomed above her, then, and entered her—gradually, prolonging the release her pent-up passions demanded. In the iron curve of his arm, he rocked her gently as he stroked that part of her that had been left hollow and filled her until she felt overripe, ready to burst.

"Alejandro!" she rasped in warning before the explosion of her senses completely blocked out him and his powerful impaling body.

Later, he cradled her while she wept more tears, this time the effluence of her emotions, her passions, her woman's body. With a frenzied abandon, she had enjoyed his lovemaking, and that would be a guilt she would bear the rest of her life.

Still later, when she lay dry-eyed and drenched in cold perspiration, she knew with a certain growing joy that although her body had responded to his skilled lovemaking, her heart, her spirit, were still untouched.

She waited, encased in ice, for Aaron.

If there was any doubt in the minds of New Orleans's French Creoles about just how far Reinette's relationship extended with Don Alejandro O'Reilly, that doubt was eliminated when they saw the couple at the round of festivities marking the Christmas and New Year holidays. On January sixth, when the King's Cake was cut at the *Bal des Rois*, the oldest of the balls held in New Orleans, O'Reilly led her out for every dance. The man of iron's eyes followed her with possessive yet tender glances that only a dolt could misconstrue.

That she satisfied him sexually she might believe, for they were like newlyweds who spent the first five to seven days in bed. Within the bedroom, she forgot all of the hatred turned on her from those without, forgot it in the throes of their lovemaking.

Then one afternoon he surprised her. He lay between her thighs, his head pillowed on her furry mound. "*Je t'aime*, Reinette.*"

When she didn't respond, he lifted his head to pierce her with his steely gaze. "It doesn't matter if you don't love me now. You will. I never lose, either on the battlefield or in the bed."

The Creoles of the New Orleans *beau monde* surreptitiously observed the general's new mistress. Whatever she wore dictated fashion. When she attended an assembly dressed in a short polonaise that exposed her delicate ankles, the shorter length of gowns became the rage. If she failed to attend a dinner, the hostess could count the night a failure.

Doña Merced was a persona non grata, and it was obvious to all of New Orleans that the Spanish widow was galled because the Frenchwoman had flourished where she had failed.

Merced was a woman of enormous pride. Her nerves were stretched so tautly by the strain of concealing her emotions that her jaw ached from clenching her teeth. At night, she lay awake reviewing the situation and inspecting it for possible holes. Frustration was alien to her. One way or another, whatever she put her mind to she always got.

Alejandro knew of Merced's devious nature and expressed some concern. Holding a naked Reinette on his lap late one evening, he said, "I will honor your request to remain with your maidservant—"

"She is not my maidservant," Reinette said, her tone liquid with the lassitude of satiated lovemaking. "Quin-Quin is a free woman."

"Regardless, *chérie*, while I am away, my lackey Neal will attend you. I want you to take care around Merced. There is no end to her machinations, I can tell you from experience."

Reinette lifted her head from his shoulder and asked, "Should I be jealous, my lord?"

"You tell me," he said, bending his silver-streaked red head to mouth one turgid nipple, while his fingers, still nestled within her, resumed their erotic stimulation.

Quin-Quin's dusky skin was taut over her mounded belly. It seemed to Reinette that the woman had been holding off her birthing until Alejandro had marched from the city at the head of three of his regiments on his inspection tour. He had been gone less than two days when Quin-Quin went into the first stage of labor.

Reinette watched her friend's pulsating stomach as it rhythmically expanded, then contracted into a hard, rounded knot, and expanded again. Wiping the perspiration from the woman's forehead, Reinette asked, "Shall I go for a midwife?"

Quin-Quin shook her head and managed a pained smile. "Who do you think would help us, girl?"

Reinette rolled her eyes. "I'll send Neal to find one of the Acadian *traiteurs*." The women were famous for their healing capabilities and attributed their gift to their Lady of the Assumption.

By the time the dapper Irish orderly returned several hours later, a stout Acadian woman in tow, Quin-Quin had already given birth to a squalling scrap of humanity. "Looks just like her scrawny father," Quin-Quin pronounced, but with all the pride and affection of a mother's love.

Reinette lifted the howling, blood-smeared infant from Quin-Quin's arms. "She's absolutely beautiful!" she told the new mother in an awed voice.

Looking down at the tiny, waving fists, Reinette felt the first stirrings of fear in her. The little mite that barely occupied the space of her spread hands would be as much an outcast as she herself had been, as would be the child she carried.

The child of her beloved, Aaron's child.

CHAPTER

40

ALTHOUGH QUIN-QUIN LET OUT several of Reinette's gowns, Reinette's petite height and delicate frame could not keep her condition secret. In fact, she looked far more than her four months pregnant. Most of the time, she remained indoors, out of sight of prying eyes, but sometimes idle hours drove her outdoors for exercise.

Usually, she escaped the house in the early afternoons, when the rest of New Orleans was sequestered in a *sieste*. She was accompanied either by the solicitous Irish orderly, Neal Donoho, or Quin-Quin, carrying her infant daughter Suzette in a split-cane basket.

Neal was a little raisin of a man, his skin just as wrinkled as one after years of exposure to the sun and wind of far continents. He treated her with the greatest respect, invariably doffing his feathered hat when in her presence. Faithfully, the Irish orderly dogged her footsteps, asking, "Mademoiselle wishes to see how the cabildo progresses?" or "Could I purchase a basket of fruit for Mademoiselle?"

On these outings, the few Creole aristocrats she encountered no longer snubbed her, but in O'Reilly's absence they were not exactly cordial either. Her condition was an open affront to them.

She was hardly cognizant of their attitude or, indeed, of anything much around her. She was trying desperately to keep her world from falling apart. The bundle of humanity she carried inside her could bind her inextricably to Alejandro if she let him believe the child was his. Then he would never let her go. Yet if he learned the truth, he might change his mind about merely commuting Aaron's sentence and instead order his death—or he might even order that the child be taken from her upon its birth. She was being torn apart by indecision, and so she let the matter drift.

One afternoon, she was walking along the levee, head down, hardly watching where she was going or even noticing the few strollers they passed. At her side, Quin-Quin, whom she had told the truth about the identity of the baby's father, quietly reproved her. 'You're not taking care of yourself, girl. You pick at your food. A mangy cur looks better fed. You're not listening to me, are you?"

Reinette looked up and said ruefully, "I'm sorry, Quin-Quin." She paused beneath a black gum tree and rubbed her aching temples. The breeze off the river was laden with the stale odors of dead fish and rotting refuse. It ruffled her lace-edged butterfly cap and fluttered loose tendrils of hair across her eyes. Absently, she pushed them back and said, "I don't know what's wrong with me any—"

Almost at the moment that a silvery flash of sunlight reflected in her eyes, a single-edged knife anchored the draping lace of her sleeve to the black gum's trunk. She scarely heard Quin-Quin's outcry. Dumbstruck, she stared at the weapon vibrating through her dress.

Immediately, Quin-Quin set down the basket and pried the blade from the tree. Little Suzette let out a wail at the lack of attention, and only then did the paralysis leave Reinette—to be replaced by a weakness that wobbled her knees. She stared at the knife balanced in Quin-Quin's palm. The ugly bolo knife belonged to Merced's diminutive Filipino lackey.

"Doña Merced won't stop with just the one attempt," Quin-Quin said that evening. "You've got to tell Neal so that he can be on guard for you."

Reinette pivoted from the chest to face Quin-Quin, who sat nursing Suzette. "No!" Agitated, she twisted her wedding band.

"No, if Alejandro learns of this, he might insist I follow him to the next post in order to protect me. I can't take that chance."

Quin-Quin transferred her gaze from the fat, flexing cheeks of her daughter to Reinette. "When he learns you're with child—what he believes to be his child—he may well do that, anyway."

"He can't!" She swung back to the chest in which the bolo lay incongruously amongst the linens and lengths of toweling, all scented with rose petals, jasmine, and lavender. With a thud of finality, she closed the lid. "We made a bargain! I've more than fulfilled my part of it—that I'd live with him until he is ordered to another post."

"And Doña Merced?" Quin-Quin persisted.

"I'll simply forgo any more outings until Alejandro returns. She won't dare attempt to harm me once he's back."

Her decision to remain cloistered in the house was easier reached than adhered to. The governor's house became a prison for her. One day faded into another, night followed upon night, with always that dream of being caught in an animal trap. She didn't know how much longer she could stand it, constantly confined by walls and ceilings. Ceaselessly, morbidly, her thoughts turned to Aaron and his imprisonment. Twenty years! And she was going mad by degrees of mere days.

This day was no different from the dozens that preceded it. With Quin-Quin at the drapers, the cook at the market, and Neal at the Royal Bank drawing on Alejandro's funds, she and Suzette were left to while away the quiet boredom.

Feeling tense, she paced the perimeters of the *salle* and the length of the hallway, mentally totaling the weeks that Alejandro had been gone. Six. He was due back any day. His return meant her release from the confinement of the house, but she still dreaded his reaction to the news of her pregnancy.

She reached the end of the hallway and turned to retrace her steps. At the other end of the hall, blocking the sunlight from the balcony doors in the *salle*, loomed an elfin silhouette. Without being able to see the face, Reinette knew the intruder's identity. The Moro.

On silent feet, he moved toward her, stalking. The nearest door . . . Oh, God, it was halfway between her and the Moro. There was no place to hide; she was a perfect target. Her recurring dream of being trapped had become reality.

A scream gurgled in her throat, but, as in her dreams, no sound came. A separate part of her mind realized that there was no one to hear, anyway; no one but Quin-Quin's baby.

The baby!

Fear of what might also happen to Suzette galvanized her moribund legs. She lifted her skirts and dashed for the bedroom doorway. The pygmy reached it at the same moment she did. For a fraction of a second, her gaze locked with his. In the ebony eyes nearly on a level with hers, she saw death grinning at her. Then before she could dart through the doorway, he looped the hemp vine about her neck with accurate ease.

"Please . . .no!" was all she got out.

He drew tighter on the vine, grinning all the while. She was so close to him that she saw his porous skin, mottled black and brown and gray, and inhaled his musky, unwashed stench. Her fingers clawed at the scratchy vine. A hot band of fire seared her throat. Red mist fogged behind her eyes. The mauve tint of her dress became gray. Behind her, Suzette awakened and began howling. Reinette's ears buzzed, drowning out the baby's cries. Her eardrums seemed about to explode.

Then something wrenched her about. Air came rushing back into her tortured lungs. The red mist faded, and she saw Neal wrestling on the floor with the pygmy. They rolled several times, fighting for the superior position. The little Irish orderly held a pistol that the pygmy was trying desperately to grab. The two were evenly matched: the orderly slightly taller, the pygmy wiry with corded muscles.

Reinette dashed to the chest, jerked open the lid, and yanked out the bolo. Even as she spun around, the pistol fired. Gray-blue smoke wreathed the motionless men. Stunned, she took two steps forward, knife poised. The Moro sprang to his feet, the smoking gun, its ball and patch spent, dangling from his hand. Blood and black powder stained the unconscious Neal's puce frock coat.

The Moro eyed the knife, flashed her a sliver of a bizarrely good-humored smile, and fled from the room.

"He's here," Quin-Quin said, stepping back quickly from the jalousies. She darted a concerned glance at Reinette, who had not been sleeping well and looked like a shadow of her former self.

Neal's murder, added to the emotional stress of the past few months, had pushed her perilously close to the breaking point.

Reinette remained seated in the brocade armchair so that she would have a few minutes' respite before the act of standing would make her condition all too apparent to Alejandro. She needed those precious few moments. Her nerves were frayed as badly as the old mooring ropes on the wharves. Her embroidery lay untouched in her lap. Waiting, she twisted her wedding band, a recent habit of which she was unaware.

She heard the rumble of masculine voices at the portal of the lower floor, then Alejandro's rapid-fire questioning of the guards Unzaga had posted only that morning and their crisp replies. She could delay no longer. Her fingers clutched the chair's arms. Within seconds, Alejandro loomed in the doorway, plumed tricorn tucked under his arm. Behind him, she caught sight of several of his officers. Her gaze cut back to his strongly boned face, searching for a clue as to how much he knew.

In three strides, he crossed the room to kneel before her and lifted her left hand, touching his forehead to the back of it in homage. When his head came up, she saw the hard glitter of restrained passion in his eyes. "Mademoiselle," he said, formally addressing her before his officers, "I came at once from the frigate. Unzaga met me at the wharf and informed me of my orderly's death yesterday. I'm relieved that you escaped harm."

Reinette's lashes lowered. "I was most fortunate, monsieur. Quin-Quin returned from the drapers in time to frighten off the intruder."

"So Unzaga reported. I'll launch a full investigation and find the culprit, you may rest assured."

"I am relieved," she replied—relieved, that was, that he had accepted her fabrication.

When he rose to dismiss his officers, Quin-Quin tactfully vanished. Reinette waited until he returned and went to the sideboard. She laid aside her embroidery and, going to him, said baldly, "There is more to tell, Alejandro. I am with child."

He paused in the act of pouring two glasses of claret. His flinty glare skimmed over her. She had chosen a modest gown of soft, dove-pearl poplin with a sacque that artfully draped about her waist. He set down the decanter and asked quietly, "The child is mine?"

"And if it isn't?" she hedged.

The back of his hand struck her cheek, whipping her head sharply to the side. She stumbled back a step, fingers pressed to her stinging face. He raised a brow. "Do I infer you made a fool of me with someone else? Have I been cuckolded, mademoiselle?"

"You will remember, our agreement was only that I give you the *honor* of my company."

She half flinched, expecting him to strike her again. Instead, he was silent for an extraordinarily long time. "You would never do well at court, Reinette," he said at last. "You haven't the guile for intrigue and lies." Still, doubt shadowed his eyes.

He put an arm around her waist and tilted back her chin. "You don't look well. You are too thin. You must rest as much as possible for the sake of our child."

Our child. She could only hope that the babe she carried inherited Aaron's auburn hair. The red highlights might just be the child's salvation—might just convince the redheaded O'Reilly beyond all doubt that the child was his own. She shuddered. Her lids closed against the fierce, possessive light in his eyes. "Alejandro . . . you promised. You promised."

She felt his lips brush hers softly, gently. "Reinette, didn't you miss me while I was away?" His fingers repentantly stroked her cheek, which carried the reddened imprint of his hand. "Don't you care for me, even a little? Deny it," he whispered against her parted lips. His hands gently cupped her breasts, overfull and aching from the changes pregnancy had wrought in her body.

She trembled again, but this time out of her involuntary response to the skillful and delicious assault of his masculinity on her senses. Shame at her betrayal of Aaron's love wormed through her, but she made no protest when Alejandro slid an arm beneath her knees and, cradling her against his chest, took her to his bed.

Quin-Quin applied the heated curling tongs to one long, honeyed swath of Reinette's hair. "Your *maquillage* doesn't cover your paleness, girl. You're certain you must attend the farewell ball tonight?"

Reinette took a deep, steadying breath. "I tried already to beg off, pleading that appearing in my condition in public was a breech of etiquette. You know the Irishman. He adores flouting public opinion." Wearily, she picked up the Spanish wool and dipped it in a jar. "Perhaps a little more rouge will enliven my skin—and give me courage, something I no longer seem to have."

Abruptly, she crossed her arms on the dressing table, scattering the jars and little boxes, and buried her head in the crook of her elbow. "Oh, Quin-Quin, what has happened to me? I'm so tired of matching wits with Alejandro! My God, I must be out of my mind," she said bitterly. "Trying to outmaneuver and stay one step ahead of a man famed for his military mind and knowledge of modern warfare!"

Two days. In two days, on March first, Alejandro was due to sail with the major portion of his troops for Cadiz. And though the issue of her going with him had not risen again, she knew that he had not even considered the idea of leaving her behind. The day before, he had ordered Quin-Quin to begin packing her mistress's belongings.

Soon Reinette knew that she and Alejandro would clash in a standoff of wills.

With a sigh of futility, she suffered through the powdering of her hair, then rose and, removing her dusting cape, went to join him.

With a frown of worry, Quin-Quin watched her mistress go. The young mistress wasn't herself anymore.

Reinette dreaded facing that insincere and gratuitous populace of New Orleans Creoles who were coming to pay their respects that evening of the departing general, whom they so deeply resented. Then, too, Doña Merced would be present. Reinette shuddered. The woman had the eyes of a wolverine.

Alejandro's staff of servants had polished the furniture and woodwork with beeswax, and dusted and mopped. The cook had spent two full days preparing dishes of tender pigeon squabs, thick and spicy ragout, and bouillabaisse, as well as the appetizing confections of custards and little cakes.

She found Alejandro in his office, slashing his quill across last-minute documents that had to be completed. He was resplendent in his red uniform trimmed with gold braid and epaulets, a rapier at his side. At her entrance, he rose and limped across the room to take her hands in his. "You're lovely, Reinette. Your beauty will put the other females all out of sorts."

She wore an off-the-shoulder gown of brown watered silk that exposed her full, milk-white breasts, faintly veined now with approaching motherhood. A pale ivory panel of lace and pearls overlapped the front of her skirt. A rope of pearls was looped through the mass of curls clustered atop her head.

"Are you ready to greet the guests?" she asked breathlessly. She tried to ignore the way his fingers lingeringly stroked her bare neck. "They should be arriving soon."

"I can feel the tension in your muscles," he told her, his eyes searching her face. "Relax."

"You know I feel awkward, appearing in public like this," she murmured.

"I don't think that is the reason, at least not all of it." His hand cupped the back of her neck, holding her immobile. "Reinette, it's my child you carry also. Do you seriously think I'd leave without you?"

She clenched her hands, dragging up resistance from somewhere inside. "I'm married to someone else."

His hand tightened about her neck. "*Sacré bleu!* Do you propose to live celibate for twenty years?"

Her eyes misted. "I love him, Alejandro."

His jaw tensed. From below came the sound of loud knocking at the portal and voices of arriving guests. "I warn you, you'll sail with me even if I have to carry you aboard."

She did not for one minute doubt his threat. Knowing his tactical mind, he would more than likely place her under house arrest before the night was out. Docilely, she let him lead her out to greet the guests, but her mind worked feverishly. If she went with Alejandro, Aaron would be lost to her forever, as she would be lost.

Close to hysteria, she accepted a glass of claret and downed it immediately, hoping to calm herself enough to think, to plan, to outwit Alejandro, who was now her jailer. She ignored his disapproving look when she took another stemmed glass of wine.

Dutifully, she moved among the Creole dandies and their haughty companions, intensely aware of the derisive looks scanning her figure. In fact, she was mortified. Her neck ached from carrying her chin high, her head held proudly; her temple throbbed incessantly.

The sight of the amiably grinning Moro waiting patiently at the doorway for his mistress shook her badly. Midway through the evening, her path crossed that of Doña Merced. The guests had been waiting all night for this confrontation. The noble-woman fanned herself rapidly. Above a cold smile, her pale blue eyes flashed. "I see you breed well, mademoiselle."

Those nearest the two women tittered or smothered snorts behind their fans. Reinette was oblivious to what was going on around her. The old Reinette might have retorted with some cutting remark, but only the shell of that young woman remained. The spirit inside was a lost child, a *feu follet*.

Still, some last vestige of self-preservation inspired her to beg in a low voice, "If you want Alejandro for yourself, then help me to escape . . . tonight."

The Spanish woman lifted a wary eyebrow. "You are trying to trick me, mademoiselle?"

"No! You must believe me. I don't want to be his mistress any more than you want me to."

Doña Merced flicked a glance at Alejandro's back, then said, "I must be a fool for believing you, but, tell me, how can I help?"

"Your cloak. It has a hood?"

The woman nodded.

"Let me leave with your Moro," Reinette said with the quiet desperation of the near mad. "I'll leave by the front door when some of the guests begin departing."

Doña Merced laughed aloud. "Your request is so implausible that I think I do believe you." She snapped her fan shut. "So be it. I'll have the pygmy accompany you as far as the palisade gates. You're on your own then, mademoiselle. But heed me. If you should change your mind, the Moro will not fail a third time in his mission. Do I make myself clear?"

"Utterly. Now, if you'll excuse me, I'll leave you to divert the general." She half turned away, then said with a brittle smile, "You may even take my place in his bed tonight."

In as inconspicuous a manner as possible, she wove her way through the crush of guests, pausing here and there to make reserved replies to stilted greetings. Time seemed to pass so slowly. At one point, she saw Doña Merced speak to the Moro.

Finally, a few guests made their *adieux*. She drifted closer to the hallway door. She dreaded looking over her shoulder, appre-hensive that she would see Alejandro watching her with those piercing eyes. She got as far as the doorway, where the pygmy had posted himself, when Alejandro said from close behind her, "You are deserting our guests so early?"

She turned, her mouth stretched in a smile, her black eyes glittering. "I was only going upstairs to repair my *maquillage* and tuck in a loose curl or two."

The wall candle revealed clearly the suspicion in his hard face. "Don't be long, Reinette."

Fear crackled up and down her spine. She should have felt some shred of guilt or shame at deserting her faithful Quin-Quin, leaving her to face Alejandro's mighty wrath, but the more primitive instinct of fear ran rampant in her soul. *Run! Run!* The words screamed through her subconscious mind, which was bordering perilously on dementia.

But run where?

An odd, tight little smile crossed her face. Why, back to the swamp, where else?

PART 4

CHAPTER

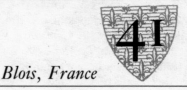

Blois, France   *March 1794*

WHILE THE REVOLUTIONARY MINDS of eighteenth-century France were holding forth on the basic tenets of *liberté, égalité,* and *fraternité,* twelve-year-old Gabrielle Fabreville preferred a simpler philosophy of life, believing among other truths that the wise thing to do with mornings was to sleep through them.

She arched her back, stretched her arms above her head, and told her new governess, a starchy woman with a pointed nose, "I think, madame, that a sunrise is a marvelous thing to look at immediately before going to bed."

"Not 'madame.' *Citoyenne.*" The middle-aged woman from a middle-class family pursed her lips and said, "The days of your *ancien régime* are over."

Gabrielle shrugged shoulders still childishly bony. Privately, she thought that vinegar rather than blood must course through the governess's veins.

The strict Carmelite nuns who had taught Gabrielle at St. Cyr had nonetheless been much more approachable. But then her father had withdrawn her from Paris's elite school for young women on the day of the queen's execution and hustled her off to Maison Bellecour.

With Marie Antoinette's execution, the Reign of Terror, something that the nuns tried to shield their charges from, reached its peak. That same month, three of the nuns themselves rode to the guillotine scaffolds in one of the rickety tumbrels that rambled through the streets daily with their cargoes of the condemned. Most were innocent victims accused by the Committee of Public Safety of charges such as failing to sing *La Marseillaise* or equally trivial denunciations by jealous or vindictive neighbors.

Gabrielle's mother had been one of the victims. Accused of madness, by whom Gabrielle knew not, her mother had been interred in La Salpêtrière. During the September Massacres of 1792, Gabrielle had inadvertently seen her mother's head paraded by on a pike; only by consciously blocking out that horror had she escaped madness herself.

She wormed out of her nightrail and subjected herself to the awful weekly bath that the fastidious governess had ordered. "*C'est odieux!*" the girl declared, but under the woman's cold eye, she lowered herself into the bathtub, a curious portable contraption shaped like a stub-nosed, high-backed shoe, and commenced to scrub herself. Soapsuds moustached her upper lip, and her nose wrinkled in a futile effort to ward off a fit of sneezing.

The loud and indelicate *ka-choos* echoed simultaneously with the thunder of musket shots from the town that fanned out below the château. Following on the heels of her sneezing could be heard a mob shouting, "*A la guillotine!*" and "Death to the Royalists! Death to the aristocrats!"

When he heard the sound of the musket fire, Guilbert Fabreville, Marquis de Marchesseau, laid down his quill and crossed to the casement window. His tailored clothes hid the fact that, at forty-five, he was running to fat. The same moment he reached the window, cannons exploded and smoke corkscrewed upward from what had been old Marboeuf's lovely mansion. Across the Loire, other rich men's houses were blown up, then collapsed in rubble one after another like falling dominoes.

"So, *Citoyen* Fouché has won the fanatics after all," Marchesseau said, then muttered even lower, lest one of the servants overhear, "Fuck the agent. Fuck the *Republique*."

For more than four years, the marquis, the great-grandson of Claude Fabreville, had evaded the ruination and execution faced by other nobles and princes of the blood through shrewd and manipulative connections. He had aligned himself with the earlier heroes, the Girondists, who in turn became the villains to the *sans-culottes*, which literally meant without fancy breeches, a form of dress associated with aristocrats. The *sans-culottes* bowed out to the Mountain, or Montagnards, who were ordered executed by the more radical Jacobins.

One after another, various men or parties emerged to seize power. Through all the turmoil, the cunning Marchesseau kept one step ahead of the rabble by anticipating the downfall of the revolutionary party presently in power. He adapted the tricolor cockade of the Republic, forwent powdering his hair, became an atheist, cursed the king and queen, denounced his wife as a *royaliste* . . . Whatever was called for, he did it.

While men like Marat met their deaths, he succeeded in surviving because he had no loyalties, no misplaced convictions or any noble ideals.

It was Marchesseau's contention that goodness and virtue were seldom rewarded but quickness of wit was. Far better to be wise, he had been taught by his grandfather, than to be good, and better still to be crafty.

He had barely escaped the September Massacres, those five days and nights of frenzied murders, cannibalism, disembowelment, and other such nauseating acts. Stomach churning, he had watched from a window in the Jacobin Club as a frenzied mob descended on La Salpêtrière where aristocrats and other unfortunates had been incarcerated, among them his timid and vapid wife. All without exception, children included, were murdered.

He had witnessed the death of the Princesse de Lamballe, once his mistress. Foolishly, she had returned from the safety of England to stand beside her friend, Marie Antoinette. Dispatched with a pike thrust, her still-beating heart was ripped from her body and devoured, her breasts were cut off, and her legs and arms were severed from her body and shot through a cannon. Several hours later, her head was jammed on a pike and paraded past the Tuileries, its blond hair billowing in the breeze.

The September Massacres necessitated another realignment of his loyalties, which he had foreseen. He removed himself and Gabrielle to the province and joined its local Jacobins. What he had not counted on was the Revolutionary Tribunal and its agents. For the past three months, Fouché had scurried like a rat about Blois, enlisting recruits and spreading dissension.

Guilbert Fabreville, or Marchesseau, as he was known, realized that his position was shaky but more than likely secure for several more weeks. The peasants and bourgeoisie of Blois might detest the Marchesseau title, but it was still the embodiment of power and influence that it had been since medieval times.

He swung away from the window and pulled a bell rope, summoning his valet. Once again, a change of residence was in order.

Toward noon of the following day, Marchesseau and his daughter set out on foot for the stagecoach offices. Gabrielle carried her sketchbook and pencils. For all she knew, she and her father were going on a jaunt to the coast, and the bourgeois clothing her father had made her don was part of the trip's revelry. She was thrilled at the prospect of riding in a stagecoach full of interesting passengers, instead of alone in the carriage with its Marchesseau coat of arms on the door panel.

Marchesseau was also costumed, in the red bonnet, short jacket, and long-striped pants of the peasant revolutionaries. With a fondness that came the closest to love that it was possible for him to feel, he watched his daughter trip away with a clatter of her wooden sabots. Hoisting up her blue skirt to expose white underpetticoats, she ran like a red Indian. She had coltish legs and unmanageable orange-red hair. "Devil hair," the nitwit governess had said. But Gabrielle had the looks that, like wine, would improve with age, and assured him of the prospects of marrying her off advantageously. If only she would stop growing; she was almost as tall as he.

Within half an hour, they reached the booking office, and Marchesseau presented the two forged passports necessary for traveling anywhere in the country. Sweat dampened his armpits, but the harried clerk didn't even look up. The stage was due to roll into the cobbled courtyard at any moment and there was still the luggage to be carted outside for loading.

The evening before, Marchesseau had sent a trunk filled with documents, coin and currency, and clothing on to Nantes, where, in a secluded cove, if all went as planned, they would board by night a boat full of other aristocratic *émigrés*.

CHAPTER

42

DANIEL DU PLESSIS STEPPED INTO the rain-washed night. His penis felt crusted, hot, and flayed. The flaxen-haired German wife of the commissary-general was insatiable.

Instinct reminded him that it wasn't safe to stand outlined in the lighted doorway of the little row cottage outside the ramparts, not with the commissary-general already suspicious that his wife Hilda had taken a lover. So Daniel stood there a little longer, welcoming whatever waited in the darkness to challenge him.

The swamp had taught him survival. Adaptability was his natural state. He learned early that nothing was ever exactly what it seemed.

He thought of the quadroon ball, which was an hour off, at eleven, and grimaced. Unlike the Creole gentlemen of his acquaintance, he found the courting tradition of the balls vastly depressing. The golden-tinted quadroons with their eager-to-please smiles left him anything but amorous.

These illegitimate daughters of white men and their mulatto mistresses were free women, raised by their mothers, much as courtesans were in France, to become mistresses of white gentlemen. Their chastity was their chief stock-in-trade, in addition to their exceptional beauty and good education. Most of them

were more white than black. For a season, they flashed their
gems, making the most of their beauty and happiness while it
lasted.

What did it matter that, after their lovers took wives, many of
the golden-tinted quadroons committed suicide? They had been
taught what to expect beforehand. No one else cared, so why
should he involve himself?

But he knew the answer to that. The nightmare that made him
first sweat with fear and then anger, had haunted him for so long
. . . How long now? Almost twenty years, wasn't it, since that
day, as a frightened five-year-old, he had first glimpsed the hideous deformities of the lepers? Twenty years since he and his
mother, who had been deranged with fever, had taken refuge in
the leper colony tucked away in the treacherous swamps outside
of New Orleans.

For nearly three years, he had remained in the colony of ramshackle palmetto huts and watched his mother's pretty body de-
teriorate, watched the hands and feet lose their digits. His stomach
still knotted and turned over at the remembered sight of his mother's face, the fleshy end of her nose eaten away by the insidious
disease.

Then one day, as she lay dying, she had extracted her deathbed
promise. "You must find the mulatto Quin-Quin and her daughter, my son . . . I deserted them. . . . She knows the truth about
your birth . . . Swear you'll take care of them."

Christ help him, he could not bring himself to kiss the wasted
woman. Dutifully, he had given his word. "*Oui, maman.*" Then,
crying his seven-year-old's heart out, he had fled from the nauseating horror that his mother had become.

Yes, Christ help him, he thought, as he stood in the sullen
drizzle. He cared little about the cloudy facts of his birth, but
his guilt and his deathbed promise had hounded him. On his
occasional visits to New Orleans, he was driven to search out the
rabbit warrens that comprised the area where the people of free
color lived and to attend the packed ballrooms located either at
Calle San Philipe or at the corners of Calle Orleans and Bourbon.

Tomorrow, he promised himself, he would devote to the main
purpose of his trips to New Orleans—the role of an intelligence
agent.

. . .

New Orleans, with its population of nearly ten thousand, vied with Cartagena, Marseilles, and the rest of the world's most notorious seaports for supremacy in outlaws, underworld, and crime in general. Its waterfront stretched nearly four miles. Moored to heavy timbers embedded in batture lay its shipping. Blunt-bowed trading brigs from all ports of Europe elbowed for room with heavy Indiamen; small craft from the Antilles were wedged next to fleets of flatboats from El Cadrón on the Arkansas River, a refuge for river pirates and English vagabonds.

Along the levee swarmed seamen from a dozen nations, rolling hogsheads of tobacco, toting butts of wine, and shifting bales of cotton. Furs from St. Louis were crated for shipment to the markets of fashion-making Europe.

Ordinarily, one nation was seldom represented at the port: the new and struggling United States of America. Spain felt that the Americans who had poured west over the Appalachian Mountains after the Revolution were a threat to her possessions, so they closed the lower Mississippi to all but ships of select nationalities.

While not stringently enforced, the directive denied Americans the use of the New Orleans port whenever the Spanish puppet governors decided to close it. The Kaintocks, as usual, were as angry as grizzlies over this, as well as by the excessive duties and restrictions an *intendente* levied on the rare occasions when they were allowed to use the port. At times their entire cargoes were confiscated. This was one of the reasons George Rogers Clark had sent Daniel du Plessis to New Orleans.

The Kaintocks offered President Washington two alternatives: either they would march down the river and seize New Orleans, or they would secede from the United States and then seize New Orleans. While Washington wasn't exactly unopposed to the idea of an independent state of Louisiana, he was more worried about the international intrigue that was rife in New Orleans.

Jacobin agents from the republic of France traveled throughout the Spanish province trying to incite revolutionary fervor among the French Creoles. England, now controlling lower Canada, was dispatching British subversives to hatch attacks on the Spanish possessions of St. Louis, New Orleans, and Santa Fe.

Yet Spain was the most dangerous power to the fledgling republic. She was biding her time, looking toward bigger stakes: the total collapse of the United States. In this game, the urbane

Governor Don Francisco Héctor, Baron de Carondelet, held a number of cards. Secret Spanish agents, some in the American army itself, were spying and fomenting trouble. Carondelet was spreading His Majesty's gold, dispatching messages in cipher, and making quiet, upriver trips to Natchez to see his Natchez subordinate, Governor Manuel Gayoso de Lemos.

Washington didn't want any European powers at America's backdoor. Then, too, New Orleans was too vital to be left under foreign domination. So Daniel, as a citizen of Spanish Natchez, was empowered by Clark to act as an intelligence agent for the United States and to keep a finger on activities along the Mississippi.

More than that, he was to keep a watchful eye on the operations of the ambitious General James Wilkinson. A trader by occupation, he had learned the craft of intrigue under Benedict Arnold in the revolutionary war and, thanks to Aaron Burr, now stood to become the ranking officer of the United States Army. Incredibly, Wilkinson was both an army officer and a Spanish agent, though no tangible proof existed that the former trader had turned traitor.

Wilkinson's protégé Philip Nolan would be attending a soiree given by Governor Carondelet two evenings hence, and Daniel intended to wangle an invitation. For the moment, though, he planned to reconnoiter the wharves.

By keeping his eyes on such ordinary things as imports and exports, he could deduce a surprising amount of information. The shipload of flour received at the wharf could mean that the recent hurricane had damaged wheat crops throughout the province. The arrival of Swiss mercenary troops signified desertions in the Spanish ranks that needed to be filled. These and other observations would be of interest to Clark.

Farther along the waterfront, a boatload of French émigrés put in. Daniel strolled with seeming idleness in that direction to watch the refugees disembark. Most looked dazed and exhausted, having hidden out for perhaps months before finding a ship to take them. Secreted among them could also be Jacobins, planning on infiltrating the city to inspire another French revolution in North America.

He studied their faces with more than just an intelligence agent's interest. Part Irish, part Indian, he also carried French blood in his veins, and he stared at these native-born Frenchmen with a sort of bemused curiosity.

At a nearby booth, an *intendente* took the names and former residences of the arriving passengers, administered the Royal Ordinance—an oath of allegiance to Spain that was required for all persons seeking asylum in Louisiana, and issued passports.

When Daniel overheard the name of Fabreville, his attention was transferred to the owner of the name, a middle-aged man of average height with a high forehead and an imperious nose that overshadowed the waxed moustache. Though his light brown hair was unpowdered, he otherwise displayed the trappings of an aristocrat: jonquil-colored knee breeches, a silk coat of robin's-egg blue, and gold-buckled heels. He wore a bicorne hat over his catogan queue and carried a slender cane the diameter of a wax candle adorned with black-ribbon streamers.

With the man was a little girl. Her hair was a frightful orange. For all her youthful ungainliness, she nonetheless moved with the untutored gestures of the self-possessed. Daniel's cursory gaze passed over her and returned to the father. Fabreville. The name stirred old, forgotten memories.

He would have wandered on down the wharf, but then he heard the man condescendingly tell the *intendente*, "My title is the Marquis de Marchesseau."

The *intendente* noted the name and dutifully asked, "Your former residence, monsieur?"

Fabreville tapped his walking cane impatiently. "Maison Bellecour—in Blois."

Daniel's attention was riveted on the nobleman. When Daniel's mother had recovered from the consuming fever, she had remembered little of her past—only the theme that had been drummed into her during her childhood years in the swamp: the need to regain the ancestral estates of Maison Bellecour one day and to avenge themselves against the Marquis de Marchesseau.

After all this time, Daniel felt little of his mother's burning need for revenge; if anything, he felt contempt for the decadent life-style that French aristocratic society had spawned, a life-style that had spilled over into Creole New Orleans. Perhaps that explained his sympathies with the brash Americans.

He clanged shut the steel door of his mind on the unwanted memories and turned his jackboots toward the famous fencing academies on Exchange Alley, a short and narrow thoroughfare between Canal and Conti streets. As he crossed the Plaza de Arma's sunburned grass, more than one young lady, strolling beneath the sycamores with her *duenna*, lifted demurely lowered eyes to follow his strapping figure.

Daniel du Plessis was hard not to notice. Inordinately tall, he strode with an unconscious but overbearing certainty of his place in the world. He wore his thick mane of flaming red hair unpowdered and clubbed. A boyish grin, which some called devilish, softened the twenty-four-year-old's square jaw.

Exchange Alley was lined by a dozen *salles d'armes*, academies for sword, rapier, and pistol training. The great *maîtres d'armes* of these academies formed a class of their own. Their skill with foils made them legends in their own time. They gave suppers for their pupils, where drinking, roistering, and swordplay took place.

Daniel had been taking lessons for several years from Bastile Roquère, a mulatto who had been educated in Paris. He taught the cream of Creole society, but never fought one duel because of his race.

At Daniel's entrance, the professor of counterpoint hailed his accomplished student. "By the looks of your eyes, you have spent more time tipping the bottle than wielding the blade."

Daniel shrugged with Gallic eloquence. "What can I say? I confess to investigating the seven deadly sins. Or at least most of them."

"Aren't the Natchez damosels enough for you?" asked Marcel Lassaut, cuffing Daniel amiably on the shoulder. "I insist you leave me to bed the beauties of New Orleans by myself."

The lanky Lassaut was one of the white French islanders who had taken refuge in Louisiana after the successful slave uprising in Saint-Domingue three years earlier. New Orleans was captivated by the easy charm of the Dominicains, their brittle wit, and their insight into the pleasures of decadence. Some Dominicains had recently opened the city's first theater, Cap Français at calles Royal and Bourbon.

While Bastile took a neophyte through the stances with buttoned épées rather than naked blades, Marcel chatted about the identity of the governor's latest mistress, the duel fought the night before in St. Anthony's Garden behind the church, and a quadroon ball held two nights earlier.

"I swear by the head of Marie Antoinette, Daniel, I saw the most beautiful mulatto today. She was riding in a carriage along the Esplanade. She had to be a griffe. Lips like coral and skin as white as pearls! I'll wager you fifty livres that before the week is out I shall set her up in a *petite maison*."

Daniel barely listened to the banter. He was waiting for the opportunity to inveigle an invitation to the governor's soiree, a grand ball.

He studied periodically under Bastile not so much to perfect his skill at weaponry but more to cultivate the friendship of the rich, young Creoles. Occasionally, he picked up useful bits of information or gained entrée to a festivity or social function, where he observed the political attitudes of various Creole dignitaries.

Possessing the Latin traits of both Spain and France, the Creole gallants loved pleasure, lived for excitement, and enjoyed any game that stirred their senses. They constituted a sort of aristocracy founded less on birth than on manners, breeding, education, and tradition. This was the golden age of Creole society, and their studied grandeur, courtly manners, and indolence amused Daniel to the point that he sincerely enjoyed their camaraderie.

There was no way of warning the Creoles that their insular society would eventually destroy them, but for a while it provided a defense against an egalitarian social system that threatened their supremacy and pride.

Raising his voice slightly to make himself heard above the clang and rasp of the foils, Daniel said, "The little drummer boy at the corner announced a ball for ladies of color and white gentlemen to be held the day after tomorrow. Perhaps the mulatto you saw will be there. Shall we go?"

"*Pardieu!*" Marcel swore. "I have Carondelet's grand ball to attend that night." Then his hazel eyes lit up. "But *ecoutez!* Why not attend the grand ball together and leave from there for the quadroon ball?"

Daniel lifted his shoulders and spread his palms. "It makes no difference to me."

Since there was no royal palace or capitol, Governor Carondelet had leased two houses and added a gallery to serve as a bridge between the two. One house did duty as his private residence, the other provided offices and entertainment rooms. Silk-clad guests were spilling out of the *grande salle*'s garden doors and onto the gallery, ornamented with filigreed wrought iron hand-crafted in Mexico.

Once inside, Marcel immediately fortified himself with a new concoction mixed in a double-ended eggcup called a *coquetier*, or cocktail, as the Americans atrociously pronounced it. With his second glass in hand, he set out leisurely to enchant, and ultimately seduce, whatever woman was available.

Daniel was bent on other pursuits. He mingled easily with the guests, extracting himself when the conversation promised to reveal nothing of significance. Several times he danced with whatever Creole beauty caught his eye, but he hardly listened to their prattle. His quick eyes were constantly scanning the large hall, noting who was bending whose ear.

Eventually, he spotted the reticent Philip Nolan in the company of the choleric Governor Carondelet, a plump, little man with an even plumper face. Nolan, an Irishman, had moody blue eyes that didn't hold one's gaze for long. Besides being a horse dealer, he sometimes acted as Wilkinson's agent between New Orleans and Kentucky, where Wilkinson retained a plantation and a trading operation. The operation, inexplicably, had a monopoly on Mississippi trade with Spanish Louisiana.

With the intention of eavesdropping, Daniel drifted toward the clique of men around Nolan and the governor. One of the men looked familiar, a moustached gentleman in a high stock and ruffled shirt carrying a ribbon-topped cane. Daniel realized it was his "kinsman," Guilbert Fabreville. The man had not wasted any time in ingratiating himself in the most influential—and corrupt—circles.

The conversation was innocuous enough, but for one moment when Carondelet lowered his voice in a confidential tone. Daniel overheard only snatches. "Wilkinson . . . right financing . . . Washington of the West."

A tipsy Marcel joined Daniel and interrupted whatever else Daniel might have overheard. "I'm bored, my friend," Marcel whispered with the mock formality of the inebriated. "Not one female here under twenty. Let's seek better company. At the quadroon ball."

The governor's conversation had already shifted to another,

less damning topic, so Daniel, feeling he had gleaned sufficient information to report back to Clark, acquiesced to Marcel's suggestion, though he didn't relish the thought of attending the quadroon ball. He would have preferred playing cards in one of the many smaller rooms in back of the ballroom, where men sat at the tables for hours and gambled, but he had a pledge to keep.

The Orleans ballroom was an immensely long room with high ceilings and a floor like glass. Its many windows looked down on to Orleans Street, and from its balconies the mulatto beauties and their Creole gentlemen could retire to enjoy the cool breeze or simply to overlook the garden just back of the church, where hundreds of duels growing out of the ball would take place. Men of color were forbidden to attend the quadroon balls, for the quadroons desired to ally themselves only with white gentlemen.

The quadroons were the most beautiful women in the world, with lovely countenances, liquid dark eyes, and smiles that seemed like eager white gashes to Daniel. Famed for their elegant dress, these free women of color tended to upstage the white women. It was no wonder the Creole ladies were indignant that so many of the Creole gallants, after a suitable appearance at their own balls, would desert the Creole ladies for the quadroon balls and leave them wallflowers.

So incensed had the young Creole ladies become that half a dozen years earlier they had prevailed upon the governor to forbid women of color to wear plumes or jewelry in their hair. They could wear only handkerchiefs on their heads. The mulattoes circumvented this by binding their hair in brilliant-colored and extravagant *tignons* that were their distinctive badge of identification.

"That's her," Marcel said. "That's the one!"

Daniel followed his lanky friend's gaze. The young woman was dancing a minuet with a painter's son whom Daniel knew vaguely. "You're right, Marcel. She is breathtaking."

The dance ended, and Marcel said, "Let's introduce ourselves!"

He was already making a beeline in her direction, shouldering his way through the mass of couples. Daniel, half-amused, half-reluctant, followed. From midway across the room, his gaze measured the petite young woman whose sloe eyes, the pale color of pralines, watched him above her fluttering fan as Marcel introduced himself. Her skin was the lovely shade of old pearls. She wore a soft rose satin gown and a matching *tignon* that lent her features a mysterious appeal.

Marcel, smirking in besodden delight, said, "Daniel, may I introduce Mademoiselle Guirard. Mademoiselle, Monsieur du Plessis."

Daniel bowed, and she curtsyed low, her eyes holding his through the tangle of her lashes. Marcel asked, "May I beg the honor of this dance, Mademoiselle Guirard?"

"Monsieur, it is late and I am weary from dancing so much." Her lovely coral lips softened the refusal with a smile. "But I would be grateful for a cup of refreshment."

After Marcel departed on his quest for his lady, she slanted a surreptitious glance at Daniel. "You two are friends, monsieur?"

"Acquaintances." Up close, she looked older than the average quadroon caught up in the *plaçage* system, his age maybe.

"Then he will not be upset if you escort me to the courtyard, will he?"

Daniel arched a brow, then said bluntly, "Mademoiselle, I have no interest in setting up a *chère amie* in a little house on the ramparts."

"Then why have you come here?" she challenged softly.

He tunneled his fingers through his hair. "I don't know."

"You have been drinking, monsieur?'

"No, but maybe I should."

"Then accompany me to the courtyard. Cordials and wine are served there."

He considered, shrugged, and then offered her his arm, saying, "Mademoiselle."

She placed her hand on his forearm and permitted him to lead her down the staircase at the rear of the ballroom. In the courtyard, quadroon ladies sat talking and laughing with Creole gentlemen at white wrought-iron tables placed beneath tropical flowering trees and shrubs. Lanterns bathed the tableau in soft, romantic light.

After he ordered two glasses of wine from an old, grizzle-haired black man, she said, "I resent your contempt, monsieur."

Her frankness caught him unprepared. "You mistake pity for contempt."

She lifted alabaster shoulders prettily. "It is all the same. Why should we be condemned when it is men like you who leave us no choice? Either we sell ourselves as slaves or we sell ourselves as mistresses."

The old man returned with two fluted glasses and the quadroon fell silent; after the man shuffled off, the quadroon lifted her glass and said quietly, "Perhaps it is you who are worse off, with your marriages arranged as social and financial alliances." Her eyes lifted from her glass to lock with his scrutinizing gaze. "At least our relationships are based on love or sexual attraction."

"And what happens when that sexual attraction wanes?" he asked bluntly. "What happens when your Creole gentleman takes a wife?"

She smiled. "I learn about it either in the *Moniteur de la Louisiane* or by gossip. Either way, I receive a letter entitling me to call my house my own. That, monsieur, is security."

She glanced over his shoulder and said, "Your friend is coming. He is very rich?"

Daniel took a sip of the sweet wine, swallowed, and said, "I don't know." With a heavy sigh, he set the glass down. He wanted to get his mission over with and get out of the place. A swelling wave of depression began to settle over him. "I'm looking for an older woman."

"To set up as your mistress?" the quadroon asked incredulously.

He ignored her question. "The woman I seek is a free woman of color. All I know is her first name, Quin-Quin—and that she had a daughter."

The rosé wine splashed over the rim of the quadroon's glass. She stared at him with wide eyes. "Quin-Quin is my mother's name."

CHAPTER

43

THE FOURTEENTH COLONY DIDN'T revolt in 1776 but remained loyal to King George; however, near the end of the revolutionary war, Governor Gálvez of Spanish Louisiana sailed up the Mississippi to take Fort Panmure, the site of the old Fort Rosalie. Spanish officials proceeded to lay out a grid of streets among an archipelago of plantations and called the town Natchez. But under Spanish rule Natchez's population, language, and philosphy remained Anglo-Saxon.

In essence, Natchez was English and pro-American—a dissimilarity to Gallic New Orleans, which thought Americans equated with barbarians. Orleansians loved the chanson; Natchezians enjoyed the reel or the cotillion. Neither was prudish; both savored a drinking song, over a glass of wine or a warm toddy.

Natchez was a dichotomy, from its genteel heights to its bawdy bottom along the river. The portion laid out by the Spanish on the bluff consisted of tranquil, jessamine-lined streets, a sunny esplanade, and the elegance of breeze-cooled heights.

Below the two-hundred-foot bluff, on a mile-long stretch of shelf, squatted Natchez-Under-the-Hill. It was rowdy and loud, with its smelly flares, the whine of red-cheeked women, and the squalor of steaming mud flats—a hell-raising, rampaging sin spot, a mecca for keelboatmen and Kaintocks who craved liquor, song, and women, all raw.

Natchez remained closer to the frontier than some cared to admit: the splendor of an imported carpet over a puncheon floor; a delicate set of carved furniture beneath the coarse beam of a ceiling. Natchez was called "the West," a jumping-off place. At Natchez were crystallized the hopes and plans of countless parties going forth to Texas and Mexico for stealthy gain.

Here, too, were hatched plots to separate the West from the East and to establish a separate republic or empire under the protection of Spain.

Three men sat discussing this problem in an isolated house within the outskirts of a murky swamp that bordered a portion of the Trace. The house suggested a primitive blockhouse, a heavy, compact place first created as a protection against savage marauders. Half-brick, half-timber, it resembled an outlaw's impregnable retreat and was a challenge to the elements. The lower, bricked floor led to a second level of wood with a wooden-railed porch. Above, a third, smaller story perched like a lookout. Within, everything was in massive scale: thick beams, wooden pegs instead of nails, doors bolted with stout bars, and a fireplace that occupied an entire wall.

Now the fortresslike house did duty as a tavern, or at least appeared to do so. Of the frontiersmen who moved down the dangerous pioneer trail, the only link over the Appalachians to the Eastern seaboard colonies, no one asked questions. If every once in a while a traveler would leave the trail to rendezvous at the blockhouse, who was the wiser?

All manner of people came and went, some staying several days, some overnight, for the trip in and out by swamp was best negotiated by the tree-filtered light of day and with the aid of a guide. Whores came from Natchez-Under-the-Hill, longriflemen from the Appalachians, courtesans from New Orleans, trappers from the Illinois country, keelboatmen from all points.

The oldest of the three men who met that particular August afternoon had built the blockhouse. Despite his nearly sixty-odd years, the gray-bearded Acadian still possessed a Samson's physique.

He sat at the table, saying nothing, only listening to the two other men, both of whom had red hair, though that of the revolutionary hero, George Rogers Clark, was lighter, less fiery, and thinning rapidly.

Paul la Ronde's gaze lingered fondly on the other man, who was only just entering manhood. Daniel had inherited the best physical attributes of his French mother and Irish father—vibrant red hair and laughing black eyes that could snap. He had also inherited the volcanic combination of Latin passion and Black Irish temperament. His engaging grin and self-deprecating good humor just saved him from being overbearing.

It was that grin that decided Paul in favor of raising the boy himself. He hadn't wanted to. Not at first, anyway.

Upon his early release from El Morro after four horror-filled years, he had returned to New Orleans only to find both Reinette and Quin-Quin missing. After almost three years of searching the backwaters and bayous and isolated villages, even tramping as far as Natchitoches, he had wandered into the leper colony. There, on the swampy little peninsula, he had discovered the little boy living among the disfigured outcasts of the human race. Reinette's son.

For an hour or so, he had been crazed with despondency over finding that Reinette had died seven months earlier. The only two women he had ever loved were dead, Emilie and Reinette. He had sworn in those demented moments that he would never again allow himself to care, that he would turn to the sea, roam the world, do anything but put down roots again.

But the little boy, clinging to his hand and grinning uncertainly with Reinette's black eyes, had changed Paul's mind.

He knew he could make a living for the two of them by trapping and trading, but he had to find a place that was beyond the pale of tyrannical governments. The Indian country, that land between the English colonies and Spanish Louisiana and disputed by both, was Paul's choice.

Only as the alarmingly backward Daniel began to grow, and grow, taking on an extraordinary height, had Paul realized there was more to parenting than feeding and clothing a child and soothing away the periodic nightmares about which the boy refused to talk.

There was also an education to see about. For more than a year, Paul had accumulated the doubloons, livres, greenbacks, and pounds that his trapping earned. Then, with a heavy heart, he had sent the twelve-year-old off to school in Williamsburg, Virginia, which was by then a part of the democracy of the United States of America.

Eight years later, Daniel had read law at William and Mary College, where he had met the likes of Thomas Jefferson and Jefferson's friend, the soldier and frontiersman George Rogers Clark. At twenty-two, the boy—no, the man—had returned, as polished as any continental. Daniel had come home, come home as Paul's son.

"It's my belief," Danial was telling Clark, "that Wilkinson is planning to separate the West from the East and build a separate republic or empire. Probably as a protectorate of Spain."

Clark's brow, heightened by his thinning red hair, furrowed. On his part, the American frontiersman was appearing to work with agents of the French Republic who wanted to seize New Orleans. "We've got to have proof, Daniel. Hearsay won't amount to a hill of beans. Not with Wilkinson's friend Burr holding sway over the Senate. Can you return to New Orleans? Hold up there as long as need be to pin down some kind of evidence as to Wilkinson's treason?"

Daniel drummed his fingers on the table. "I've got a backlog of cases waiting for me in Natchez." He flicked a meaningful glance at Paul and told Clark, "Let me put my affairs in order. It shouldn't take more than a week. Then I'll find an excuse to return to New Orleans."

Natchez's earliest residences were similar to those of the West Indies, with iron balconies and piazzas and the flavor of half-tropical living. The Creoles of Natchez built their houses stuccoed in the manner of the dons and raised high to catch the air and escape the dampness.

Daniel's small house and office, the lower half brick and the upper half timber, was located just off the green-hung plaza near the esplanade. From the balcony, the tawny river could be surveyed through the branches of a magnolia tree, but on most summer evenings a haze floated over the town limiting the view. That evening, when Daniel arrived home, was no different. Here and there the first stars of twilight peeked through the romantic haze.

He was halfway past the little garden's creaking iron gate before he sighted Suzette Guirard on the gallery. He walked on up the brick path to where the bent myrtle tree overhung the gallery steps. She stood at the head of the steps. "You wanted to talk with me?" he asked.

She looked over her shoulder. "I didn't want Mama to overhear. Can we walk in the garden?"

He nodded and offered his arm. There in Natchez she hadn't bothered to wear the *tignon*, and her hair, the color of pecans, was coiled beneath a lacy cap. He said nothing, waiting. At last he spoke. "Monsieur, you have been most generous in bringing Mama and myself into your home."

He grinned. "This speech sounds rehearsed." Despite the gathering dusk, he saw the blush that suffused her cheeks.

"*Oui*," she said softly. "But you haven't explained . . . I don't understand my position here. Mama and I've been here more than three days and you've yet to—" She broke off, and he knew she was too embarrassed to continue.

He took her hand from his forearm and turned to face her, clasping her slender hands in his. He felt the tremor of her hands but didn't release them. "I want nothing from you, mademoiselle. As I told you, it's a debt I owe your mother. You're welcome to stay here as long as you wish. As the Spanish say, '*Mi casa es su casa.*' "

"But Mama says very little. Only that your mother and she were friends."

"I'm afraid I know very little more. Before I leave, I hope to talk further with your mother."

"You are leaving?" Her liquid dark eyes searched his face in bewilderment.

"Only for a couple of weeks. I've business that I need to complete in New Orleans. Now let's go in and talk to your mother."

Suzette's mother was a tall woman who had undoubtedly once been handsome. She still carried herself with a queenly dignity despite an accumulation of fat. Now she was a mammoth woman with whom few men dared to argue. Daniel and Suzette found her in the kitchen at the rear of the house. She was preparing boula boula, a savory dish of crabmeat made with cream and cognac.

Gently removing the wooden spoon from the old woman, Daniel said, "I didn't bring you here to do housework, Quin-Quin. Where is the cook?"

Quin-Quin put her hands on her ample hips. "I sent her packing, Monsieur Daniel. If you think that my daughter and I are going to laze around, you've got another thought coming in that brain of yours."

Daniel rolled his eyes. "Were you as domineering with my mother?"

"Didn't need to be. We understood each other."

He braced his palms on the table and said, "Tell me about my mother. I know so little. She—she wasn't herelf those last few years. She talked more about her childhood years in the swamp—and revenge—than she did about the rest of her life."

"Then you'd better sit and have a drink because this will take a while. You, too, Suzette. Hand me that spoon, son. We might as well eat in here while we're at it. Now, to begin with, your mother's favorite flower was the gardenia. As a child, she'd . . .

Drinks were downed and dinner polished off before Quin-Quin finished her story, closing with the arrests of Aaron, Paul, and Etienne. "And, so, when it became apparent Aaron had left your mother with child—"

"Wait," Daniel said, stunned. "I thought an Irishman was my father."

As Quin-Quin shook her head in denial, her jowls waggled. "Uh-uh, child. Maybe your mother feared for your life and was afraid to ever reveal the truth to you or to anyone. Maybe that's why she gave you the old family name of du Plessis. I don't know what was going on in her head—she was half out of her mind with fear and worry, but I do know that O'Reilly was going to force her to leave New Orleans with him. She fled instead. O'Reilly thought I knew where she went and threatened to have me whipped. I escaped and hid out in Pointe Coupe until the need to support Suzette drove me back to New Orleans. That's all I know, child. I've been waiting for you to tell me the rest."

He finished off the last of the after-dinner brandy in his glass, wondering how he would tell this old woman what she didn't know. He tilted back on his chair's rear legs, his thumbs tucked into the band of his breeches, his long legs stretched beneath the rickety table and said forthrightly, "I can tell you what happened to the three men sent to El Morro, Quin-Quin."

Her deep bosom heaved with a quickly indrawn breath. "You know, son? How?"

He came forward on the chair, his black eyes searching her rounded face for some clue as to just how much he should tell her of what Paul had revealed to him. He settled for the minimum. The full extent of Etienne's suffering could do nothing but bring pain to the old woman.

"After four years, Paul la Ronde was freed from El Morro. He returned to Louisiana to search for my mother, but by the time he stumbled onto the leper colony in the swamps outside of New Orleans, she was already dead. He took me out of the colony with him. He lives not twenty-five miles to the north, on the Trace."

"And Etienne?" The fatty folds of her throat worked up and down.

"Etienne died in prison, Quin-Quin," he said softly. "Of some malady. I doubt if the doctors had been there with their leeches, he would have lived any longer than what he did. His last words, Paul said, were of his love for you."

Tears cascaded from the black woman's lids, and her face folded in on itself. Suzette rose and put her arms about her mother, but Quin-Quin waved her away. "I had prepared myself a long time ago for the worse. I'll be all right." She looked at Daniel. "What about Aaron?"

Aaron. His father. A Jew. Incredible. Daniel shook his head. "Paul didn't know. Aaron was separated from him and Etienne and put in solitary. If he's still alive after all these years, he's no doubt crazy as a loon."

Quin-Quin levered herself up from her chair and said in a tired voice, "The past repeating itself."

"What?" he asked.

"Your grandmother's first husband, Philippe du Plessis, was imprisoned and escaped. By that time he was *tête de bois*, crazy as a loon, as you say. He made his way to Natchitoches and murdered your grandparents. I was there," she finished, her hooded eyes glazed with her reverie. "I can still remember the wild look in his eyes when he came toward me. I fought to keep your mother with me, she was just a toddler. But it's true, Daniel—about madmen having great strength. He took her off into the swamp, and that was the last I saw of her for almost a decade."

"It's late and time we went to bed, Mama." Suzette took her

mother's arm and tenderly led the behemoth woman from the kitchen.

For a long time, Daniel lay awake in his bed, thinking over what had been said that night, about Quin-Quin's remark that the past repeated itself. *Mon Dieu*, he hoped not! The memory of his own past and of the hideously deformed lepers spilled over into his nightmare.

Their arms, deformed appendages with nubs for hands, reached out to embrace him. He ran, first this way and then that, but always another leper rose up from behind a rotted cypress stump or a clump of palmetto branches to grab hold of him. The stench of their putrefying flesh and limbs was so overwhelming that he closed his eyes—and saw his mother's accusing glare.

His lids snapped open. Surrounded, he screamed as the lepers tugged him with them, pulling him under . . . down into the swamp's quagmire.

"Daniel! Daniel!"

He sprang to a sitting position, staring, breathing hard. The sheet clung damply to his naked thighs. His eyes focused on the face in front of him, Suzette's. Her unbound hair sleekly framed her exotic features. Her almond eyes studied him with compassion.

"You were having a nightmare," she said.

He pushed back the mass of thick red hair and drew a steadying breath. "An old one. I'm all right now."

Her fingers tentatively brushed his bare shoulder. "I'm not, Daniel."

He stared up into her shadowed face, trying to see her expression.

"My mother worked hard as a seamstress so that I could receive an education, so that I could wear the finest clothes and one day be presented at a quadroon ball. She wanted security for me. A young Creole gentleman set me up in a little house near the ramparts, but like every quadroon, I believed that my partner would prove an exception to the role of desertion."

"That was why were you at the quadroon ball last week? To form connection?"

She leaned across him, her arms encircling his shoulders, and he could smell her musky perfume. "I was trained to do one thing well, Daniel," she said softly. "To do nothing but give and receive love. Don't waste what I was expressly made for."

He kissed her fluttering lids and tasted her tears. He felt himself growing hard. "I want you, Suzette," he said huskily. "Badly. But can't you see that it would be against the pledge I made my mother? To care for you and Quin-Quin?"

"No, I don't see that at all," she whispered.

CHAPTER

44

FROM BEYOND THE GALLERY THAT
bridged the two houses came the muted rasp of the violin. Governor Carondelet was entertaining that night. The elite of New
Orleans had been invited to listen to chamber music. Daniel was
not among the guests, but then an invitation was not necessary
since his previous visit had gleaned information pertinent to his
present task—such as the location of the governor's office.

His previous visit to New Orleans had also saddled him with
a lovely young quadroon who was tempting his restraint beyond
its limits. Sending Suzette, untouched, back to her room had
required a great deal of moral effort, which he had never considered one of his more sterling qualities. Once his job was finished
there at the governor's house, he meant to rendezvous with the
pretty blond German at the little cottage outside of the ramparts
and appease his combustible lower half.

As he had expected, the gallery doors opening into the office
were locked. A guard patroled the perimeter of the two houses
but, according to Daniel's calculation, was not due to pass by
again for another twenty minutes or so. The crescendoing chamber music muffled the sound of his pistol breaking the window.
He thrust his arm through the jagged aperture and lifted the door
lever. Fingers of light from flambeaux on the gallery spread into

the darkened room and pointed the way to the governor's oaken desk.

When the desk drawer didn't give, he took his pistol butt and, after several attempts, smashed the lock. A quick search of the middle drawer revealed nothing of importance: bills of lading, invitations, official correspondence with the governors of Havana and Mexico City.

Daniel reckoned that he had another ten minutes before the guard made another pass. As a Spanish citizen, if caught he faced the charge of treason and its penalty—death. His fingers rifled more rapidly through a drawer on the left but found only papers of a personal nature such as tailor bills and an order for a shipment of Madeira.

He pried open the bottom drawer. A stack of proclamations, some crossed out here and there with revisions, others already signed. He almost closed the drawer when he noticed the red leather portfolio tucked beneath the proclamations. Removing it, he unwound the gold cord and withdrew several papers. He examined them in the faint light streaming through the doorway. A slow grin pleated either side of his mouth.

The first letter was from Wilkinson to Carondelet, ostensibly discussing a shipment of horses from his plantation in Frankfort, Kentucky. But the governor had already deciphered it. Every fourth word had been underlined. "For the love of God and friendship," read the deciphered portion of Wilkinson's letter, "enjoin great secrecy and caution in all our concerns. Never suffer my name to be written or spoken."

The letter went on to report his apoplectic agitation at being deprived by great treachery or robbery the money due him from Spain.

With it was what appeared to be a ledger sheet. Beside the noted sum of six thousand dollars was written, "Agent 13 . . . Wilkinson."

So much for Wilkinson's claim that his connection with the Spaniards was purely commercial.

The second letter was unfinished. It was addressed to the Spanish minister, Godoy, enthusiastically praising Guilbert Fabreville's offer of financial backing of Wilkinson's plot to take trans-Appalachia from the United States. In exchange, Fabreville wanted a portion of the new empire.

At the sudden increase in light, Daniel whipped around. The plump Carondelet stood in the doorway, a bronze candlestick in his hand. Next to him was a soldier, his musket leveled at Daniel's midsection, and behind the guard Daniel glimpsed the face of Guilbert Fabreville, Marquis de Marchesseau.

"It seems you did indeed hear something, sergeant," Carondelet said. "I commend you for your alertness." He stepped inside the room and put out his hand. In the pumpkin-round face, his eyes burned like a jack-o'-lantern's. "I'll take those letters, monsieur."

Daniel flicked a glance toward his pistol, lying on the desk, and Carondelet said, "Don't try it. At this range, the musket would blow away your stomach. A pity, wouldn't you think Monsieur—?"

"Daniel du Plessis," Daniel said. Certainly the name of du Plessis should elicit some response from Marchesseau.

At the doorway, Marchesseau showed no recognition of the name, and Daniel said, "The name should be familiar to you, Marchesseau. Your great-grandfather acquired by treachery all of the estates and wealth of Philippe du Plessis, beginning with the Maison Bellecour in Blois. Treachery seems to run in your family."

Marchesseau stepped into the room to see Daniel better. Above his imperious nose, his brows were drawn together in frowning puzzlement. "Philippe du Plessis had no children. Who are you, really?"

"His wife was my grandmother." Daniel's hand inched toward the pistol.

The furrow of Marchesseau's brow smoothed. "Ah, yes. As a child, I had heard stories that the woman had escaped to Louisiana." He opened an ivory-lidded box and took out a pinch of snuff. Inhaling it delicately, he slid a look at the baffled governor. "A problem of family rivalry, Baron. I recommend you rid Louisiana once and for all of the du Plessis strain."

The governor clasped his pudgy hands. "That should not be too difficult. A spy . . . yes, execution in the plaza should serve the purpose most befittingly."

Marchesseau snapped closed the snuffbox lid and nodded almost imperceptibly toward the papers Daniel held. "I don't think so. The man might have the opportunity to talk about confidential matters before the appointed hour. I suggest killing him now. After all, the sergeant here would be expected to shoot an intru—"

Daniel flung the papers at the guard and grabbed for the pistol. The musket went off first, and Daniel's world exploded around him.

The darkness of Hades had swallowed him up. The slime and stench of Dante's hell seeped into the naked man's pores. Daniel came to his senses by infinitesimal degrees. Only after a quarter of an hour was he able to ascertain that he lay in the dark, dank hold of a wave-tossed ship, a slaver by its putrid smell. His forehead and right shoulder were burning with fevered pain. Tentatively, he raised his hand to his right side to search out the source of the throbbing ache and discovered he had been clapped in chains.

With the clanking of his chains came his last memory before unconsciousness had claimed him. The thunder of the musket discharging . . . its acrid, burnt-powder odor . . . Guests charging into the room . . . Strange faces looking down at him . . . and a babble of startled voices. No doubt it was their presence that saved him from being finished off by the guard. As it was, it would seem that the governor and Marchesseau had managed to fob him off on one of the smuggler ships, where he had no doubt been left to die.

Thirst raged in his throat. He called out for water. As angry as he was, his voice was little more than a rasp, and no one responded. At some point, he lost consciousness.

Dank water splashing over him brought him around sometime later. He sputtered and opened his crusted lids. A raw-boned, red-faced man in a felt hat leaned over him, a wooden-staved bucket in his hands.

"You were having a nightmare about sores or something, Frenchy." The barrel-chested man nodded at the bucket. "Besides, saltwater's good for your sore." He had a horrendous French accent.

"Who are you?" Daniel managed to ask.

"Brown. Oliver Brown, late of the *Sally B.* out of El Cadrón up on the Arkansas."

An Englishman. No, American now. Feebly, Daniel fixed his

gaze on the red turkey feather tucked into the floppy hat brim.
"And Cock of the Walk, also?" he said, this time in English.

"Why, damme, you're not the bloody French popinjay I took
you for. You frequent Natchez-Under-the-Hill?"

Daniel nodded. His head felt loaded with bricks. "At times."
Though he had to be pretty far gone in drink to visit that hellhole.

One thing he had learned early on in his visits there was to
respect the brawling, brawny, bawdy breed called keelboatmen.
They continuously engaged in the most outlandish kinds of fighting—from gouging out eyes to biting off ears, claiming this kept
them physically tough to keel, pole, bushwhack, or cordelle their
boats on the arduous journey back upriver. The toughest man
aboard each keelboat was called the Cock of the Walk, and to
signify his rank among his peers, he wore a red turkey feather in
his hat.

Daniel eyed the broad-faced, grinning jackanapes, who had a
missing front tooth, and asked, 'What's a keelboatman doing aboard
a slaver?"

Oliver flung aside the bucket and said, "I had the misfortune
to drink myself into a stupor in one of those wharfside taverns.
That was two days ago."

"Two days?" Daniel groaned.

"Two days. You and I, Frenchy, have been impressed by the
dons of this ship. Bound for Spanish Guinea, she is. You ever
seen seaman duty aboard a frigate? Once we reach the high seas,
if you live that long, which from the likes of you, you will, the
two of us will be put to work."

Daniel groaned again and mercifully passed out.

By the end of the first week, he was laboring, shirtless and
barefoot, alongside Oliver Brown and other seamen of all nationalities: coiling hawsers, splicing hemp ropes, scrubbing decks with
holystone, repairing sails.

By the end of the second week, his skin had burned, peeled,
and burned again.

By the end of the third week, he was plotting how he could
escape once Spanish Guinea was reached.

Spanish Guinea was never reached, which was the worse for
Daniel and Oliver.

A storm broke off the coast of West Africa. For days, the
timbers groaned as if they would split asunder. Waves higher

than the masthead washed over the vessel, rolling her from one side to the other. The immense crests lifted her up and plunged her into the troughs. Several hands were lost overboard before the frigate went down.

However, the remainder of the crew were saved, thanks be to Allah—and the Barbary corsairs.

CHAPTER

45

THE RAIS, OR CORSAIR CAPTAIN, sailed into the Turkish-controlled harbor of Algiers with his cargo of Christian captives. As a city of pirates, Algiers was at the same time an arsenal and a port of refuge. From the Mediterranean, it took on the aspect of a fortress bristling with defenses against attacks by sea. Its seaport was protected by two towers and a parapet, crenellated and pierced with embrasures for muskets and cannon. The wall surrounding the town was over forty feet high and almost two miles long, constructed of unbaked brick and protected by a moat over twenty-five feet deep and fifty feet across.

Daniel, Oliver, and the twenty captives were chained with large iron shackles that were bolted and riveted above their ankles and at their wrists. Then, chained at the waist, they were marched under the high arch of one of the five gates, the Customs or Fishery Gate that opened onto the road leading up from the harbor. In the confined space within the walls, white houses were grouped closely together with terraces rising in tiers, their overhangs supported on beams jutting so far out over the narrow streets that they sometimes appeared to join those across the way. Nearly a hundred mosques, octagonal in plan, domed the skyline.

As Daniel and the surviving seamen passed by single file and chained, the Moors and Arabs spit on them and reviled them with cries of "Infidel dog!" and Arabic and Turkish words, which was the official language, words that Daniel didn't understand. He half expected to be beheaded.

Algiers in September was hot and blindingly sunny. He was paralyzed by the dust and dry, roasting heat and fetid odor of the narrow alleys they trod. After having known the green, shaded lushness of Louisiana and Virginia, the open-oven effect of white-hot skies and bleak, lifeless landscape was a whole new world. It shook his confidence, something that had rarely happened before.

Toward the center of the town was the Kasbah. They passed several souks, which were no more than shuttered and roofed alleyways, displaying rush mats, leather workers, basket sellers, and an open-air pottery market. The men were shouting and badgering and jingling their wares.

At last the captives were ushered into the *Berka*, or the slave market, a small open space with three covered ways. Ahead of Daniel, Oliver growled, "I think this is going to be bloody unpleasant."

It was. Before a crowd of purchasers, all of the captives were stripped bare except for Oliver, who insisted on keeping his battered, turkey-feathered hat. Thinking him slightly touched in the head, the captors humored him.

The purchasers looked them over like beasts on market day, inspecting their teeth, their eyes and hands, prodding their flesh. Values varied according to the use or profit the buyer expected to get. Particularly sought after were girls and boys, for whom only one fate awaited; next were persons supposedly of quality, who might be good for ransom.

With his red mane of hair and red beard covering Daniel's face, he attracted the notice of all. His fierce pride burned under their intimate inspection. His teeth clenched, and his eyes stared wide and unseeing. This was the ultimate humiliation, after weeks of beatings by the seamen, that his aristocratic attitude had brought upon him. He faced the dirty Arabs haggling over him with his head erect, his mouth curling in contempt.

"Don't be worrying yourself," Oliver muttered. "We're a fresh piece of merchandise and it isn't in anyone's best interest to damage. They won't be making choirboys of us at least."

"Nor do I wish to be some local bey's play toy," Daniel snapped.

He had heard lurid tales at William and Mary of the perverted sexual mores the Turks practiced.

Surprisingly, he found that no sale took place that day. Instead, after several hours of being inspected, the Christian captives were herded to one of seven bagnios, a sort of state prison, where they were shut up with almost two thousand other prisoners, most of them also Christians—and quite a few of them Americans. Janissaries, dressed in open jackets with sleeves and linen breeches held up by a strip of crimson woolen cloth rolled round the waist and belted with two-handed swords, guarded the place.

The bagnio provided beds slung one above another. Here, the captive's waist chains were removed for the night. Daniel lay in his hammock, listening to the others' stories and their tales of the Ottoman's piracy. He learned that more than thirty thousand captives were imprisoned in the military state of Tripolitania alone.

As he listened, he took heed of all that was said, for he meant somehow to escape. Every piece of information would be invaluable.

The next day, bidding began in earnest on the slaves, or *abids*, who were placed on the auction block. When Daniel's turn came, the bidding soared. A dark, moustached man in a tasseled red fez raised the bid each time with an imperious lift of his forefinger.

"Looks like you're going to be a lapdog to some wealthy merchant," Oliver said behind him. Immediately, the keelboatman was struck across his broad face with a thin whip wielded by the warden-*bashi*. One by one, the other bidders dropped out of the auction until the haughty man in the fez and a proud, fierce-faced man swathed in flowing blue robes were left. Beneath the outer robe, the tip of a curved scimitar could be seen. At a closer look, Daniel was startled to see that the man had blue eyes—and smelled mightily.

The man in the fez frowned as the blue-clad nomad kept pace with the bidding. All at once, the bidding ended, and Daniel found himself with a master, the nomad, who made several other human purchases, including Oliver Brown.

"I like Anglos," the nomad said in heavy English. "They're the hardest workers. They survive the longest."

Daniel and Oliver looked at each other with raised brows; their prospects did not bode well.

That afternoon, Daniel and Oliver and three others, starved-looking Americans from the state of Massachusetts, had their waist chains and leg and hand shackles removed. Then, under the gun, they were marched out of Algiers, this time by the Holy War Gate to the south. This entry was the most important since people came in by it from the countryside and it was linked by a long, mercantile road that led to the other two Turkish military states that composed the Barbary Coast, those of Tunisia and Tripolitania.

Caravans of camels, strings of black slaves, and Bedouin tribesmen herding sheep streamed through the gate. Once outside, beyond the clusters of mud-brick houses and tents that made up the city's suburbs, stretched an infinity of sand.

"Today we rest," said their master, Hassan, addressing them in a lingua franca of Arabic, Spanish, Turkish, French, Italian, and English. "Tomorrow at dawn we fold our tents and begin our journey."

The sand felt pleasurably warm on Daniel's feet, and had it not been for the muskets trained on him, he might have enjoyed the short trek to the tasseled tent shelters. Inside the cool dimness of one tent, the slaves were allowed to rest and eat.

On sandaled feet, a daughter of the desert entered, her blue Berber eyes glowing above the swatch of veil, her hair hidden by an indigo turban. Her sultry eyes, curious, slid covertly over Daniel's flaming red hair before they lowered demurely. A wealth of gold bracelets jingled about her blue-skinned wrists. She carried a tray of sticky sweet tea in earthen cups, fruit, and *couscous* in wooden bowls, which the three Americans fell to consuming by the handfuls.

Oliver eyed the blue-skinned girl, who silently departed, and said, "This may not be such a bad fate after all, Frenchy."

Escape, not women, was the only thing on Daniel's mind. For the first time since being impressed in New Orleans, he slept soundly, chains and all. When he awoke, stars were fading in the chocolate-brown heavens. Hassan pushed back the tent flap. "We make ready to leave, infidels." He dropped a bundle of clothing just inside the opening. "Dress in these."

Almost with relief, the captives shed their filthy breeches for baggy pants; pulled down over their heads the flowing, long blue robes of the desert, called *ghutra*; and donned single-strapped sandals. Wrapping the ten-foot length of cotton cloth about their heads was more difficult.

Outside, the glaring Sahara sun was already rimming the flat horizon, and the Berbers were rolling up their prayer rugs. Daniel was puzzled as to just what kind of work he was to do. He was soon to learn. But first he fell in line with the other captives behind the fierce, camel-mounted warriors and headed out into one of the world's most forbidding landscapes.

The camel riders, perhaps a hundred of them, were proud, tall, Berber warriors. Daniel privately dubbed them the Blue Men because of their skin, dyed by the indigo that rubbed off from their clothing. They prized their blue skin and even claimed descendancy from the Biblical Philistines and, in particular, from Goliath.

Each dromedary was made to stand after it was loaded, then the beasts were roped tail to nose, with many a Berber shout and gargling retort from the camels. The strings moved in no precise order. Sometimes they marched in one line, sometimes in parallel rows, for there was no path that Daniel could ascertain to encourage a single-file procession across the desert. Behind the camels trailed herds of goats and sheep, driven by the women and children and followed by the chained captives.

In the beginning, they walked, he learned, to spare the camels, traveling interminable corridors between dunes. By day, the Berbers were guided by the wind and the blazing sun and the fetch of the dunes. Sometimes later, the camelteers dismounted and spread out their rugs for another of their five daily prayers, and Daniel discovered what part of the captives' task was to be. The *abids*, who had been purchased on earlier trips to Algiers, ran to grab the camels' halters, for no pack camel would go forward unless someone was leading it.

The *abids*' task was to lead the camels on whenever the devout Muslims halted to pray, for the caravan couldn't pause even for a moment until the long halt of the night. If it did, the camels would kneel, a jerking movement that could pitch the loads over their heads.

As the slaves walked, they ate their lunch: millet, pounded, dried goat cheese, and water stored in goatskins, which the desert men rashly drank as if there were no shortage. In all other caravan matters, they were so careful and took so few chances. Yet with water, the most important substance of all, they seemed almost bent on proving their faith. Allah would provide.

Daniel took only one gulp. *"Tonnerre!"* he swore, spitting out the foul water. Oliver quickly followed suit. Looking closely at the fluid in their palms, they saw goat and camel hairs, an ample quantity of mud, and some green vegetation of a sort that was supposed to make the goatskin containers leak-proof.

The march continued at a slow pace beneath the yellow glare, no more than one to two miles an hour. The newer captives were brought forward and distributed down the line of camels. Daniel found that walking in the soft sand was growing more difficult. Finally, everyone was allowed to mount. The nomads watched the newest captives' efforts with amusement.

Frustrated, Daniel jerked his camel's head down by the tuft of its throat. The beast roared and shied away, but Daniel grabbed an ear and hauled himself up. Looking around, he observed from the Berber's expressions that he had gained stature in their eyes. The other captives had more or less managed to mount up also.

But, *merde*, his back began to ache from the constant rocking of the beast, and he wondered if they would never make camp. Occasionally, a breeze would come out of nowhere, though Daniel swore that it had to be spawned from an oven. At last darkness arrived. Still the caravan went onward beneath the glaze of stars. Hassan was guiding on one and pointed to it, saying, "Allah's gift to us."

"D'accord," Daniel replied ruefully, and Hassan grinned.

At last the caravan halted. Hassan instructed the *abids* to put the newer slaves to work. Daniel now learned his primary job on the trek. They were to help unload, as they would unload at every halt—unload completely. Everything. Then they hobbled the camels and gave them the forage packed along for the trek.

That done, Daniel straigthened and looked around him in the dark. Tiny fires made with sticks carried by the camels were springing up. The tents were not erected, which pleased Daniel immensely, for he knew he would be instructed to do that chore, too. Windscreens of pack saddles sheltered the caravaneers. The women broke out, for themselves and the children, low beds of tamarisk wood that collapsed for travel.

Under cover of night, and unchained, he could escape. But where to? He could not navigate as the desert men did. To do so without sufficient water would be suicide if he became lost. Attuned to the swamp, he was out of his element.

An apathy settled over him, and he took only a sip of water. Emulating the Bedouins, he scooped out his bed in the sand and wrapped his blanket around him, ready to seek the sleep of forgetfulness.

The old dream of flesh-denuded lepers returned to keep him company, and he groaned and tossed restlessly in his blanket until a hand on his shoulder brought him upright. By the faint light of the stars, he saw the half-veiled face of the girl who had served him and the other captives the night before. She placed her finger before her lips, then moved off silently into the night.

The caravan was four days into the Sahara. Every day became the same for Daniel. The pitiless sun, the sand, the cloudless sky that never changed.

Monotony. *Swish, swish, swish.* The platter-size camel feet made soft sounds in the sand; the cadence never varied. Sometimes, the Berbers sang on the heat-blistered journey—songs of love, ballads of battle. The *abids* would join in. Daniel and the more recent captives didn't, for using his voice made him thirsty. As the water in the goatskins dwindled, Hassan announced that everyone must ration himself.

"At last he has aided Allah," Daniel said wearily to Oliver that night after the backbreaking unloading.

"Do you know where we are going, Frenchy?"

Daniel thought about the desert girl with the sultry blue eyes. She couldn't be more than fifteen. Misha'il was her name, he had learned. The niece of Hassan indicated by lingua franca and sorrowful eyes that they were going somewhere that had something to do with salt.

When the keelboatman heard that, he emitted a stream of sulphuric oaths and obscenities. Daniel stared at him, and he explained, "The desert salt pits! It kills men, Frenchy! Why do you suppose they have to replace their captives every year?"

Daniel became adept at swathing his head in the blue cloth, just as he became adept at loading and unloading the camels. The Berbers watched him and Oliver closely but casually. They approved of the captives' efforts and laughed at their errors in Ta-

mahaqua, their official language. Daniel got to the point where
he didn't mind the dreadful green camel spit, for no more than
they, who rarely washed, did he keep himself clean in the desert
where water was only for drinking. Now he knew why Hassan
smelled like a camel.

He found some amusement in the antics of the camels. They
looked like old men, kneeling at night, all in a ring around a pile
of fodder, looking down their noses and occasionally nipping a
neighbor or superciliously peering into the desert when a jackal
howled beyond the campfires.

Once a Sahara sandstorm hit and the camels were rapidly unloaded and turned loose to fend for themselves. The camelteers,
blasted by the grit, cowered under blankets behind a fort of
saddles, packs, and mats. The very desert seemed to rise and
move. Nothing could face the abrasive grit without pain.

Another time, when water was low, the Bedouins scooped a
hole in a dry wadi known to hide water. Daniel stored all this
away for reference when the time was ripe for escape.

After the evening meals, the men rested, joked, and drank their
tea, three small cups for each man. The women plaited ropes of
date-palm fiber or made fancy leathercraft such as the open-sided
goatskin tents and bed cushions. And so it was that on their third
week into the journey something awoke him in the night and he
saw a pair of Bedouin boots, stout but soft, in yellow leather and
tooled in red.

The next day, Misha'il's timid glance at the boots he wore
revealed the source of his gift. They fitted him perfectly. When
others developed trail-worn toes, toughened enough by the burning sand to serve as pegs for twisting strands of palm frond in
rope making, Daniel's feet were protected.

At midday, the caravan reached a stagnant pond, which the
camelteers avoided. Daniel was terribly thirsty, but he followed
suit. Hassan pointed to a cliff in the distance, a mere shadow
upon the horizon. "*Fachi*," he said. An oasis, the only one they
would see between Algiers and the salt pits.

Toward sundown, the cliff seemed a little nearer, although now
Daniel could plainly see a notch in the cliff that led to the oasis
beyond. About three hours before midnight, they passed through
the notch in the cliff and slowly descended a long slope. By

midnight, Daniel could see palm trees by the light of a crescent moon.

The thump of wooden pestles grinding millet in wooden mortars came down with the wind. And the sound of dogs. A desert man with a goatskin of water greeted the caravan as it padded softly in from the desert. By the light of the moon, Daniel counted almost five hundred camels that were watering at the oasis that night. As he dismounted, four or five dogs, the gaunt salukis, snapped at his heels viciously. Somehow they knew he was different.

That night Hassan said over tea, "I have heard that in your country men descend to pressing their lips against those of their wives. Is this true?"

Oliver burst out laughing. Grinning, Daniel asked, "Is it true that Berber men descend to exchanging sniffs of the noses with their wives?"

Hassan stared at him a moment, then chuckled. *"Touché."*

From the darkness beyond the fire, Daniel sensed Misha'il's sultry gaze.

After a two-day layover, the caravan departed again. The next water, a well marked by a single scrawny acacia, lay but three days' march away, so only half of the goatskins were filled. Daniel had trouble with Hassan's principal camel because it kept kneeling and refusing to arise without drastic urging.

"When do we reach the salt pits?" Oliver asked one afternoon.

Daniel found himself answering in the Islamic manner. "When Allah so wills."

Squish. Squish. Squish. Finally, the Berbers reached the end of the four-hundred-mile route. Daniel stared, stunned.

Jagged heaps of rubble from abandoned diggings rose between the camels and a meager, palm-shaded oasis. Scattered about the oasis were rough, stone abodes—the workers' shelters. Cadaverous men staggered out to greet the caravan. Some coughed violently, their lungs eaten away by breathing the salt.

This was to be Daniel's future.

The task of removing salt from the pits wasn't difficult to learn, but it was backbreaking under the relentless, baking sun—and deadly monotonous. Daniel could understand why the slaves marooned at the pit seemed almost deranged, moving about with vacant expressions.

A mere five guards, one of them in charge of the other four, stood watch at the oasis with lethal-looking scimitars. But there was nowhere to escape to, and work in the pits was the only diversion offered; the guards rarely had to exert their authority over the slaves.

Two of the twenty-odd slaves had survived there, ten and twelve years apiece. A third one, a Spaniard, had been in captivity for twenty long years but had worked in the salt pits only the last four, having been sold to Hassan after the death of his former master in Algiers. The slave, Ortez, was forty-five but looked sixty-five.

"I came in seventy-five to fight the Algerians with ten thousand men under Count O'Reilly," Ortez said one evening. "The four thousand who died were lucky; the few who returned to Spain with O'Reilly were even luckier. The rest of us . . . ." He shrugged his gaunt shoulders and gnashed the boiled mutton from the bone he held.

"What is it, Frenchy? You don't look so good. Is it the mutton?" asked Oliver.

"My mother was O'Reilly's mistress," he said. Both Oliver and Ortez looked at him as if the sun had driven him out of his head. He grinned drily and added, "At least so goes the story."

Each day, Daniel, along with the rest of the slaves, worked one of three shifts. The first team poured water into the shallow pits to loosen the salt. Another team coaxed the salt chunked from the walls with a flat shovel. Still a third team cast the moist salt into wooden molds.

The dried blocks resembled long-stemmed mushrooms with flat tops. They broke into impossible pieces when they were dropped, which brought down the flat of either of the guards' scimitars on the back of the man unfortunate enough to drop one. Neither Daniel nor Oliver was that careless. But, then, they still possessed the stamina of youth and good health.

All in all, Daniel had to admit that Hassan was a congenial-enough man and realized he could have a more cruel man for a master. Hassan's caravan remained at the site, sheltered by their pitched tents, for about a week while they recuperated, unloaded the dried-food provisions for the slaves, and loaded the forty-pound, rock-hard salt cones bundled in straw matting, six to a camel.

At the campfire on the caravan's last night at the oasis, Hassan beckoned to Daniel, who ate with the newly purchased slaves, to come sit with him. Daniel knew enough of the customs by now to kneel and sit back on his legs with anyone considered of higher rank. Those of equal rank sat cross-legged.

"You are thinking of escaping, Daniel du Plessis of New Orleans," Hassan said formally.

It was a statement not a question, but Daniel replied, "*Oui*," anyway.

"It would be folly. From here our caravan travels south to areas of cattle raising, where there is no salt. To attempt to follow us would only take you farther from the coast and transportation. We will not return to Algiers again until the need to replace slaves demands the trip; that could be as long as a year and a half or two years. For you to try to make the four-hundred-mile journey on your own . . ." The Bedouin shrugged his shoulders expressively.

The will to survive was strong in Daniel, and he didn't let the Bedouin's words deter him from his eventual goal of escape. He swallowed the black bread and said nothing.

At dawn the following morning, he awoke to find the veiled Misha'il bending over him. For a long moment, she stared at his visage, then she bent to nuzzle his nose with hers gently and scampered away before his hands could grasp her slender, bracelet-encircled arms.

He was not to see her again—or another caravan—for almost six months.

During those six months, he twice became glare-blind; Oliver went crazy and Daniel had to punch him to keep him from running off wildly into the empty desert. Most of the slaves paired off with another male as a substitute mate. Neither Daniel nor Oliver got that desperate, but Daniel agonized over what changes would be wrought in him involuntarily over a period of years at that isolated oasis.

Years!

"Don't think about it, Frenchy," Oliver counseled, "or you'll go stark, raving mad like the rest of these Beelzebubs here."

What Daniel did think about was revenge. The beginning of

an overwhelming hatred for the Marchesseau family took seed in
him, and a need for revenge that was greater than that which his
mother had sought. Somehow . . . someday . . .

When Misha'il and Hassan next returned, it was spring. One
of the Americans spotted the caravan first, and when word passed
around, one would have thought their liberator was arriving rather
than their master.

After the campfires were lit that evening, Hassan summoned
Daniel to his tent. Daniel pushed back the tasseled flap and entered. Across from Hassan on a large square divan covered with
sheepskin sat another Bedouin, his *thobe* of the finest white cotton.
From beneath the flowing *gandurah*, held in place by black-ribbed
head ropes, intelligent blue eyes studied him.

The Bedouin stretched out one veined hand, and Daniel pressed
his forehead to the back of the old man's hand. To be disrespectful
could incur one hundred blows on the soles of the feet.

Hassan indicated one of the silken cushions, and Daniel dropped
down on the back of his heels to wait. He had learned patience.

Hassan snapped his fingers for the serving of the tea.

When the Bedouin was ready, Daniel knew the subject at hand
would be broached. Tea was drunk while Hassan inquired politely into the salt operations and Daniel replied respectfully. The
other Bedouin said nothing, only observed.

From there the slightly one-sided conversation progressed in
rather uncustomary form to Daniel's antecedents. Daniel didn't
elaborate, only replied that both his parents were French—his
mother of the du Plessis line, his father one Aaron Simon.

As if satisfied, Hassan's gaze then settled suggestively on Daniel's slightly worn, yellow leather boots. After the traditional third
cup of tea, he said, "You understand now what your future is
here. My brother-in-law wishes to offer you something better."

Daniel raised a brow but remained silent.

"Marriage to his stepdaughter—my niece, Misha'il. I fear she
has taken a liking to you. Wedded to Misha'il, your life would
be appreciably improved."

So that was what this interrogation was all about.

"Ibn Rajhi is a wealthy man," Hassan continued. "You would
not be required to accept the Islamic faith, no more than he has.
But you must give him your word you will not try to escape but
will remain with Misha'il as her husband."

To commit himself for the rest of his life to the nomad's way of living . . . But the alternative was too drastic to dwell on.

On his part, he made only one request, that Oliver be released to him as his manservant. For that one act, he gained the man's everlasting devotion.

It was the Bedouin custom for a new bride to defend her modesty on the first night of marriage. She would fight off her husband as a token of her chastity, and the women of the tribe would listen outside the bridal tent. The sounds of struggle proved her honor, and the struggle might last for quite a while.

But on this night the struggle was brief, indeed, and in no time the women were running out with the bloodstained wedding sheet. They displayed it, as was their custom, to prove that the bride has been a virgin.

The childlike Misha'il might have been a virgin that night, but at her fingertips—and lips—Daniel learned over the years an exquisite art of Eastern lovemaking of which all the mistresses and whores and simpering young ladies of New Orleans, Natchez, and Williamsburg were abysmally ignorant.

CHAPTER

46

DURING DANIEL'S EIGHT-YEAR absence, New Orleans had changed immensely, due, for the most part, to a large fire in 1794, which took place only a few months after Daniel's impressment. The New Orleans of 1802 might belong once more to France, this time under Napoleon's rule, it might possess a French culture, language, and cuisine, but its architecture was totally Spanish as a result of the rebuilding after the fire.

This time, the city had been built to withstand the ravages of wind, weather, and fire—a brick and plaster city, with proud arches of heavy masonry and roofs of tile, reminding Daniel of Algiers. New were the Cabildo and Presbytère that flanked the Gothic-windowed Cathedral of St. Louis with its twin spires. The rebuilt homes were painted with vibrant pastel colors and roofed with fire-resistant tiles. In addition, a few homesteads dotted the wilderness on the bank opposite the teaming city.

As the new city was different, so was the freshly shaven Daniel. At thirty-two, he was a man in all ways. His mettle had been tested; he had survived. He returned to New Orleans, this time, an incredibly wealthy man, thanks to the benevolence of the Sheik Ibn Rajhi. He returned to New Orleans, this time, a bitter man, bent on revenge. Gone was the engaging grin, replaced by an astringent curl of the lips that passed for a smile.

His casual stroll of the streets, now cobbled or layered with crushed oyster shell in most places, was anything but. His idle drinking with Oliver in the taverns and cafés those next two days was a deception. He listened, he watched, he learned. A word too many over a glass of rum or too few in responding to a toast told him much. He was in no hurry. He had acquired the Arab's habit of patient, endless waiting. Over the years, he had had to resort to that blankness of mind with which one got through the damned dead spots of Arab life.

By the time he and Oliver were ready to journey on to Natchez, he was amply informed for what he had in mind: the complete and total destruction of Guilbert Fabreville, Marquis de Marchesseau.

At Natchez, he found the changes even greater. In his absence, Natchez had been ceded by Spain to the United States by the Treaty of San Lorenzo back in 1795.

He was now an American! He even wore his red mane unclubbed and loose about his shoulders in the style set by Thomas Jefferson.

Natchez had been designated the capital of the Mississippi Territory, and with the invention of Whitney's cotton gin, it became the capital of a cotton empire, an El Dorado.

Though three hundred miles upriver, Natchez had become a full-fledged seaport. Its wharves received goods directly from Europe. The planters sold part of their cotton to Paris, Liverpool, and London. Fortunes multiplied or failed with a resounding crash. Through all the gold that gilded Natchez shone a bright flash of tinsel.

By 1802, it had surpassed New Orleans as the most profligate place in the world. Although a stable element strolled Natchez's breeze-swept heights, another element squalored in precarious existence of Under-the-Hill's musty depths.

Natchez's riverfront, and especially Under-the-Hill's Silver Street, was the wickedest locale. At the landing, hundreds of vessels moored in a bobbing, shifting line. Crews cursed each other. At the wharves, mounded with cotton bales, yellow-skinned hawkers told of joys beyond, on Silver Street just below the esplanade.

That mile-long stretch of land was a western boomtown comprised of houses of ill-repute, dance halls, peep shows, rooming houses, gaming halls, barrooms, and even a racetrack. Under-the-Hill possessed an international flavor ranging from Spaniards to Scotsmen, Italians to Greek to Cajuns. Plantation owners with lace cuffs and ruffled shirts sauntered down there for a risqué evening, alongside keelboatmen, card sharks, and thieves. Riots broke out hourly.

Daniel could not have chosen a better spot for his base of operations.

He hadn't really given any thought as to what his reception in Natchez would be. Long ago, he had put Paul, who was like a father to him, from his thoughts. During those years in North Africa, it had seemed to Daniel that the Western world was forever forbidden to him. Longing for the people dear to him only brought depression.

He had tried, really tried, to adapt himself to his new country. He had tried to love the childlike Misha'il, who had been illiterate and indifferent to anything beyond him. Perhaps, in the end, he had come to love her after all. But, after years of being barren, the little Misha'il had conceived. With that conception also came her death warrant—and that of the infant, Daniel's daughter. Maybe it was Misha'il's tiny frame, maybe it was the complications of primitive birthing conditions, whatever it was, mother and child died within hours of each other.

Daniel had wept tears that he thought the desert had dried up. Ibn Rajhi had touched Daniel's heaving shoulders and said simply, *"Insh'allah."* It was the Muslim's answer to almost every question. "As God wills."

The old merchant sheik had apparently felt that it was God's will that Daniel return to his people. As Paul had been a substitute father, so had Ibn Rajhi, and Daniel had come to care deeply for the wise old man. With Ibn Rajhi's blessings and a mass of gold coins and bullion, a settlement made upon Misha'il's death, he had left the desert people.

With Oliver lumbering behind, Daniel strode up to the small house off the esplanade. The yard looked well tended with the creeper vines cut back, and the house's Doric columns were freshly painted. At the door, Daniel paused, and Oliver said, "Well, blimey, hain't you going in?"

No decision was necessary since the door was thrown open, and Suzette stood there, gaping. At thirty-three, she was just as lovely, her figure still sylphlike, although a few faint lines creased the pinnacles of her cheekbones. Daniel parodied Oliver's words. "Well, aren't you going to ask me in?"

"Da—Daniel," she said, disbelief widening her almond-shaped eyes. Then she flung her arms about his neck. "I thought you were dead!" she mumbled against his sun-glazed neck, choked tears breaking her voice.

He set her from him and smiled stringently. "As you can see, I'm not. I'm flesh and blood."

She stared up at him, shook her head marvelingly, and said, "But you're different. Somehow, I can't put my . . . But come and take off your hat and make yourself at home. You must tell me all that has happened to—" She broke off, noticing for the first time the big, raw-boned man standing behind him.

"Oliver Brown," Daniel said, introducing the keelboatman. "Previously of the Arkansas Territory, of late a full-fledged citizen of Algeria, like myself, and now, I perceive, a citizen of the United States."

Her mouth wide open, Suzette sank slowly to the sofa. "I think you're going to need to tell me everything."

Daniel told the story as briefly as possible and kept all emotion from his voice, which wasn't that hard. Only one emotion funneled through his veins now.

Oliver kept silent, twisting his worn felt hat in his hands. The shredded plume dropped sadly. Daniel had tried to buy him a hat in New Orleans, but the keelboatman clung to his old one. He had slicked his longish hair back with bear grease for the occasion.

Daniel suspected that, like himself, Oliver felt uneasy in the comforts of civilization.

"Amazing!" Suzette said when Daniel finished the tale of his odyssey. "If I had a horse pistol, I think I would shoot that vile Marchesseau myself."

"I plan something much more entertaining," he said softly, and she shivered at the tenor of his voice. "Now, you must tell me what has happened here," he said. "How is Paul? Where is your mother? I was surprised to find you still here. Sometimes I imag-

ined you married with a cluster of chicks clinging to your knees."
That was, if he allowed himself to reminisce at all.

Suzette rubbed the fingers of one hand against the others. "Daniel . . . eight years is a long time. Paul and Mama both died,"
she blurted.

A nerve in Daniel's temple twitched. "How?"

"It was in July of ninety-seven. They called the epidemic the
Stranger's Fever because it seemed to come up from Under-the-
Hill. A lot of Natchezians died from it."

"I see." He stood and walked about the small room, his thumbs
hooked into the short, horizontal lines of his pockets. His home-
coming had been centered around seeing Paul again. Now he felt
such a deep, gnawing emptiness.

He turned back to Suzette, who watched him with eyes that
said she still loved him. "How have you managed to get along?"

"When Paul knew he—he wasn't going to live, he summoned
a lawyer. Paul never believed that you were dead. The will provided for the annual taxes on your house and enough left over as
a stipend for me to care for the house until your return. But you
must see Seth Dickerson, Daniel." She blushed, and her lashes
lowered. "He's the lawyer who has been administering the will."

Daniel promptly did just that, while Oliver deserted him to
search out old friends in Under-the-Hill. Daniel found the attorney at South Wall and State streets. Practically the entire block
had once been devoted to a Spanish military commissary. Now
the commissary had been converted to a string of small quarters
occupied by lawyers.

Within the confining quarters of the attorney, Daniel studied
the man on the other side of the desk. Dressed like a dandy.
Blond, curling hair, merry blue eyes, and an open face. But looks
were deceiving. He would listen and then make up his mind about
the lawyer.

"With the American regime, Natchez has become a lawyer's
paradise," the *bon vivant* Dickerson was saying. "The laws, especially in regard to land, are hopelessly confused. Who owns
what? Will the American government follow the Spanish land
grants? And what about the English and French property dealings
prior to that? Men rush about, claiming squatters' rights to land
they've never seen."

Daniel said nothing about having read law himself. "So you are getting rich by merely filing claims." It was a statement.

Dickerson smiled charmingly. "Not as rich as I want to be."

"You have a plan?"

"Since your return to Natchez, have you looked around? Really looked? Did you notice all the unattached males strolling about the hotels, lolling at the bars, surveying Natchez through the smoke of their cigars? Besides being a paradise for lawyers, this is a paradise for professional wife hunters. There are so many eligible planters' daughters with assured incomes for years ahead. . . ."

Dickerson's long, expressive fingers fluffed the ruffles of his stock. "So," he continued, "I have refurbished my wardrobe, gathered letters of introduction, and am ready when the right planter's daughter comes along."

"Then you're pretending to practice law, but your real business is marrying for money?"

Dickerson grinned amiably. "I'd marry if the bride was as ugly as original sin and only had enough breath in her to say yes to the preacher."

Daniel decided then to trust the man.

"About the inheritance Paul la Ronde left you, it's a nice sum of—let me check the last bank draft."

He started to rise, and Daniel said, "That's not important. I want you to represent me in certain dealings. The only stipulation is that my name is not to be revealed in these dealings. You will be handsomely paid for your efforts."

Dickerson sat down again. "This promises to be quite interesting. Do tell me more, Mr.—"

"Daniel will do fine. I want to bankrupt a certain morally corrupt man. Bankrupt him both financially and spiritually."

With a smile of anticipation, the lawyer offered Daniel a cheroot. "You have a plan?" he asked, playing on the same question Daniel had asked of him earlier.

Daniel shook his head to the offer and withdrew instead from his waistcoat pocket a tin of smaller, hand-rolled papers of cut tobacco. "I picked up the habit from a Turkish officer in Algiers. Much milder and more pleasurable than the Spanish cigar."

He lit up the cigarette and exhaled a helix of smoke before

replying to Dickerson's question about a plan. "With a great deal of careful questioning, I've ascertained that this so-called gentleman prizes two things highly. His wealth. And his daughter. His current intentions are to increase the first by marrying the second off advantageously. His daughter is twenty years old and still single, so I doubt she is any great beauty, but she is being courted by the son of an exiled French count with a sugar plantation over in St. Martinville."

Dickerson shook his head disparagingly and clicked his tongue. "The nobleman's no doubt an impoverished and unscrupulous fortune hunter."

"That is one observation you may be sure is erroneous. Fabreville, I am certain, has had the count thoroughly investigated, beginning a hundred years back at the least."

"Guilbert Fabreville? The Marquis of Marchesseau?" Dickerson whistled softly. "You've picked on one of New Orleans's most influential men—second only to the Spanish governor, Salcedo, who administers the province for France. Why, Daniel, Marchesseau's considered above reproach. Salcedo relies on the man's advice heavily. You've got your work cut out for you if you're going to bring Marchesseau tumbling down."

"No, you're going to bring Marchesseau tumbling down for me. I'm going to tumble his precious investment, Gabrielle Fabreville."

CHAPTER

47

Creole supremacy was threatened as New Orleans grew beyond its French-held stronghold of the Vieux Carré, or old square. The main artery, rue de Royale, retained its character—the Old World ambiance of banks, exchanges, and cafés, interspersed with elegant residences. Rue de Bourbon had changed radically from a street of pitiful shanties to an elite avenue of fine homes. The resplendent shops on the rue de Chartres had moved to a street known as Canal.

Here the Yankee invasion had begun. Several American exporters and importers, sugar and cotton brokers, were permitted by the French to do business in the city and had begun to build their own suburb on the other side of Canal Street.

The Yankees might have invaded the mercantile system of New Orleans, but those crude, pushy interlopers were ostracized from its Creole social hierarchy. Americans were synonymous with "barbarians." Creoles still equated Americans with the coarse and revolting Kaintocks, who boasted of being half-alligator, half-horse.

A brave few of the American merchant princes sometimes risked Creole wrath by secretly attending the fancy costumed *bals masqués*, which had been forbidden under the Spanish regime. Usually, the Creoles were aware of this subterfuge but pretended

ignorance. The Yankee presence just added to the titillation of
the masked ball.

The tall man with the flaming red hair had to be an American,
though his French was impeccable. There was, however, the
slightest hint of an intriguing accent. More than one Creole maiden
had cast flirtatious glances in his direction and asked her partners
if they recognized the eyes that glittered from behind the red
domino.

The masquerader's identity was a mystery.

The intruder was difficult not to notice, and Gabrielle Fabreville also wondered, for just a brief moment, who he might be;
she knew everyone. And everyone knew her, the daughter of the
wealthiest man in Louisiana.

That night, she chose to dress in the daring Greek classical
style that the *ancien régime* had found shockingly indecent. Perhaps
she did so out of ennui, to shake the pretentious Creoles from
their smugness.

She wore her hair swept up from her face and neck by an
ostrich-plume bandeau and secured in a cluster of long ringlets.
From below the daring, square décolletage of her alabaster bosom
draped a soft, semitransparent gown of bottle-green muslin over
a pair of light green pantaloons tied at the ankle with a black
twist. An Amazon of a woman, she could only be thankful that
the fashion in footwear was flat slippers with ribbon ties.

From behind her gold, ruffled mask, she stared at the interloper,
perplexed as to his identity; then, just as quickly, she dismissed
the puzzle and devoted her attention to her current partner: a
sweet, attentive young man with the perfect profile of an Adonis.
A bore. And her father's choicest candidate for her husband.

"Mademoiselle, you have not heard a word I've said," chastened
Robert de Bourgogne.

She looked into his handsome face, wondering what was wrong
with her that she felt no particular excitement in the presence of
the men who courted her. The problem was that she had everything: adulation, wealth, position, and arresting features that people mistakenly called beautiful. However, she felt these so-called
striking looks were decidedly of an intellectual cast. "I'm sorry,
you were saying?"

Could she suffer the young man through the rest of the evening, much less the rest of her life? Her father would no doubt despair and then rant and rage if she turned down Robert's proposal, but it was, after all, her father's fault.

His lack of attention to her, while in pursuit of wealth, had fostered an almost masculine independence in her that her suitors found disconcerting. Since she had never known love, love did not exist for her. If her mother had lived, perhaps she could have made her conform to the acceptable standards of feminine behavior.

Lately, though, Gabrielle felt the prickling of the long neglected child in her, a shy, little girl who wanted to be taken care of, who craved some vaguely seen but all-powerful man on whom she could depend. She snorted at her own absurdity, then sighed, thinking that sooner or later she should settle on a husband and perform the duty expected of a woman by bearing children.

Careful that no one should see, Robert captured her hand. His soulful eyes searched her face for a clue to her feelings. "I said that I would like to call on your father tomorrow. Will he be at home?"

Relieved, she answered honestly, "No, we're spending the weekend at Maison Bellecour. But you may call upon our return." Three whole days to postpone what seemed inevitable.

When she would have withdrawn her hand, he said, "Mademoiselle, surely you are aware of my deep feelings for you. Thoughts of you are constantly in my mind!"

She made a little movement of impatience. She had awakened an emotion that she herself did not understand in certain men. She stared at him without a trace of self-consciousness. "I'm certain you will find other things to think about before twenty-four hours have passed."

He looked miserable. "Your reputation for complete indifference to admiration is—"

"May I have this dance, mademoiselle?"

Gabrielle glanced over Robert's shoulder at the taller man. The man with the vibrant red hair. Behind the crimson domino, his eyes burned cruelly like the black fires of hell. What bravado he had in approaching her.

Robert's unavoidable ardor tempted her to dance with the crass interloper, but she would just be exchanging the inconvenience of one male for another. At least she knew Robert and liked him well enough. With a dismissive smile, she said, "I'm afraid not, monsieur."

She offered no excuse, such as not having been formally introduced or being weary or having promised that dance on her card to another. Pampered by a retinue of old and familiar servants, she was unaccustomed to compromise even for the sake of propriety.

She expected the polite but disappointed response of "My misfortune, but perhaps later." Instead, the man said nothing. Below the domino, the strongly defined lips curved in a feral smile that chilled her. He merely bowed and departed.

She shrugged her broad shoulders and turned her attention back to Robert, but the stranger continued to pique her interest, even after she went to bed that night . . . so much so that she awoke in the deep of the night, with his haunting, masked face shimmering before her wide, staring eyes. An after-effect of a dream and nothing more. The gallery doors of her bedroom were open to the cooling breezes off Lake Pontchartrain . . . doors she had thought she had closed before retiring.

She shook her head, trying to clear it of sleep cobwebs. She was not the kind of female who let her imagination run rampant. Determined to go back to sleep, she lay down again, but her sleep was fitful.

The next morning, she felt lethargic. She and her father were to desert the city later that morning for the pastoral interlude of the family plantation. She barely conversed with him as they traveled in the stuffy carriage. For his part, he was caught up in reading *Le Moniteur de la Louisiane*.

At one point, though, he looked up and said, "You enjoyed yourself at the ball last night?"

She knew what was coming. The pressure to marry. "It was pleasant enough."

"Young Robert de Bourgogne is not a bad catch."

She met her father's questioning gaze with cool gray eyes that were unusually clear and steady. "I have no interest in him, Father, and have discouraged his courtship."

"You are too obstinate for your own good, Gabrielle," he warned furiously.

The determined jut of her chin matched his. "You have made

me what I am—obstinate. Or should I say your absences have made me what I am?"

"I will talk to young Burgogne," he snapped, "and try to repair the damage you have done."

She shrugged and transferred her attention to the passing jungle landscape outside the coach window, but her thoughts remained with the heated discussion that had just ended. The fettered existence of marriage, even a marriage based on mutual consideration and forbearance, was repugnant to her. She was revolted by the idea of being bound irrevocably to the will of a man who would have the right to demand obedience.

The Marchesseau indigo plantation and sugar fields were reached by the River Road that led away from the city. The house, really more a palace, stood at the end of a broad avenue of giant oaks and cypresses that dripped Spanish moss.

Maison Bellecour, modeled after the Marchesseau château in Blois, had taken Guilbert Fabreville fully eight years to re-create, and the building was still in process. Bathed in golden sunlight under the powder-blue sky, the house was breathtaking. The three-story front was a ninety-eight-foot expanse of quarried stone and marble imported from Italy, with a single-story wing extending on either side.

The only alteration to the exterior plan was an open gallery, supported by massive white pillars in the Greek Revival style, which encircled the immense house.

Inside, the original guardroom with its cavernous fireplace was altered in the plans into a baroque Grand Salon; the cloister was glassed in as a sculpture gallery; and the astonishingly large apartments on the second floor were divided into cozy guest rooms sumptuously decorated for the visitors Marchesseau forever entertained, mostly politicians or wealthy planters and their wives. What had been a chapel in the Blois garden was converted in the house plans into a separate suite, where Governor Salcedo would be staying that weekend.

Later that afternoon, when the guests had retired to the cool, shadowed rooms for an hour or so of *sieste*, Gabrielle dressed to go riding in an expensive riding habit of black velvet with emerald-green lapels and matching hat and veil. Matilda, the plump housekeeper, lectured her with a stern German accent. "Your beauty rest is important."

Gabrielle's scornful mouth and firm chin showed plainly her opinion of one's concern for beauty; she thought of her supposed beauty no more than she did her wealth.

Matilda warned, "Mind you, you're young. But wait. Time will tell!"

Lovingly, Gabrielle kissed her ruddy, ample cheek and strode out to the stables, her crop snapping against her knee. A groom helped her to mount one of her father's cherished horses brought downriver from Kentucky. Old Pierre, married and a grandfather, had replaced the previous groom, a lusty young man of twenty. When her father had witnessed her resounding slap on the amorous groom's cheek and learned the reason, he had had the young man horsewhipped and sent packing.

She set out along the river road, with Pierre in attendance. Utterly fearless, she would rather have ridden alone, but her father had ordered that she take an escort on her rides, for it was neither safe nor decorous for a young woman to travel the river road alone.

Soon, though, with a reckless, little laugh, she urged her mount into a freedom-inspired gallop. The indolence of Creole life stifled her. Coffee or mint juleps brought to their apartment in the morning, then breakfast on the gallery. Afterward, morning visits or lounging until dinner at two; then rich Creole dishes, followed by the *sieste*. Before sunset, a tea table set in the garden and a stroll until bedtime. The most activity a Creole woman might attempt was a game of croquet or whist. One tended to quit thinking and start dreaming.

"Mademoiselle," Pierre called, and nodded warningly to the horseman cantering toward her. In her preoccupation, she had failed to see him in the dappled shadows of the overhanging branches. She slowed her Thoroughbred to a walk, and Pierre moved up alongside her as a precaution.

As she drew nearer, there was no mistaking the red-haired devil. It couldn't be coincidence that she should encounter him twice within twenty-four hours. At least she would give him credit for being persistent.

She felt no fear, and the lack of it had nothing to do with the small pistol she carried in her boot. Those who had lived through the Reign of Terror during the worst part of the French Revolution were either left cowed or made fearless. She supposed she was the latter. She really didn't give the past much thought if she could help it.

She decided to ignore the stranger, no matter how courteous he might be this time.

He reined in his magnificent white Arabian a dozen or so yards ahead of her. As she approached, she had an irresistible urge to look at his face, unconcealed now by the domino, but she lifted her chin in her most arrogant manner and fixed her eyes directly ahead. Astonishingly, he said not one word when she drew abreast of him, but she felt his black-smoked eyes raking her, assessing her, with a sinister air of deliberation.

She was accustomed to being stared at. She was tall, big-boned, with the square, severe face of her father and the same temperamental mouth that did not brook interference—though her father had tried, more often in her childhood years than of late. Since she could do nothing about her hideously orange hair, the bane of her youth, she no longer tried to hide it but rather flaunted it. Surprisingly, had she been prone to vanity, her shockingly brilliant hair would have been a major source.

Unable to stop herself, she risked looking behind her. All she saw was the man's broad back as he cantered on. Perhaps their meeting *was* just coincidence. The rude boor!

That evening, her father entertained their guests in the Petit Salon, which had floor-to-ceiling windows that opened to give couples access to the balcony and a white floor of painted maple, that was easier to dance on than cypress.

As was customary, she presided as his hostess over the small dinner. Feeling utterly bored and restless, she sat at one end of the long table, which was topped with porphyry. Even there in the countryside, the redheaded stranger was on the tip of several female tongues.

"He must be one of those brash Yankees," said a young matron two seats down from her. The woman's tone was disparaging, but her eyes glittered with the avaricious curiosity of a discontented wife. "But, *ciel*, what red hair—and black eyes! They fairly make one shiver."

At the other end of the table, Guilbert Fabreville inquired as to the name of the man being discussed. Naturally, no one knew, which made the man an even greater enigma. Marchesseau's heavy brows met over his arrogant nose in a frown of puzzlement, then just as rapidly eased as the topic turned to the undeclared war between France and the United States.

When the evening was at last over, Gabrielle retired to her bedroom. Her fitful sleep of the night before should have left her yawning and heavy-lidded; in fact, she did fall asleep without any problem, as was normal for her. But just as it happened the previous night, she awoke with the lingering sensation of someone in the room with her.

For a long moment, she stared at the dark shadows of her furniture. Her gaze moved past the bedposts, hand-carved in pineapple and acanthus-leaf pattern, over the English rosewood chest, a porcelain lamp, the mahogany *duchesse*, a silver vase, the dropleaf card table. Nothing looked amiss.

Impatient with her feminine flights of fancy, she flung aside the mosquito *baire* and strolled across the hexagonal terra-cotta tile floor to the gallery doors, closed this time.

Outside, the magnolias scented the night air with a heavy, sweet fragrance. Clad in a thin, silky dishabille, she padded across the gallery to lean her palms on the balustrade and to search the maze of the box garden, pruned cypresses, and banana trees just beyond the low, ocher wall for the phantom that had disturbed her sleep. Satisfied—and laughing silently at her foolishness—she tossed her thick braid back over her shoulder and swung around to return to bed.

The handkerchief that gagged her mouth . . . the burlap bag that enveloped her body . . . were no hallucinations.

CHAPTER

48

Time was a blur of sensations for Gabrielle, but always there was the predominant sensation of traveling. Carried at first, then doubled over the back of a horse. When the horse halted, she could hear it blowing wind puffs. Later, she detected the *swish, swish* of oars against water.

She was determined not to panic, for that would only hamper her escape, but the gag in her mouth, the smothering effect of the scratchy burlap bag, the ropes abrading her wrists and ankles tried even her noted levelheadedness.

She tried to gauge in what direction the boat—a canoe, she judged, by the width of the ribs—was presently traveling. She knew it negotiated a bayou, for there was no sense of current. In her mind's eye, she pictured several bayous that meandered through the lush land around the plantations. The sudden chirping of birds that broke the night's stillness told her dawn had arrived. A time lapse, then, of perhaps three or four hours. Surely a destination would be reached soon.

Such was not the case, for within the hour she felt the sudden buffeting of the canoe and knew that it had swung into a river and was moving against the current. A big river by the sound of the slapping water. The Mississippi.

This confirmed her suspicion that she had been kidnapped for ransom; she was being taken far from the reach of her father's influence.

All day, she and her abductor traveled. Only a little air reached her where the burlap bag gaped about her knees so that between the lack of oxygen and her growing hunger she felt weak and unable to think coherently. She squirmed in furious protest but garnered no reaction from her abductor. Who was he? Whoever had toted her had to be big.

A fleeting thought that he might be the redheaded stranger who had been watching her was vanquished when the canoe shifted with a change of weight, was dragged ashore, and she was lifted from the prow to be deposited on her feet on solid ground.

The burlap bag was removed. In the twilight of evening, she looked into a disreputable, broad-boned face shadowed with beard stubble. He wore a shirt and trousers of canvas that were black, greasy, and tattered. The turkey feather in his hat proclaimed, she knew, even with her limited knowledge of the waterfront, that this ferocious-looking man was one of those legendary keel-boatmen that a decent person avoided at all costs.

Above the gag, her eyes glared at him. She resented mightily being viewed in her revealing nightclothes. She gave no thought to her personal safety, for it was obviously money he was interested in and not the other. That could be had from any dockside doxy.

His leering gaze ran up and down her, and he nodded approvingly. "Damme, if ol' Frenchy doesn't have himself a bargain."

English! She made muffled grunts behind the gag, and he caught her meaning.

"You can yell all you want once I get this off," he said, this time in French, and came around behind her to work clumsily at the knots. "No one to hear you but the Houmas, and they'd be a lot less friendly toward you than I would. So don't bother to yell out your lungs."

She swallowed the fuzzy taste on her tongue and inhaled the sweet, fresh air, then said in English, "I have no intention of wasting my breath on screaming. I only want to reach some sort of negotiation with you so we can get this ridiculous farce over with. How much money are you asking from my father?"

"Money? You best speak to Frenchy, miss."

"Frenchy?"

"All in good time. Now if you'll just settle down on that log, I'll drag out something to eat."

She wasn't planning on waiting around long enough to speak to Frenchy.

The rapscallion trotted back to the canoe and returned with bedrolls and a saddlebag, no less. From one of its pouches, he produced a long cloak with a hood. Astonished, she let him fasten it about her shoulders. A cloak, to cover her near nudity, had been thought of beforehand. The realization chilled her. What had happened . . . It had all been carefully planned out.

She said, "My hands, won't you release them so I can eat?"

He grinned in a reassuring fashion, displaying a missing tooth. "Sorry about that, miss, but I got to feed you. Won't be but a matter of a couple of days, and you can feed yourself."

Did that mean she'd go free in a couple of days? And who *was* Frenchy?

From another pouch, the oaf produced a long, crusty loaf of bread, cold meat, and cheese. All cut beforehand into bite-size pieces. This was just one more example of how well planned the abduction was. Her previous hunger evaporated, but she forced herself to eat the pieces he plopped into her mouth with hands that weren't all that clean. She was going to need all the strength she could summon to escape, when the moment was right.

After they had eaten, he laid out two bedrolls. He stretched out on one and immediately started to snore. She lay silent in hers, trying to make sense of what had happened. With her wrists bound behind her, she was uncomfortable, but she knew it was useless to ask him to untie her. Just after dawn, she awoke to find him moving about the clearing, repacking the canoe.

When he came back up the gentle slope, she said, "I will see that you are rewarded with a princely sum if you'll just return me to my home. I've done nothing to hurt you. All I want to do is go back home."

A pitying look crept into his eyes. "I'm sorry, miss. That's not for me to do. That's between you and Frenchy."

Frenchy again. Her shoulders sagged.

When the keelboatman picked up the burlap bag, she said, "Please, not again. It's not necessary, is it?"

He looked at the bag and then back at her. "Not really, miss."

After they were on their way once more, she asked of him, "Where are you taking me?"

He swung the oar from side to side in great whacks. "Natchez," he said, and spit a stream of tobacco over the side.

She sat silently, ruminating on that piece of information. Surely she'd find someone to help her there. Buoyed by that hope, she was able to endure the discomfort of being bound through the rest of that day and the ones following.

Beneath the onslaught of the July sun, her skin began to blister. Beneath the cloak, her satin nightrail clung to her perspiring body. He released her rope bonds only when she made it known, as discreetly as she could manage, that she needed to relieve herself. Even then he remained within hearing distance, so that at the slightest crunch of leaves underfoot she could expect him to appear.

Because of the sandbars, they didn't travel at night. It was during those nights that she felt another presence beside the keelboatman's, perhaps that of watching Indians, which made sleep impossible for her.

Occasionally, they passed other boats, most of them flatboats traveling downriver. She thought about shouting for help, but from the looks of the occupants, she judged she might be landing herself in a worse mess.

Toward dusk of the fourth day, he put into Natchez-Under-the-Hill. Something in her expression must have given her away.

"Don't be getting thoughts of running for it, miss, 'cause there are men in Under-the-Hill who'll think nothing of splitting your throat ear to ear. Natchez proper isn't much better; the folks there just pretend at propriety. If a plantation madame or mademoiselle proves too ladylike, there's always good-humored girls of yellow or even white skin in shacks in Under-the-Hill. Why the man up at Connelly's Tavern is a regular wife beater, but doesn't nobody say a word. 'Round here, witnesses know better than to remember what they seen."

One glance at the teaming quarter and she knew she had better do as he advised. Weatherbeaten shacks occupied every square foot of ground, extending to the water's edge, where they perched on stilts. Chickens, pigs, dogs, and dirty children prowled the littered streets.

Tawdrily clad and highly rouged girls leaned out of second-story windows to wave enticingly at the men passing below. From the nearest dive came the tinkle of a tinny spinet, the high laughter of women, and the clatter of dicing games.

Indians reeled naked on the broken and half-sunken boardwalks from too much firewater. Boatmen, tired of long isolation on the water and bursting for action, shouldered their way into the barrelhouses. Obscenities that she heard as she passed by were not reassuring, and she drew even closer to the big keelboatman.

Through the crowd sped carts and drays. Lines of cattle stumbled under the drover's whip, and files of slaves, heads covered with bandannas, trudged alongside her and the keelboatman as they made their way up the narrow ledge of roadway to the hill above. Even though the sun had set, the place was still hot and stinking and congested. Her nose wrinkled at the combined odor of squalor, musk, and decay.

When she reached the top of the bluff, she saw a contradiction of Under-the-Hill. A wide esplanade bordered by fragrant oleander . . . the soft, dappled shadows of twilight . . . the gentle breeze that stirred the damp tendrils clinging to her temples and cheekbones.

A few people strolled along the esplanade. An open carriage clattered by with a woman occupant. Beside it, a man rode *à cheval*. Dare she hail the passersby for help?

Reading her thoughts, the keelboatman said gruffly, "They would think you half mad." Suggestively, his gaze took in the hem of her nightrail trailing the ground. Who, indeed, would believe her?

Weary beyond comprehension, disoriented, she wanted only to end the nightmare of a journey and return to her former life, a life she had thought unbearably complacent.

Soon, soon, she told herself, and straightened her shoulders. Soon she would meet this Frenchy with whom she could strike a bargain.

Just a block over from the esplanade, the keelboatman turned into a wrought-iron-fenced yard. Set back behind magnolias and oaks was a small, two-story house, the second and main floor reached by flagstone steps to its gallery. The house of half-brick, half-timber looked decent enough and lent her hope, as did the woman who greeted her at the door, a woman with saffron skin and a lovely, serene face—except for the eyes. She saw there the same pitying look she had glimpsed in the keelboatman's glance.

"I know you're exhausted," the woman said kindly as if the appearance of a strange woman at the door were not something out of the ordinary. "I've prepared a room for you downstairs."

Rage coursed through Gabrielle that she should so meekly accept such a fate. Her eyes flashed an unholy gray. "I do not wish to be shown to a room you've prepared. I wish to be returned to my father."

The woman looked uncertainly at the keelboatman, then said, "You will be in time, I am sure. But, still, you would need to rest before making another such journey. Please, come with me. Wouldn't you like a glass of cool lemonade?"

The woman's logic was irrefutable. Bone-tired, Gabrielle had to acknowledge that she didn't have the strength to attempt an escape. She would rest, negotiate with this Frenchy, and return home as soon as possible.

Reluctantly, and against her better judgment, she followed the woman down a narrow staircase. Once she rested, she knew she would be able to think more clearly and to formulate some plan. The room on the lower floor was acceptably furnished with a white chenille spread thrown over the tented bed, and a hand-woven rug covered the brick floor. Yet Gabrielle wasn't reassured. After the woman departed, leaving the door open, she glanced about her suspiciously. The room, like most rooms on lower floors, had been built expressly for slaves. No windows lightened the room, only the bronze candlestick. The door was made to be barred from the outside.

"No," she murmured to herself, "no, I'm not staying here a minute longer."

"Yes, you are, *mon coeur*."

CHAPTER

49

THE MAN WITH THE EXTRAVA-
gant red hair blocked the doorway. He wore riding breeches of
doeskin and a loosely bloused white cambric shirt. His tall and
powerful frame, in spite of its relaxed posture, held a leashed
strength.

"You!" Gabrielle spat.

Leisurely, he sauntered toward her. His spurs clanked softly,
dangerously. What looked to be a short cheroot, half-smoked,
dangled between his thumb and forefinger. She held her ground,
refusing to quail, for she sensed somehow that he wanted her to
cower, to grovel, to weep and beg.

"What do you want of me? I can assure you that if one hair
on my head is harmed, my father will not only refuse to pay a
ransom but will see to it that you never see the light of day again."

"He already tried just that—and failed."

She tensed. Up close she saw his face fully: the warrior's scimitar cheekbones and bladed nose, the slash of dark brows over
black, black eyes. His sensuous lips were rendered insensate by
the ruthless curl of their ends.

"I don't understand what you're talking about. You didn't answer me. What do you want?"

He reached out and fingered the fat braid that lay over her

heaving breast. Until four days ago, no man had dared lay a finger on her. Her teeth clenched at the outrage.

"I think you know what I want." He raised his mocking stare to meet hers, his eyes challenging. Her breath drew in sharply, and he taunted, "Don't tell me you're about to swoon." And then he added with an enigmatic smile, "Perhaps it would be better if you did."

"I don't swoon, Monsieur . . . ?"

"Daniel du Plessis. I will make certain you remember my name."

A shiver crawled up her spine. "Neither am I intimidated by bullies."

He unbuttoned the top frog of her cardinal. "Oh, I don't plan to intimidate you but to initiate you."

He pushed the cloak from her wide shoulders, and it slithered to the floor. Her square chin shot up, and her mouth opened to protest indignantly. But she saw that he watched her, sensed that he would take pleasure in just such a response.

Repressing the urge to cross her arms protectively before her chest, she met a raking gaze that appraised her sexually and said, "I can promise you more money than you'd know what to do with if you'll only let me go."

"When I'm finished with you—and in my own good time—I'll release you."

The tiny hairs on her nape prickled. Then, before she could react, his hand clutched the lace-frilled neckline of her negligee and ripped it down the center all the way to the hem. A scream choked in her throat. She lunged to one side of him. His arm was quicker. Its steely strength curled about her waist and yanked her against him. She was taller than most women, but he hoisted her effortlessly so that her bare feet flailed in the air.

He looked down into her wide eyes glazed with shock and shook his head wonderingly. "You're not the homely little girl I remembered." That frightened her as nothing else yet had. "This will be much more pleasurable than I could have anticipated those long, empty eight years."

She didn't care what he had to say. Her lips trembled. "Please . . ."

Whatever she had been about to tell him was forgotten as he literally dropped her on the bed. She scrambled to her knees and faced him with flashing eyes and hissing breath.

"Have it your way. It shall be by force then."

He drew the white cambric shirt over his head. Next he removed first one top boot, then the other. Watching her—almost,
she thought, as a tabby does a dormouse—he began to unbutton
the flap of his breeches. She felt the flush of heat rising from the
pools of her collarbone up the column of her neck, and immediately lowered her lids. Her eyes settled on the pillow. With all
the force she could muster, she hurled it at his chest and sprang
like a coiled snake from the bed.

His hand moved so quickly that he had her by each wrist before
she could dash past him. No compassion or pity glowed in his
eyes. "What kind of rock did you climb out from under?" she
hissed.

"A desert of rocks. Salt rocks."

"You're demented!"

He didn't bother to reply to her charge. With merely the blunt
tips of his fingers, he nudged her so that she toppled backward
onto the bed. Her ripped gown fell to either side, exposing the
white globes of her breasts. Frantically, she tried to shield herself
from his ravaging gaze, which was her undoing.

In that moment that she averted her eyes, he fell upon her.
She was astonished by his weight—and fully realized for the first
time the position of submission imposed upon a woman in this
most intimate of acts. Beneath him, she kicked and scratched and
hit out, refusing to cry out loud even in those moments of shame,
but he easily anchored both her wrists above her head with the
iron-strong fingers of one hand.

"This is for that moment I stood on the auction block and was
sold like a piece of merchandise," he whispered in her ear—then
plunged brutally into her.

Her head jerked at the punishment inflicted on her. A whimper
bubbled up from her throat. When he plunged again, this time
rending her inner tissue of flesh, her hips arched with the sheer
pain of his thrust.

She lay there, unresisting, as he violated her, his powerful body
slamming into her time after time with a fury that crackled the
air about them. For once she wished she were as other women
and prayed for unconsciousness. At last, when his seed soiled her
and he lay inert atop her, his head lifted, and his eyes watched
her through the slits of his lids.

If he expected her to weep, he was to be disappointed. Fire crackled in her head. Her hand jerked loose from his lax grasp and swung against his bricklike jaw with a mighty impact, of which few females were capable.

His head snapped to the side. A blistering red spot welted where her palm had struck his cheek. She gloated at the stunned look in his eyes. Let him strike back; she welcomed combat. To fight would be good. It would be an outlet for the shame that burned deeply in her soul.

"So the dog can sit up and walk," he said, his eyes glittering with fury.

He rolled from her, and she averted her eyes from the jutting shaft that was streaked with her maiden's blood. He crossed the room to where his clothing mounded the floor. Covering her exposed body with crossed arms, she watched him warily, tensely. Never had she seen a naked man, and she couldn't help but stare. Grudgingly, she conceded to the toasted perfection of his body. Only his small, rounded buttocks, straited with muscles, were white; dark whorls of hair shaded the hard-columned legs.

Mon Dieu, but she hated him, hated his smell that he had imbued her with.

When he turned to face her, she gasped. He held a curved knife in his hand. She snapped upright feeling the pain sharp between her thighs. She shrank against the headboard, and he laughed lowly. "Oh, I'm not going to kill you. That would put a short end to my vengeance."

His free hand jerked cruelly at the braid that fell over one naked breast. "Don't move," he ordered with galling insouciance, "or the blade might mar your lovely skin."

He hacked at her plait of orange-red hair with the knife. As her braid was shorn, wisps of her remaining hair curled about her neck and ears and temples. Dumbly, all she could think of was the proverb that pride goeth before a fall.

She twisted her face up to his. "Why," she cried, "why are you doing this to me? What have I ever done to you?"

"It's what the house of Marchesseau has done to the du Plessises for over a hundred years," he said, not bothering to keep the hatred and bitterness from his voice.

"You *are* mad!" she said.

"Yes, but it took eight years to carry out my madness, eight years that I spent working in the salt pits of the Sahara—all because of your father."

She tried to twist around to see the American's face. "What does my father have to do with this?"

"Turn around." He jerked her head with the vicious slashing of her hair.

She sat stiffly, feeling bursting knots of rage curling through her belly until she thought she would throw up with loathing.

After he severed her yard-long braid, he said, "When your father receives this gift from his distant kinsman, he'll know the reason for my madness. Ask him."

"I'm asking you! Just what has my father done to you to warrant this—what you've done to me?"

"I found proof that your father was involved in a conspiracy against the United States, and he tried to have me killed. When that didn't work, he had me impressed on a Spanish slaver."

"You call it a conspiracy; my father might call it patriotism."

"Your father has no feelings of loyalty to anyone but himself!"

He paused again before his mound of clothing. "Please consider yourself my guest, *mon coeur*, until I decide to return you to your father. As my mistress, you have the freedom of the house, and Suzette is at your service."

"As your mistress?" she spat, disbelievingly.

He shrugged, indifferent that his flaccid manhood hung exposed from the nest of dark hair at his crotch. "I can turn you out onto the streets to make your way on your own, though I wouldn't advise it. The choice is yours."

He waited, as patient as a wolf, at the door for her reply, and she said trenchantly, "I've seen Natchez-Under-the-Hill. The men there can't be much worse than the likes of you. However, I desire to return in one piece to my father." She fingered her short, curly locks and added with a morbid twist to her lips, "Such that is left of me. Until then, I'll consider myself your guest."

He grinned, and his face might have been indecently handsome had the flash of his teeth held warmth. "But not my mistress?"

"Mistress implies a willingness—of which you'll never find me capable."

He cocked a brow. "Testing that statement might afford me some amusement while we wait."

Then he was gone, not even bothering to bar the door. So he, indeed, believed her cowardly enough not to entertain the idea of escape.

In the act of viciously scrubbing his salty essence from her thighs with the rumpled bed sheet, she looked up to find the woman—Suzette, she supposed—standing in the doorway, staring, aghast, at her cropped hair.

Gabrielle drew the sheet up over her breasts. At her accusing glare, the woman lowered her eyes and glided into the room to set the tray she carried on a nightstand. Over one arm was draped some sort of clothing. "You must be hungry for a real dinner after all this time."

The steaming rice, moated with butter, watered Gabrielle's mouth, but seething virulence overrode hunger. "How could you participate in—in this defilement!"

Suzette stepped back and looked at her with liquid brown eyes. "I can't justify what Daniel has done to you, mademoiselle. It's terribly wrong. If I could have dissuaded him . . . But I couldn't. At least, as another woman, I can try to ease the pain of the violation." She gestured at the folded wet cloth and jar of salve on one corner of the tray.

"Violation? What he did was an abomination!"

"If only you knew what he suffered at your father's hand, you'd understand a little of the reason . . . for all this."

"You . . . why, I believe you love that—that rutting beast!"

"He saved me from the *plaçage* system."

A mulatto! To Gabrielle, the woman looked almost as white as she.

"I owe him much," Suzette was saying, "and, *oui*, I love him."

"I find it impossible to credit that such a man would be capable of inspiring love. I would gladly bury his knife in his back."

"Don't be so hasty to judge him, mademoiselle." Suzette took the clothing draped over her arm and laid it at the foot of the bed. "I've brought you another gown and a morning dress. Tomorrow I'll find additional clothing for you that should fit somewhat better. You see," she said apologetically, "Daniel didn't forewarn me about your height or size."

Gabrielle bristled. "Don't concern yourself. Your Daniel was thorough in everything else dealing with my abduction."

A blush suffused Suzette's honeyed skin. After she left, Gabrielle consumed the rice, the meat pie, and the sugared apricots. A dainty appetite had never been one of her qualities. The wine she left untouched, not because she suspected it of containing some kind of sleeping agent, but because she was going to need her sharpest wits about her.

Her one fear was that the redheaded devil would return some-time during the night to carry out further vengeance on her. She lay wide-eyed in the bed, waiting, as the night deepened. Behind her lids, her mind replayed the disgusting and painful scene of a few hours earlier.

Rage filled her, blind, passionate rage against the man who had dared to touch her, who had dared to lay his hands on her inti-mately. She was choking with fury that she had been compelled by the restraint of his arms to endure his hateful body inside her own! Before that night . . . Why, she had shrunk instinctively from even the thought of passion with the same fastidiousness as she did from actual physical uncleanliness.

In the dark, her mouth pressed firmly and a new keenness came into her eyes. The house quieted. Her ears strained at every creak of the timbers. When she judged it sufficiently late, too late for Daniel du Plessis to think about paying his guest a visit, she rose and dressed quietly in the morning gown Suzette had provided, covering her shorn, shocking-red hair with the cloak hood.

With thudding heart, she ascended the staircase. The parlor was pitch dark. To get that far and knock against a piece of furniture, rousing everyone, would be unbearable. Luck was with her, and she slipped out into the cool night. Her plan was to hide out among the ramshackle buildings that sagged drunkenly against each other in Natchez Under-the-Hill; then when dawn brought activity to the wharf, she would go down to the docks and bargain for passage on one of the New Orleans–bound ships, promising payment upon her delivery.

Even that late at night, or early in the morning as it was, Natchez-Under-the-Hill was still going strong. In the ghostly fog, the place was a bacchanalia. The stench of Monongahela whiskey and an even rawer local brew filled her nostrils.

Like a wraith, she moved through alleys that were dank and dark. For the first time in her life, she was nervous, and there was a hollow feeling in the pit of her stomach. At one rear door-way, a parrot on a stand squawked, scaring her terribly. In an-

other alley, she almost stumbled over a drunk who had rolled up
in a blanket to sleep where he could. A sign over one door said:

NO MORE THAN FOUR TO A BED.

She rounded a corner, always heading closer to where she
believed the docks to be, and almost collided with a naked sailor
who ran from a shack, shouting, "I've been rolled!"

Several people came to doorways and laughed, then returned
to their gaming and drinking.

Down another winding street, two men, plantation gentlemen
by their elegant clothes, fought on a tavern's upper gallery. The
light of the flambeaux attached to metal holders outside the tavern's doors flickered over the knife one wielded. *Swish . . . swish
. . .* a shriek of pain . . . The other went hurtling over the railing
to land with a sickening thud not far from where she pressed up
against a weatherboard siding.

He twitched violently, and only then did she see his intestines
hanging from a ripped stomach. The few witnesses turned away.
Gabrielle remained frozen, appalled and perilously sick to her
stomach.

Within minutes, stealthy figures crept out of the gray fog that
arose from the river to rifle through the man's clothing. She
watched in horror as his body was dragged to the nearest dock
and rolled off it to float like a cork in the black water.

Hand against her mouth, she shrank back against the rough
wall. Only through sovereign luck had she so far avoided such a
fate. She had to find someplace to hide out until dawn. In the
midst of such squalor, the flambeaux illuminated one reputable-
looking house. She recognized it for what it was: A palace of
prostitutes, but one of discretion.

All right, she could play the country bumpkin looking for a
way to earn a lot of money and stall for time. Lifting her skirts,
she climbed the stairs leading to the second floor. She knocked
at the door, and a peephole was opened. She felt terribly uncomfortable being observed that way. Then the door was partially
opened by an extraordinarily tall, thin woman in a richly cut
gown of burgundy-violet taffeta. At six foot eight, she was taller

than Gabrielle by a good eight inches. She asked, "You're looking for your husband?"

Gabrielle shook her head. "No. I'm not mar— I'm looking for work."

The woman opened the door wider. Even from the gallery, Gabrielle scented the pervasive odor of perfume. "I'm Madame Aivoges. Come in, *si'l vous plaît*."

Gabrielle followed the woman. The parlor was carpeted with red plush. Over in a corner, a golden girl softly played the spinet for a client. On a maroon damasked couch, a couple talked and drank from stemmed glasses that most likely didn't contain Under-the-Hill's standard Monongahela whiskey.

Madame Aivoges took her to a large anteroom, similarly decorated but with a desk instead of a spinet in the corner. "Now tell me," she asked, settling her bony hips on the edge of the desk, "why you would select this ungodly hour of the morning to apply for work here."

Without asking permission, for she never had in her life, Gabrielle gracefully settled her skirts on the divan. "I'm running away."

The middle-aged woman took a cigar from a pewter box on the desk and bit off the end. "Someone with your quality breeding doesn't run away. Only slaves do. Want to try another story?"

Gabrielle spread her palms. "Regardless, I am. From a forced marriage. I'd rather have clients of my own choosing than the old goat my father has selected."

Madame Aivoges reflectively rolled the cigar between her thumb and forefinger. After a moment, she said, "There are other options besides prostitution for a woman of your obvious education."

The woman was shrewd. "True." Gabrielle let a conspiratorial smile curl her lips. "But I seek to live in a manner to which my father has accustomed me. I think you can understand my feelings. I was told that this was one of the most elegant establishments. For that reason I chose to come here first."

"Not one of the most. The *most* elegant." She put down the cigar. "I will have to talk this over with my girls. Do you wish to wait—or return tomorrow morning?"

"No, no. I'll wait."

"I hope you'll change your mind by then. I don't think you

would do well in this profession, if you don't mind me saying that. If you'll excuse me, I'll check with our housekeeper and see if there is an unoccupied room for you to sleep in for the remainder of the night. Tomorrow I'll let you know my decision."

Gabrielle should have felt relief that all was going so well, but she was weary beyond any other time in her life; even wearier than the day she had fought her way through the rabid *sans-culottes*, her eyes streaming at the sight of her mother's severed head.

Within minutes, the woman returned. "We have a room, an end one that is exposed to all the noise of the street below, but it is yours until morning."

Gabrielle followed her down the softly lit hallway. The madam showed her to a small but well-furnished room, replete with a large gilded mirror and furniture lavishly ornamented with curlicues. She crossed to the gallery doors and checked the lock. "The streets are not safe at any hour, but especially not at this hour—as surely you must have noticed."

"Yes," Gabrielle murmured. "I saw a man killed—and no one did anything about it."

The woman fixed her with an eagle eye. "Let me tell you why. The witnesses turned away because they know the victor and know better than to remember what they had seen. By morning, some shanty-boat dweller will drag the body to land with a rope in hopes of a reward. What happens here is no one's business. This might be United States territory now, but there's no law here. Under-the-Hill is a place where anybody can get away with anything he wishes if he has big enough fists or a trigger finger to support him. A man takes what he wants and dares the rest of the world to challenge him for it. And he keeps what he caught until a stronger man comes along and guts him for it. Remember what I've told you."

"I've already been convinced," Gabrielle said, grim-faced.

When the madam left, Gabrielle didn't even bother to disrobe but lay down crosswise on the four-poster. At once she was asleep. A mere half hour later, the door opened. She stirred, moaned at the interruption of her sleep, and slit her eyes against the faint, early-dawn light slipping in through the jalousies.

Dear God, no!

Daniel, the damned redheaded *canaille*, closed the door behind him. "Get up," he said, anger sparking his midnight eyes.

Instantly, she was soberly awake. "I won't go with you. I'll scream. I'll raise such a—"

"You stupid, arrogant aristocrat!" He strode to her and jerked her to her feet. "How do you think I found you? I buy the services of every scurrilous river rat at the wharf—and every whore. You can't go anyplace without my knowledge. Why do you think I left the door unlocked? But, by God, I didn't think you would be foolish enough to wander the streets."

She yanked her arms from his biting grasp. "I'd be foolish enough to do anything to escape. Nothing could be worse, do you hear me!"

"Oh, really?" he drawled. "Let me tell you about another kind of abduction that goes on here. There are gangs who abduct women of quality—virgins, specifically—for resale here. A performance is scheduled; the attraction open only to an approved few. The woman is put onstage, and the curtains part to reveal the genteel but quite naked lady who is up for inspection. Intimate inspection. Then begins the bidding. After she's no longer a virgin, she is sold again and again, each time bringing a lesser price, until she dies of drink, disease, or by her own hand."

Her smoke-gray eyes fired an annihilating glance at him. "And you think rape at your hands is preferable than at the hands of another river rat? *Mon Dieu*, you set a high store on your prowess!"

He cocked his head; his lips curled satanically. "Mademoiselle, you have yet to test my prowess."

She had goaded him too far. With each step he advanced, she retreated. The wall blocked further retreat. She stood stiffly, waiting for the inevitable violation, the pain, the shame that followed. "Go ahead, rip my clothing!" she bit out, fighting back the weakness of tears. "Bruise and bloody my flesh. Violence seems to give you great pleasure."

His lips tightened. "Perhaps, then, I can resort to something else. Something that would give me equal or greater pleasure. Yes, I think your total capitulation—in every way—would be a rewarding pleasure."

"I'll never surrender to you. You'll never see me cry or beg or—"

He planted his palms on the wall at either side of her head, and her words trailed off in a shudder of repulsion. Her lids closed, blocking out the sight of those cruel eyes. His breath played over her cheek. She could smell the faint scent of those small, odd-looking cheroots he smoked, so unlike the harsher odor of the Spanish cigar and snuff.

When she felt his lips brush softly, beguilingly, over hers, her teeth clenched in resistance. Somehow this was an even worse violation of her, for the first time had been an impersonal attack involving her body only. But now he attacked her senses . . . an intimate invasion of her emotions, touching deep down to her soul.

His big hands deserted the wall to cup her face, his fingers aligned with her strong jawbone, holding her thrashing head immobile. Her breath hissed in at this outrage.

"Doucement, doucement," he whispered against her lips, filling her mouth with his scented breath. It was like a narcotic . . . his breath . . . his kiss . . . she wasn't certain which. A lassitude seeped through her veins so that the act of merely standing was a monumental effort.

"Please," she said, "don't do this."

He lifted his head. In the false light of dawn, his black eyes gleamed like dark silver, the deadly dark silver of the scimitar's blade or the pistol's barrel. "Are you begging me?"

She shook her head in denial. "Never." It was the merest sound, the sound of a single leaf rustled by the first breeze that presaged a hurricane.

"We shall see, mademoiselle."

At the determined glint in his eyes, she said in an agonized voice, "Not here . . . not in a brothel."

He threw back his head and laughed, really laughed, startling her. Then before she knew what he was about, he slipped his arms about her waist and knees and hefted her dead weight against his chest.

She had fought him the first time; that had not kept him from having his way with her. Indeed, it had seemed only to inflame him more. This time she would grit her teeth, set her mind somewhere far away, and lie passively until the sordid mess was over. He would not—by God—touch her soul; he would not leave his mark on that part of her.

His hands worked leisurely at her clothing. The bodice buttons gave way beneath his supple fingers like wagered picayunes.

I am lying beside a shallow stream. The gurgling water is cool to my feverish fingertips.

His lips burnished the proud column of her neck and nuzzled the hollow of her collarbone. His fingers gently encircled the tip of one breast. "I know you are capable of passion, mademoiselle."

The blue-green stream bubbles over mossy rocks, carrying me with it to some peaceful destination.

His hands skimmed the concave plane of her stomach, his fingers tracing the rise of her hipbone and following its gentle slope to the down of red-flamed curls. Then his fingers found that secret place.

The stream . . . it's flowing faster, churning . . . hurtling me toward . . . God . . . oh, God . . . it feels so good.

He paused, his hand still nestled between her thighs. "Beg me, mademoiselle."

The glazed look filmed her eyes. She fixed her dilated pupils on his sun-browned face. Her voice was like raw whiskey. "Never."

CHAPTER

50

To travel along the Natchez Trace was to trek with darkness and death. The five-hundred-mile trail twisted between its terminals of Natchez and the hamlet of Nashville like slack rope around vine-hung forests and steaming swamps that couldn't be skirted.

Hundreds of buffalo first established the trail, picking the easiest passages along the ridges that led to the south. Then Indians discovered it and whacked narrow trails through the undergrowth. White men marked the trees and cut the twisting trail ever deeper, so that in places almost perpendicular walls of twenty-five feet or more banked it. Only in China and a few other places could be found this soft loess soil that eroded so rapidly. The sunken Trace was a cool tunnel of thick vegetation, the roots of trees and shrubs curling like fingers from the walls. Damp and rustling with fallen leaves, it was fragrant with pine and crushed flowers and the elemental smell of wet earth.

Floods could turn low spots into bogs in which horses were caught so tight they never could escape. Vengeful Choctaws and drunken cutthroats waited in the gloomy copses for the travelers whose only prayer was that they might survive the risks of the Natchez Trace. Nameless corpses rotted beside the dried bogs.

Nonetheless, as communication became important between

Congress and its new Mississippi Territory, a mail service was put into effect. President Jefferson was especially interested in what was happening at the western end of the Trace.

His confidant, George Rogers Clark, sat at a table on the third floor of the makeshift tavern that looked as if it had once been a retreat for all the outlaws that scourged the Trace. From below came the raucous noise of the various agents quartered at the moment in the blockhouse.

Across from Clark sat Daniel, who passed him one of his cigarettes, holding a candle stub to light it. Clark inhaled on the cut tobacco and slowly let the smoke spiral out of his barrel chest. He held up the cigarette and twirled it between his fingers. "From the taste of this, I'd say those years in Algeria weren't a waste after all."

Daniel thought of those years as the lowest point in his life. Because of the Fabrevilles, he had been stripped of his humanity and treated like an animal. Eight years of his life gone. He despised Guilbert Fabreville and even more so his daughter, who partook of the fruits of her father's slimy dealings but was too far above "the likes of him," as she had put it. It had pleasured him greatly to humble her that morning the week before at Madame Aivoges.

She had been waiting for him like a blank bank draft. Had Gabrielle Fabreville truly thought that he would let her escape so easily? From the moment he had taken her from her father's plantation—and it amused Daniel greatly to let her think the abductor had been Oliver—she had been meant for him and him only to deflower. He would entrust no one else with her, not even the faithful and loyal Oliver.

And yet, despising her, how could he have any hunger for her?

Because I wish to have her beneath me, struggling, begging for the pleasure that I can give her—or withhold; because in coupling with her I dominate her. And that she detests.

Yes, having her at his mercy was a most suitable revenge on the female half of the Marchesseaux.

Clark leaned forward and lowered his voice, though there was no need to do so. The walls were three feet thick, and the blockhouse occupants—Oliver and the cook he had hired upon his return, a widow with a small son—were completely trustworthy.

"Jefferson has ordered our American minister to France to talk to the French officials about the possibility of the United States buying the Isle of Orleans. Livingston is to treat these instructions as a secret mission, because the Constitution doesn't give the President the power of purchasing territory. Tom could be impeached for such an authoritarian action."

Daniel sat back, reflecting on this bit of news. He thought about Paul la Ronde, a Huguenot; Aaron Simon, a Jew; Nicolas Brissac, a Canadian half-breed; Natalie du Plessis, a French noblewoman. They had all sought out Louisiana because it offered the promise of freedom. Maybe soon the promise would be fulfilled. And he might be a part of that. A part of the making of America. It staggered the mind.

All he said, though, was, "It won't do Livingston any good to talk to French officials. He must get the ear of Napoleon. Napoleon is the dictator of France. There is no people, no legislature, no counselors. One man is everything. His ministers are mere clerks, and his legislature and counselors are puppets."

Clark knocked the cigarette ash into a spittoon on the hearth. "That's why every eye in the United States is fixed on Louisiana affairs. France holds Louisiana, but Spain still governs it. So what the hell is going on? We depend on the information your contacts bring us."

"You say that France is about to go to war with England," Daniel said. "A British agent in Detroit brought word not long ago that it's rumored the English are already making plans to send a large fleet to capture Louisiana just as soon as the war starts."

He paused to draw thoughtfully on the cigarette, then said, "This would be a good bargaining point against Napoleon. If he thought he might lose the colony, he might be more willing to sell it first."

The door opened, and Marchesseau's daughter entered. She wore a wash-worn peasant blouse that laced low and a drab, hickory-nut homespun skirt that he had instructed Miriam to find for her, but Gabrielle Fabreville stood before him like a queen, her head balanced imperiously on the passionate column of her strong neck.

"Your whiskey," she said, her eyes snapping.

Clark flicked him a questioning glance, which he ignored for the moment.

"Bring it here and set in on the table," he ordered, switching from English to French. He watched her cross to the table and knew she would like to crash the earthen jug over his head. To be at his beck and call, to have to wait tables, was galling to a woman of her monumental pride. Her iridescent skin was flushed, and her lips set in a mutinous line—those lips that he could bruise like rose petals so that they swelled soft with passion. Beneath his hungry hands, her flesh was as smooth as Cathay silk.

She thudded the jug on the table, not deigning to look at either him or his companion. He had shamed her, but she would never acknowledge it. At least not if she had her way. But she wasn't going to; it would be his way.

"Glasses?" he drawled. "Or did you expect us to drink straight from the jug's mouth?"

Her incensed gaze flickered from Clark's tactfully sober countenance to resettle on his face. "I expected you to wallow in it like the swine you are."

His hand clamped over her wrist. "I won't have my friends insulted. You will apologize."

"It's all right," Clark began. "I took no—"

"No, she will apologize," Daniel ground out. His hand manacled her wrist so tightly that any more exertion of pressure and the bone would snap. His glare clashed with hers in a contest of two powerful wills.

Her eyes blazed. Her lips tightened so that her teeth were almost bared in a snarl. He rotated his hand ever so slightly, and she was forced to lean forward to neutralize the additional pressure. The glimpse of her full, swaying breasts only angered him, reminding him of the power she unknowingly held.

"For God's sake!" Clark said. "It's not that important!"

"You have no idea how important it is," he growled. "Eight years' worth."

Surprising him, she whirled to confront Clark. "If an apology from a woman kept as a prisoner and her body used as—as . . ." —her dense lashes lowered—". . . is worth anything, than I offer it." Her lids snapped wide, her eyes glinting defiantly. "But only to you, sir. Obviously, you are a gentleman of compassion. It was ill bred of me to include you in my sweeping statement of swine."

At that, Daniel laughed shortly and released her. "My friend doesn't understand French, but your apology will suffice . . . for the moment."

As she spun to leave, he said, "And bring two glasses."

She never turned around but slammed the door behind her.

Clark said, "You've actually pressed the girl into service! Why, Daniel? This isn't like you."

He lifted the earthen jug and, holding it backward over his arm, swilled from the mouth, anyway. Then he wiped his mouth across his sleeve and said, "I'm not the man you knew eight years ago."

"Who is she?"

"Marchesseau's daughter."

"Gawdamighty," Clark swore softly.

Daniel closed the door behind him, and Marchesseau's daughter whirled from the open window, her pupils pinpoints of wariness. "Don't think about running away again," he said, "because this time you would not be so lucky as the last. Have you ever seen a human sucked down into a bog? I did. I watched the quicksand fill the shipwright's screaming mouth and ears and nostrils, and then swallow him whole, so that it was as if he never existed."

He left her bedroom doorway and strode toward her, a cigarette held shielded by his palm the way the janissaries smoked. She didn't look happy, but she didn't look defeated, either. He was still infuriated by her outburst earlier that day. He flicked the cigarette out the window.

"There's also the alligators. You should know about their powerful, gnashing jaws and lashing tail. At night, their eyes gleam above the slime, where they lie in wait for some unfortunate animal—or human."

"You can't keep me captive forever. One day . . . one day, I'll escape."

"I can keep you as long as I want," he said languidly, "by simply doing what one man did in Natchez. Declared his wife insane and had her chained up in the madhouse."

In her eyes, he saw fear, and her breasts heaved with the fury of her impotence. He recalled the sight and touch of them. Heavy enough to fill a man's hands, young and firm with unfurled pink nipples that glistened; not the dry, dark, dusky aureoles of the Arab maidens.

He marveled at his turn of luck. She was a giantess of a woman, with hair like pale fire and long, tapered gray eyes and passionately proud lips. Deep down inside, he was pleased that she had known no other man but himself.

He had reduced her to servility. It gratified him to see the house of Marchesseau humbled. He was determined to keep her as long as it continued to please him.

"However, I don't plan to keep you captive forever. Just until I tire of you, until I've used you and used you and there is nothing left of you that any man would want."

Like a scalded cat, she hissed at him. She flung herself at him, her fingers arched to claw at his eyes. He dodged her easily, but the nails of one hand raked his cheek. He gave her a push that sent her pitching forward onto her knees. He didn't lose any time. He unbuttoned the flap of his breeches and crouched down over her.

Her eyes enormous, she tried to roll away from him. He was in one hell of a hurry to possess her. The urge had taken hold of him very suddenly. He was irate with her, but he admitted to himself, reluctantly, that she was also damned alluring. There had been nothing much to do in the hours since Clark left but think about her, about what it would be like to lay on a woman almost as long as he. He had always been so afraid of crushing Misha'il.

Over and over in his imagination he had disrobed the woman beneath him. He remembered those breasts, as ripe and heavy as muskmelons. He imagined her smooth and naked, with his body stretched over hers and his mouth locked on her lips.

Only her damned clothes were so difficult to get off. She resisted him with all her strength, rolling from side to side to make it harder and trying to free a fist to lash out at him. He fended off her flailing hands. "Stop it now," he growled, "or I swear I'll thrash you."

She halted her struggling, genuinely amazed. "No one, not even my father, has ever dared!" she breathed, sibilant as a viper.

"Then it's time." He held on to her, trying to get the blouse's drawstrings loosened. "Just because your father's wealthy, you think you're too good for everyone else!" He pushed her shoulders back against the rug. "Your illustrious lineage," he told her, panting, "has gone to your head."

He pressed her flat, trying to hold her still long enough to kiss her mouth, but she yanked her head to the side. He didn't have any intention of returning to the men, drinking and eating below, with a woman's nail marks scratched into his flesh for all to see. He braced his forearm over her neck and managed to break the damned drawstring.

"Don't tear my blouse," she whispered. "I haven't got anything else to wear."

Her square face under him was ashen. Her eyes, gray as Spanish moss, were wide open and stared up at him as though confronted with some awful mental picture.

What might have been remorse passed briefly over him, but she was setting him on fire; just looking at her, he felt he was burning up with the need to take her.

"Don't maul me," she said in a small but dignified voice. She began to loosen the remainder of the drawstring.

"Leave the blouse on," he told her. He was in a haste to have her. "Just leave it parted."

He heard her draw in a rasping, uneven breath, but she did as he instructed, spreading the blouse's flaps back to display the soft, faintly blue-veined breasts, the nipples taut and teasing. She looked as if she wanted to cry, but she didn't.

He buried his face between those lovely, pillowy globes. He could feel her shrinking back. He held her protective hands away and rubbed his nose against her flesh. He smelled a sweet odor of gardens and flowers blended with her perspiration.

"Just get on with your disgusting business," she breathed between her clenched teeth.

Grim-eyed, he thrust her frayed skirt above her hips, pushed her knees apart but went into her slowly, something of an achievement considering his haste. She gripped his shoulders with digging nails and bit her bottom lip to keep from making any betraying sound.

For a moment, it was as difficult as getting a camel to kneel. She was very tight, but he went ahead, unable to stop, anyway. He stroked her as Misha'il had taught him, the long, even motion of withdrawing and entering, of tilting his pelvis with each entry so that the tip of his penis found that "hidden garden of pleasure" that Misha'il had shyly shown him.

A long shudder rippled down the length of the woman beneath him. Finally, her mouth opened a little under his, responding against her will. He increased the rhythm he had established, lifting her slightly with his hands under her hips until he felt her limbs stiffen, her muscles tighten in an anticipation she wasn't even aware of. She seemed surprised. Her eyes darkened with consternation. Her reactions to him grew wilder until he felt her heat passing into him. He didn't let himself finish until she dropped her head back, eyes half-closed, gasping a little.

It was good. Not like anything he had expected from her. It was obvious that she could be a very passionate woman. She moved with untutored responses. He put his head down against the hollow of her neck and tried to catch his breath. It was as though he couldn't get enough of her. "Again," he muttered because he still wasn't satisfied.

"Do I have any choice?" she asked bitterly.

He raised his head and saw now, at last, the tears glistening in her eyes—and the supercilious look that defied him.

He was tempted to tell her that he had tired of her, after all, that her clumsy manner bored him. But he really wanted her; it was driving him to a frenzied madness. He was astonished that she could elicit such a response from him. "No."

She pressed the back of her hand against her mouth to keep from crying out when he moved more deeply into her. Her clear gray eyes darkened into shadowed lagoons. Her hands pushed at his shoulders, but even then she tried to respond as fiercely—he suspected, to keep from being overpowered. She was no match for him.

He wanted to get it over with, to be finished with her. Twice within the hour he had possessed her totally and thoroughly, and it should have been enough. But it was as if he was in touch once more with the vast cosmos, with nature's flow and ebb, with the things that madden one and yet comfort, also.

When he ejaculated at last, her chin was set stubbornly. Her mouth was a little swollen. Several wisps of her shortened hair clung to one corner of her lips.

"You're crushing my ribs" was all she said.

He could see that it would be very easy to become infuriated

with her. Nothing seemed to make any impression on her at all.
He levered himself off her, buttoned his pants over his painfully
sensitive erection, and strode from the room without saying a
word to her.

Drinking that night with the tavern's guests, three Kaintocks
in greasy buckskins and molty coonskin caps, his exasperation
with the young woman mellowed. He knew his full pleasure in
revenge would come with her father's downfall.

CHAPTER

A WAR COUNCIL OF SORTS WAS being held in the private upper chamber of the blockhouse. At the table sat Daniel, Oliver, and Seth Dickerson. Suzette stood near the window, arms crossed, watching the men talk. During the night, she had pursuaded Seth to bring her with him for this conference.

She studied the young lawyer. Last night that golden head had been counterpoint to the dark thatch of curls between her legs. Seth was a magnificent lover, and in his arms, they had set the night afire. Better than the lovemaking between them, however, was their *accord*. They both understood the need to marry for money.

Seth accepted that her love and loyalty belonged to Daniel; she accepted the fact that Seth would marry a plantation heiress. Suzette was all too aware that, even as he made passionate love to her during the nights, he spent his days courting Naysmyth's dough-face daughter and the daughter of the bitter Tory, Marlborough—when he wasn't carrying out the mission charged to him by Daniel.

Her gaze settled on Daniel. His extraordinary flaming red hair was a contrast to the austere flowing white robes he wore that hot afternoon. In the Eastern garb, he looked both foreign and unapproachable. She wondered if it was true what Oliver had told her, that Daniel's father-in-law had adopted him, making Daniel a sheik in his own right.

His involvement with Marchesseau's daughter puzzled her. He had had his revenge on the young woman, yet he continued to keep her a prisoner—for more than three weeks now. This wasn't like Daniel. From the way Paul had talked, Daniel had discarded women at the drop of a handkerchief.

His hatred and bitterness had to be consuming him for him to continue to subjugate the proud young woman—or else, he was . . .

Suzette's reflections, as well as the men's discussion, which both centered on the same topic, Gabrielle Fabreville, were interrupted by her entry. Even her shorn red-gold hair didn't detract from her handsomeness. A statuesque beauty to the discerning eye.

She bore a wicker tray of glasses and a bottle of Madeira. Suzette watched her closely as she set the bottle, then the glasses, on the table. Her lids were lowered. The hollows beneath her cheekbones flexed in what Suzette suspected was an effort to suppress her boiling wrath.

Suzette flicked a glance at Daniel. He was also watching the woman. One slashed brow was raised, as if he were silently taunting her. Why, the rakehell wanted to provoke the young woman into an outburst!

"That will be all," Daniel told her curtly.

The woman's lids snapped up, and fire crackled in her eyes. With what had to be an elephantine effort at self-control, she said nothing but sailed majestically from the room.

"No wonder Marchesseau is tearing New Orleans down, board by board, looking for his daughter," Oliver said after the door slammed shut. "If the bloke's anything like his daughter, he's a hotspur."

"He is that, let me assure you, and more," Seth said. For once, his merry blue eyes were stern with disapproval, but Daniel noted that he said nothing about the impressment of the noblewoman. He accepted the glass that Daniel passed him. "The day after he received your . . . uh, message—"

"His daughter's braid of hair," Daniel said dryly, the short cigarette bobbing between his compressed lips.

"Exactly," Seth said. "The day after that there wasn't a café in New Orleans that didn't have a poster or a tree that wasn't tacked with a broadside, offering a reward for the whereabouts of one Daniel du Plessis and describing your person."

Oliver fingered his lantern jaw thoughtfully and said, "I can have the keelboatmen going ashore in New Orleans put out the word that you're either hiding out with his daughter in Texas's No Man's Land or in the British-held Floridas."

"By now," Daniel said, "I'm certain Marchesseau has tracked me down to somewhere in the Mississippi Territory—beyond the reach of Spanish authority." He took the cigarette from between his lips, holding it in the Turkish fashion, and asked of Seth, "How is your part in this going?"

Seth sighed. "I'm earning the money you're paying me, believe me, friend. That Marchesseau is a wily and thoroughly unscrupulous fox. Through some expert investigation work, if you don't mind me saying so, I've uncovered some interesting data. He has established a complex and elaborate system of funding his enterprises."

The lawyer leaned forward in the rush-seated chair. "Marchesseau can be compared to the agents and quartermasters of the sixteenth-century European courts who made their fortunes catering for the palaces, armies, and private pleasures of their princes. Marchesseau is in league with the British, the French, the Spanish, and no doubt Beelzebub himself on a multitude of commercial ventures in which he rakes in enormous profits in commissions.

"Let me give you an example of how he works. At the moment, he is secretly trying to buy up so much of the South's cotton that come spring he can control the market and set the price himself. From what I can ascertain, he is one of the richest men in the New World, outside of yourself; nevertheless, he has had to resort to borrowing from international contacts to pull off a deal of this magnitude."

Daniel smiled thinly. "A simple concept of supply and demand, then. It works both ways. Oliver, I have a trip I want you to make—by the fastest schooner out of New Orleans. I want you to return to Algeria. Seek out Sheik Rajhi. Ask him to purchase for us all the cotton coming out of North Africa, Egypt especially."

Seth grinned. "By God, Daniel, if you're not the redheaded devil people claim! An ingenious idea. Come spring and the cotton shortage Marchesseau has engineered, you dump the Middle East's cotton on the market."

Daniel stabbed out the cigarette. "Exactly. Flood the market and the price of cotton bottoms out. A chunk of the Marchesseau estate will have to go on the auction block for him to meet his financial obligations. Little by little, Seth, I plan to ruin the man. At this point, I want him to know who is responsible. Tell me, do you think he'll eventually come down to auctioning off his daughter?"

Suzette saw the glacier ice that frosted the wintry dark eyes and shivered.

Gabrielle dashed the boar brush in the bucket of dirty water, watching from the corner of her eye as Daniel descended the stairs with the two men and Suzette. Never had he looked so barbaric, so formidable, as he did when dressed in Arabian regalia of robe and sandals. The knuckles of Gabrielle's chapped hands tightened until they showed white from the strain. At that moment, she wanted nothing better than to hurl the bucket at the insolent, red head.

She had been chagrined, waiting on the various people who passed through; she had been humiliated serving the frontiersman Clark; but she was mortified beyond words when she acted the scullery maid before the dandified lawyer, a man of breeding and education. Somehow, she vowed, she would find a way to escape the fortress—a safe way. Serving as food for the alligators was not to her liking.

The cook's three-year-old towheaded son deserted his mother's side to fling his birdlike arms about one of Daniel's long legs. Daniel stooped, hefted the boy Jeremy onto one broad shoulder, and continued on out the door with his visitors, his desert robe swishing close to where Gabrielle knelt on the plaster-covered brick floor.

Only when the boy was out of sight did the rawboned widow turn her attention back to the kettle suspended from the fireplace's crane—and back to Gabrielle. Like the woman's son, rarely was Gabrielle permitted out of the cook's sight.

Grudgingly, Gabrielle had to admit that Miriam could have lorded it over her, delegating many more chores to Gabrielle than she did. If the woman was curious about the reasons behind Gabrielle's enforced presence at the blockhouse, she never inquired. She was a tight-lipped woman who noticed everything, worked hard, and was intensely devoted to Daniel's welfare. When he returned from one of his periodical visits to Natchez, Miriam always had hot food and drink ready for him. Lately, the woman had food and drink ready for Oliver also, and Gabrielle suspected the two had eyes for each other.

Gabrielle nodded toward the open door, from where Daniel's low voice could be heard, bidding his visitors farewell. "Your son, Jeremy—is he related to the *maître*?" It galled her to refer to the barbarian as the master, but she had little choice.

"Nope. Jeremy's father was knifed in Under-the-Hill. A month before his son's birth."

Well, that canceled out the possibility of a paternal relationship. Her mouth set, Gabrielle went back to scouring the floor before the hearth where old grease drippings darkened it. The soap of leach lye removed the stains but also ate away the skin on her hands. Hands that had once been famed for their porcelain beauty!

She was more than a maidservant; she was a mere slave of the passions of Daniel du Plessis—unconsidered, disregarded, reduced to the level of an animal. The starkly hideous reality of her position made her quiver and hang her head. Where now was the young, reckless female who had laughed at the aroused passions of her suitors?

Though she continued to fight Daniel du Plessis until the unequal struggle left her exhausted and helpless in arms that forced her compliance, her courageous spirit was crushed by the realization of her own powerlessness and by the strange fear the man himself had awakened in her. She loathed herself with bitter contempt.

Jeremy came toddling back through the door toward her, a crooked smile lighting his round, little face. "Sweet?" he asked, holding out a dimpled hand.

Gabrielle paused and withdrew the handkerchief from her apron's pocket. It contained broken bits of praline that she doled out to Jeremy.

"You'll spoil the boy," Miriam chided but, as usual, didn't forbid Gabrielle the pleasure that she received in watching Jeremy's grin ripen.

Jeremy padded off, drooling the praline's sugar onto his chin, and Gabrielle went back to her mopping. A shadow spilled across the floor, then she saw the muddied sandals, their owner striding carelessly across the newly scrubbed floor.

Rage misted her vision. "You sniveling, uncouth jackanapes!" she shouted.

Miriam froze, appalled. Daniel turned slowly, his brow raised in cool inquiry.

Gabrielle's self-control snapped. She did what she had been wanting to do all day—picked up the bucket and flung its dirty contents. Water puddled about the sandaled feet. By increments, her gaze was raised past the wet robe, which was molded to his thighs; upward past the expanse of chest, where dark hair sprang from the robe's deep V neckline; and settled on his face. His features were rigid but for a muscle that ticked furiously in his jaw.

Miriam chose that moment to leave the room discreetly.

"You know," he said, fists planted low on his hips, "I'm afraid I have been lax about the running of the tavern. In the old days, a slave waited for the appearance of a guest with a hot toddy and hot water to wash the traveler's feet for him. Presently, Miriam will bring a drink for me, but for now I want you to—"

"No," she gritted, low. "I will not—ever—wash your feet."

"You will. And you will do it now."

She faced him like a sparring boxer on fair day, cautiously circling. "And if I don't?" she jeered. "What will you do? Will you thrash me as you threatened?"

"No," he said, rubbing his jaw thoughtfully, "I think it's too late for that; you're far past childhood. No, I will simply do what any wise master does with a recalcitrant slave. Rather than damage his property by whipping it, the master sells the slave 'downriver,' so to speak."

"You wouldn't dare!"

He shrugged. "I'm weary of your defiance."

She drew several steadying breaths. Servitude to Daniel was better than the uncertainty of her fate at another man's hands. But, *mon Dieu*, she hated Daniel du Plessis! She lowered her lashes so that he couldn't see the tears that threatened to spill over. Incredible that this incident should breach her defenses, when his repeated violation of her had not. "I'll draw the water."

He took a seat in one of the cane-backed chairs, his hands flat on his thighs, elbows out. "Don't dawdle. My patience wears thin."

When she returned with the basin of water, his leather-thonged sandals were off and his robes drawn up past the knotted muscles of his calves. Gingerly, with great distaste, she lifted one foot and placed it in the basin. She ran the wet cloth down over his heel and under the instep of the strongly formed foot.

"Between my toes, also," he instructed, and she knew he was enjoying humbling her immensely.

She risked a daggered glance of venom up at his face. He smiled back and raised his brows.

"The other foot," she snapped.

He complied, saying, "Perhaps, with only a little discipline, you will make a good servant woman after all."

"God rot you," she mumbled, diligently washing between his toes.

Naked, Daniel stood at the window, watching Gabrielle work in the courtyard below. Her red-orange hair, which had grown past her nape now, was hidden from his view by a frilled muslin coronet cap. With a grace that reminded him of the lithe Bedouin women, she poured water from her bucket into a large jar that contained alum and charcoal for filtering the tavern's drinking water. The long line of water jars resembled something out of "Ali Baba and the Forty Thieves."

When Miriam appeared in the courtyard to carry in one of the filled jars, he turned away. In the strong autumn sunlight shafting through the window, he subjected his sun-baked flesh to the usual inspection, checking for spots or lesions. The fear of leprosy was an obsession that haunted him.

That done, he quickly dressed for the meeting with Seth. He found him in the taproom below, bouncing Jeremy on his knee, but as soon as the boy glimpsed Daniel, he squirmed off and tottered over to him, his arms uplifted, demanding to be picked up.

Daniel did so, letting the boy, who was infatuated with his red hair, tug at the curls while Seth talked. He was the blockhouse's only visitor that afternoon, and he spoke freely of what had transpired in the month since his last visit.

"Marchesseau's located several people who knew you in New Orleans. The commissary-general's wife and the *maître de'armes*, Bastile Roquère, to name two. Fortunately for Marcel Lassaut, he is touring Europe and is unavailable for Marchesseau's interrogation and blackmail."

Daniel sat down at the table, balancing the wiggling tot in one arm. "Tell me more."

Miriam appeared with a decanter of rum and two large pewter mugs on a tray and said, "Let me relieve you of Jeremy, *maître*."

Jeremy went, albeit unwillingly, into his mother's arms, and Seth settled into his story. "Both claimed to know nothing of your whereabouts. Marchesseau brought pressure to bear on them. When Roquère could offer no further information, he was put up for auction at Maspero's Exchange."

Daniel's eyes glittered with jet hardness. "Roquère was a *gens de couleur libre*!"

Seth shrugged. "That didn't stop Marchesseau. Nothing does."

"Hilda?"

"The commissary-general's wife? I am told that when Marchesseau threatened to expose her . . . extramarital affairs, she wept and begged him not to do so, swearing she hadn't seen you in more than eight years. I don't doubt that Marchesseau believed her, but he revealed her past, anyway, I think half out of helpless fury and half as an example to others. Her husband kicked her out into the street. She took up whoring down on the levee."

Daniel studied his hands. He knew the strength they possessed and didn't know if he could control them. He locked them around the pewter mug. "I want you to find who bought Roquère and buy him—"

"I already have, Daniel. A planter out of Mobile bought him. I paid four times the price for the fencing master, and the last time I heard he was on his way to Haiti, a free man. Unfortunately, I couldn't do anything for the German woman. She took her life. Purchased a dram of poison from some voodoo mistress."

Daniel finished his rum and said, "Thank you. You're an excellent lawyer and an even better friend." He cursorily assessed the affable sybarite. "The costly suit you wear is made to order in Philadelphia, isn't it? Cost you approximately a hundred dollars, Seth, and I know you have three or four for winter alone. You live profusely, you have a taste for the good life, you drink costly port—"

"Not here I don't," Seth retorted, chuckling.

Daniel shrugged. "Regardless, you need an affluent income to sustain such a life-style. Seeing as how you haven't had time to do any serious courting, I suggest you invest some of the wages I pay you in New Orleans real estate."

"You don't pay me enough to compete with magnates like Marchesseau."

"Don't bother buying prime land, Seth. Buy swampland, derelict property, whatever you can afford."

Seth blinked incredulously. "Are you out of your mind, Daniel? What would I do with swampland?"

"Sell it for a hefty profit within the year." He poured both of them another round of rum, saying, "This is to go no further than this taproom, Seth. The United States is bargaining with France—not only for the Isle of Orleans but for all of the Louisiana territory. If it goes through, that would drive New Orleans real estate up sky-high."

Seth rubbed his chin. "The United States doesn't have that much money in its treasury."

"Jefferson will get it, let me assure you."

Seth grinned. "I owe you one, Daniel!"

"Call us even."

During the remainder of the evening, the two men played backgammon, with the jubilant Seth for once winning three out of five times. But then Daniel's mind wasn't on the game. He thought of Marchesseau's villainy, and a quiet anger gradually built in him.

Late that night, he went to Gabrielle's bedroom. He would bend her to his will once and for all. He banged open her door, and she bolted upright. In the glow of his candlestick, his narrowed lids didn't hide the hearts of dark passion in his eyes. His gaze raked over the Titian red of her tousled hair that just reached her shoulders. Defensively, she drew the sheet up higher to shield herself.

The act infuriated him. He set the candlestick on the one-drawer stand. "Take off your clothes." His command brooked no resistance.

She stared at him in frozen concentration, as if locked in a violent inner struggle between submitting and facing the consequences if she didn't.

Her face expressionless, she slid from between the muslin sheets. With a rabid glitter in his eyes, he watched her slowly divest herself of her nightrail. The phenomenon of her translucent flesh never ceased to stun him.

He know that what he was about to do was wrong, taking out his anger on her since Marchesseau was not beneath his hands at the moment for retribution, but he couldn't help himself. His entrails wrenched with the need to dominate her.

"Now take off mine."

A shuddering breath went out of her. "Daniel, I overheard you and Seth this afternoon. About how my father blackmailed those people who had known you. I can understand how you must hate him. What he did was terrible. But, please, don't do this to me."

"I said, take off my clothes."

Something in her great gray eyes, the reproachful look of a puppy, shamed him so that, when she padded over to him, his hands locked brutally in her tresses and forced her to her knees in straining quiescence.

His breath came raggedly as he watched her fingers fumble at the buttons of his breeches. She looked up at him, tears glistening in her eyes. Furious with himself, he tore open his breeches and, without taking them off, plunged into her violently, grinding her down against the plank boards with his big, hot body until he shuddered with a mighty release.

He rolled from her, not even having the courage to look at her, and stalked from her chamber.

CHAPTER

52

FURY EXPLODED IN DANIEL, BLIND and violent and shouting down the walls. Gabrielle was gone.

Something had awakened him. For a few drowsy moments, he had prowled his chamber, trying to deny his need for her beneath him. With purposeful strides, he had gone to fetch her—only to find that she had fled from the blockhouse.

He jammed his nightshirt into a rumpled pair of breeches, rolled the sleeves back, and hunted for his boots.

He should have known. For the past three weeks, ever since the night he stormed into her chamber to violate her on the floor like a mindless, rutting animal, she had avoided him like he had the plague—or leprosy.

At the foot of the bed . . . under the table . . . Damn! Where had he left them?

In truth, he had avoided her also. He was ashamed but never would he beg the pardon of a Fabreville.

His boots—they were downstairs, where she had polished them of course.

He grabbed the ax from above the mantel. Briefly, he considered taking the lard lantern and decided against it. The moon was nearing its second quarter. He stormed out the door, telling himself that, by God, he was going to keep the woman until it pleased him otherwise! And it pleased him to no end to see the house of Marchesseau humbled.

In the moonlit landscape, her tracks were easy enough to follow in the mulch of vegetation. If only she stuck to the trail, but it was deceptive even to the most seasoned woodsman, and at night . . .

After three miles, he lost her footprints; he backtracked and found where they had wandered down a blind trail. He swore softly. His lips pressed together, grim and narrow. The trail she followed died out at the brink of a swampy region.

Even as he stalked her, his leg muscles picked up the subtle change in the earth, its solidity giving way to a sponginess. Automatically, he shifted the center of his weight from the balls of his feet to his knees.

The stillness of the dense woods was as heavy as a coffin lid. He didn't bother to push aside the dead moss that occasionally reached down to brush across his face and shoulders like long, skeletal fingers. Mist rose from the strands of water. His gaze intent on trying to pick up her trail, he almost missed the brown scrap of material caught on a thorny vine some yards away. She didn't know it, but she was traveling in a circle, a circle that would pass through the worst of the swamp.

The bellow of a bull alligator broke the stillness of the night. Immediately, Daniel set off at a clipped pace in that direction. To run might mean the fatal misjudgment of a step. Briars and fines slapped him in the face. His heart thudded heavily behind his breastbone. He found a channel and followed it, ax lying ready in his grip as he searched the banks for an alligator's den, which sometimes tunneled as much as fifteen feet beneath the soggy earth.

Minutes later, he stumbled upon the muddy trail of clawed prints littered with the remains of fish and waterfowl. Gabrielle must have disturbed the alligator during its dinner. Daniel smelled the musky odor given off by the glands in the alligator's head at the same time he saw Gabrielle. A dim apparition in the swamp's dark gloom, her hair of pale fire gave her away. She was a *feu follet*. She shrank into a corner hollowed by the roots of a giant bald cypress, dirty water lapping at her calves.

Immediately, Daniel's gaze scanned the murky terrain and spotted only yards away the gleam of the alligator's eyes perched above its broad snout. As if the reptile recognized a worthy foe, it lashed its tail against the marshy water. The tail could break a man in half. Daniel judged the alligator to be an old one, reaching a length of perhaps seventeen feet and easily weighing seven hundred pounds.

The ancient, lizardlike thing was wily. Despite Daniel's appearance on the scene, it wasn't about to give up the prey it had cornered. Almost lazily, the olive-gray beast cruised toward Gabrielle. Her shrill scream sent the night's winged creatures rustling up out of their perches in the trees. The animal world came alive: frogs croaking, an owl screeching. They sensed impending death.

Only a bullet or an ax blade between the eyes could stop an alligator, and its whipping tail taunted Daniel, who was out of position for such a throw.

With no other alternative, he plunged into the water. He tried to circle the alligator, but no clear shot at the snout presented itself. To miss meant the loss of a weapon. For the moment, he tucked the ax handle into the band of his breeches.

Then, with a sudden lunge, he locked his arms and legs about the alligator's midsection. Its tough hide was slimy and hard to hold on to. The monstrous tail thrashed wildly. The alligator rolled, and Daniel went underwater. The head whipped from side to side, the teeth trying to tear at its foe. Up Daniel came again. The musky smell was overpowering now.

The jaws—if he could hold them shut for a moment, he might have one chance to bury the ax between its eyes. Its teeth were bared, gleaming yellow against the surrounding dark. Enraged, it bellowed again. Its jaws snapped viciously. Daniel made a grab for the great snout, but the alligator plunged under the water's surface once more. Daniel sucked in water, choking, and almost lost his hold.

When the alligator surfaced, Daniel gasped for air. Water drops clinging to his lashes blinded him. He shook his head, flinging off water like a wet mastiff. His strength was dwindling. With a Herculean effort, he seized the snout between his hands. The blood pounded in his ears. His biceps strained. The tendons in his forearms stood out like hawsers.

In gradual increments, he pressed the jaws shut. He had only a maximum of seconds. His right hand jerked the ax from the band of his breeches. The alligator's jaws escaped the hold of his left hand. He swung the ax in a mighty arc and sank it into the skull midway between the eyes.

The bull alligator bellowed a death call, lashed its tail feebly, and rolled beneath the water.

Daniel found his footing in the mire and stood, waist-deep, in the blood-pooling water. He quaffed deep quantities of stagnant air. Then, plowing back the wet hair plastered to his face, he plodded toward the cypress, where Gabrielle pressed against its trunk. Her eyes were enormous in her white face. Her wet skirt clung to her hips and thighs revealingly.

At his approach, she shrank even farther into the cypress hollow, if that were possible—as though she thought he would kill her next. Just as he reached her, she sagged, and he caught her in his arms. Gently, his muddy hand turned her face up to his. "Chasing after you is getting to be tedious, *mon coeur*."

Like an animal moving one paw at a time, Gabrielle inched toward the awful truth. Dear God, she was in love with her captor. She was in love with Daniel du Plessis.

She lay beside him in his great bed, staring sightlessly at the dark, vaulted ceiling. Their naked bodies were sprawled in a passionate tangle. In the moonlight that spilled through the window, his sun-browned skin glowed as if it had been buffed with saddle wax. His heavy arm, flung across her ribs, trapped her. . . . just as her feelings for this enemy were building a cage around her.

She tried to deal with these feelings, turbulent feelings she had never known before. She was powerfully alive to him. Gone now was her independence. Did she even have free will left, or had she surrendered that, too? He had conquered her, leaving her nothing, not even her pride. At least there had been a dignity in her animosity.

Would she ever get enough of him—and, oh, God, what would she do when he no longer wanted to vent his revenge on her?

Daniel's fingers cupped her cheek, turning her face toward his. She lowered her lids so that his probing gaze wouldn't see the love revealed in her eyes. Upon their return from the swamp, he had carried her to this bed, where he had taken her with a wild and feral passion—and within the hour possessed her again, this time with a tenderness and consideration that left her off balance, reeling in her newly discovered sensuality. This was the first time she had really known what her body was for.

"I thought you were asleep," she murmured, feeling a shortness of breath and a sudden shyness despite his now thorough knowledge of her.

"From tonight on, you will sleep here with me," he said, irritation compressing his sensuous lips. "I don't trust you not to try to run away a third time."

He was a satyr, this desert sheik who had captured her soul and heart. How could she run away? She managed an insouciant shrug of her shoulders. "You have no need to worry. I don't care to repeat tonight's experience."

He arched a brow and flicked her a fulminating glance. "Which experience?"

Instantly, she perceived his meaning. "Neither one," she said, turning her heard from his scrutiny.

He raised himself on one elbow and stared down at her with annoyance. "You know, *mon coeur*, you once swore you would never beg me. I think it's time I make you recant that promise."

Her mouth was parched. How could she ever keep the knowledge of her love from him? Her love seared her soul; it consumed her with an intensity that was an agony; it was a happiness that mocked her with its hollowness.

He lowered his head and brushed his lips gently across her temple. The gentleness would surely be her undoing, and he knew it! His lips played over hers in a long, surpassing kiss that didn't demand any response from her, yet still left her breathless.

"Your mouth was made for a man's pleasure," he said, and traced its outline with one callused fingertip as if he actually took real pleasure in something as simple as her lips' symmetry.

"You could have let the alligator devour me," she said in an attempt to divert his attention from his quest. "It would have been a fitting end to your enemy's daughter."

"What? And deprive myself of your loveliness?" His hand caressed her shoulder, her arm, her palm, with infinite tenderness. Her nerve endings were frazzled by this sensual assault. "Lately," he said lazily, "it has occurred to me that we're two of a kind.

Redheaded, hot-tempered, extraordinarily tall, and each determined to have our own way. It will be interesting to see which one of us does."

"You are taking into account, of course, that our goals are mutually incompatible."

"Of course."

His mouth burnished her neck, and she shivered at the pleasant sensation. When he slipped down to nuzzle his face against the red riot of kinky curls, she lost all hope of self-containment. His rough tongue stroked the velvet folds of skin, and something hot and demanding took hold of her. Incoherent words trembled on her lips. She locked her legs across the muscled ridges of his shoulders and arched her hips upward in an offering.

Supporting the small of her back, he lifted his head. His lips glistened. "My love," he asked quietly, "will you concede that in this one case our goals are mutually compatible?"

At either side of her, her fists crushed the rumpled sheet. *"Oui,"* she gasped.

He had broken her. But it had taken four long months to do so. And still sometimes he thought he caught a certain defiant gleam in her eyes or the indomitable set of her mouth. He should have felt some sort of satisfaction, but he felt only emptiness. Not until the house of Marchesseau was totally destroyed would he allow himself to feel again.

He sat across from Seth and Sheik Ibn Rajhi, who had journeyed back with Oliver. Daniel almost hadn't recognized his former father-in-law in the Western garb of buff frock coat, embroidered cream satin vest, and nankeen breeches. Without the *ghutra*, the Arabian cloth headdress, the sheik looked older, but distinguished, with his silver hair cropped à la Titus.

The wise and sharp blue eyes watched him from out of the sun-leathered face. Those eyes possessed a curious power, his gaunt body a grandeur that Daniel couldn't explain. Daniel respected the man greatly. He still retained that inclination to kneel and touch his forehead to the back of the sheik's hand as he used to do in the man's presence, but, obviously, the man expected no such obeisance.

When he took a drink of the coffee Miriam had served, Daniel said with a wry smile, "It's as thick and syrupy as Turkish coffee, isn't it?"

"I find many similarities in the two cultures, my son."

Daniel raised a brow, waiting for an explanation, but the old man said instead, "I arranged for the purchase of the Middle East cotton you requested. You owe me nothing, the money belonged to you, anyway."

"I dumped the cotton on six ports this week," Seth said. "Charleston, Mobile, Savannah, Pensacola, Norfolk—and, of course, New Orleans. At lowest prices—and in your name. Before the month's out, Marchesseau should be feeling the pinch."

Daniel ground out the cigarette and leaned forward. "Good. Here's what I want you to do next. Go to the New Orleans exchange and investigate what companies are for sale. Pick one that's both sound and doing well. Buy controlling stock in the company under an assumed name. Start funneling money into the company. Then, when the stock goes up enough points to interest our greedy opportunist, I want you to approach him with an offer to sell forty-nine percent of the stock and—"

"—and then funnel the money right back out," Seth finished with a pleased look on his handsome face.

Daniel's look matched it. "Exactly."

The little boy's voice whimpered, and in her half-sleep, Gabrielle thought it was Jeremy. Sleepily, she told herself that Miriam would go to comfort her son; but when the child's weeping continued, Gabrielle dragged her mind up from its somnolent state.

Groggily, she pushed back her hair, which had grown to where the curling ends just brushed her shoulder blades. Jeremy . . . She had to check on Jeremy.

Then she realized the boy's whimpering belonged to Daniel. It wasn't the first time in the span of six months that he had awakened her by his tossings and mutterings. But this was the first time he had cried out in such a pathetic little voice. The sheet was soaked with his perspiration, as was his hair.

The way he whimpered tore at her heart, and she cradled his head against her breast. She loved the woodsy smell of his skin. "Daniel . . . Daniel, it's all right, love." She smoothed back the sweat-dampened curls from his temples. She wanted so badly to kiss him, to kiss away the hurt that ate at his soul.

He stirred and opened his eyes, their black shade as soft as velvet. With the return of consciousness, their color would harden to jet. She sighed. "You were having a nightmare."

"The lepers . . ." he murmured. He laid his hand over hers and nuzzled his cheek against her palm.

"What about them?" she asked. She could feel his heart thudding against her flesh.

"They were reaching out to . . ."

He pulled away from her, sitting up and tunneling his fingers through his rumpled hair. She could see that he regretted that moment of indiscretion. His voice was suddenly not childish at all but cold and definite like a nutcracker coming down on a pecan. "An old dream is all it was, nothing more."

"You have it quite often."

He turned to her, anchoring his hand in her tresses, and his eyes grazed over her breasts, heavy with her need of him. She recognized that arrested look stamped on his powerful features. Against her thigh, the cylinder of flesh and the wrinkled bag dangling from the dark crotch steadily hardened. "But you have the means to make me forget it," he said with all his former male arrogance.

He took her hand and instructed her what to do, quietly, re-assuringly, just like a priest, she thought. Then she forgot to think at all. A warmth melted her and made her yield like candlewax. Time and silence enclosed her, swelling, drifting, passing in great waves.

"You are a beast," she murmured, enveloped within her self-induced languidness.

"*Oui*, a beast who brings pleasure, my love."

"Cruel pleasures," she qualified, but made herself accessible to him, anyway.

Gabrielle rotated the short-handled paddle among the clothes in the staved washtub. The sunlight of a warm May afternoon penciled through the courtyard's tupelo trees to fall on her pensive face. She reflected that ten months before she had been the belle of the ball—and now she was a washwoman, scrubbing clean even Daniel's intimate apparel. In the heat of the afternoon, she flushed, thinking that pride did indeed go before a fall. Her old haughtiness had been vanquished by Daniel's repeated subjugation of her.

In the weeks that had slipped away since her mad dash for freedom, she had come to know a vivid happiness that was mixed with poignant suffering. The perfect joy of being with him was marred by the passionate longing for his love. She treasured the cool dawn mornings when she lay with him and listened to the raucous twitter of the awakening forest birds, the times when he casually shared bits of information about the exotic life of the Middle East and unintentionally revealing scenarios about his own life as a slave . . . and sometimes taunting her with tidbits about his Arab wife. Her death he mentioned in as few words as possible.

A shadow fell across the wooden tub, and she looked up to see the old sheik. He was dressed in the robe of his desert people. "Good morning, daughter," he said courteously.

In the three weeks he had been at the blockhouse, she had come to like him, with his grave and quiet dignity. In him, she sensed a sympathy for her plight, though the few times they had talked their conversations had been of Rousseau, the opera, and Paris, which the sheik had visited. He was a surprisingly learned man. According to Suzette, he was as rich as Croesus.

Glad for a respite, she rose and dried her hands on her apron. "You look vastly different in the Arabian robe and headdress, Sheik Rajhi."

"I am preparing to return to my country shortly." He gestured toward the ceiling of leafy branches above them. "I miss the open skies of the desert, no matter how much I enjoy visiting with my son-in-law."

"I will be sorry to see you go," she said sincerely. Unconsciously, she rubbed her fingertips together, where the flesh was wrinkled by the wash water. "You love Daniel almost like your own son."

"Yes, I do. I know you may find it hard to believe, my daughter, but he's a good man, an honorable man, despite this grievous thing he has done to you."

She couldn't help but blush at the reference to her position there at the blockhouse. She looked away from the discerning old eyes.

"His pride has led him to commit many errors," the sheik continued. "When Oliver came to Algeria to see me about a cotton purchase and I learned what had transpired, I decided to find out for myself what Daniel was about."

"And have you?"

The sheik wandered over to a gardenia bush, plucked a flower, and sniffed its exotic fragrance. "The most beautiful of flowers," he murmured, and then said, "Your fate, Daniel's fate, is in Allah's hands." The Mediterranean-blue eyes that watched her over the gardenia's waxy-white petals were enigmatic.

She sighed. "I don't think Daniel is afraid of anything, even of your Allah."

"He is a man, my daughter, and has fears like all men."

She thought of Daniel's dreams that awakened him at nights and said, "He has nightmares about lepers."

"Ah, yes." The sheik's tone held a great sadness. "I understand that, as a child, he lived in a colony of lepers, that he watched his mother disintegrate with the disease. I am told she was a beautiful woman."

"She was."

Gabrielle spun to see Daniel standing behind her. His black gaze swung from the sheik to her. "Tomorrow," he said, "we leave for New Orleans to see my father-in-law off next week for North Africa. All of us."

Her heartbeat accelerated. "You are letting me return home also?"

"No."

She looked imploringly at the Sheik Rajhi. He spread his hands, palms up, and said, "*Insh'allah*."

As God wills.

CHAPTER

53

Daniel DREW ON THE CIG-
arette, and its flare briefly illuminated his hard, handsome
face. Gabrielle, lying in the cradle of his arm, thought that any
hope for his love was as insubstantial as the cigarette's light.
In those moments he possessed her body, he called her his
heart or his love, and in those moments she chose to deceive herself, to believe he really did care, really did love her. If so,
that love was like the cigarette's light; a single word could
extinguish it.

She transferred her gaze from his strong profile to the shadowed
ceiling of the New Orleans apartment he had taken for
them. "Daniel," she asked in a low voice, "if my father learns
of your presence here in New Orleans, he will have you
killed."

"What? Are you concerned for my safety?" he jeered softly.

Without looking at him, she replied, "I don't want the blood
of any man on my hands."

"Have no fear. Your hands shall remain lily-white."

"Why did you drive me past Maison Bellecour today?"

He turned slightly from her and ground out his cigarette in
the ashtray, then rolled to half cover her. "Because, my love, I

thought you might like to see it one more time before your father gives it up."

Her gaze slashed to his. "What are you talking about? Father would never sell it."

"Nevertheless, your father's hope of surviving the financial crises he finds himself in depends on his selling it. By next week, Maison Bellecour should be on the auction block."

"And you plan to buy it, don't you?"

"No, I don't. I will take it from your father without giving away a single doubloon."

"You really mean to ruin him," she said in an incredulous whisper.

"Utterly. Financially and morally."

"You *are* some sort of monster!"

He rubbed his knuckle along the undercurve of her cheek. "Tonight I believe I shall take you to the opera."

"I won't go. I won't let you humiliate me any more than you have already."

"Yes, *mon coeur*, you will. And as my mistress, you will hold your head high. You wouldn't want me to do what the husband I pointed out to you did—have you declared quite insane and put in the madhouse for the rest of your life?"

Fear crawled from her nape to the base of her spine. She recalled her mother, interned in the madhouse of La Salpêtrière, and in that awful moment came the realization that her father had been responsible for that act.

She found the courage to say, "Daniel, can't you see what you're doing makes you no different from my father?"

"Why, because I would rid the world of a cockroach of a man?"

She knew then that his obsession for revenge would destroy not only her father but himself—and any hope for their love. "We are in New Orleans," she said quietly, proudly. "You do not hold the supreme power here in French territory that you do in Natchez. I will find a way to leave you, I swear."

"There is no place you can go that I won't find you. Don't you know that by now?"

She turned her face from his devouring gaze, but he caught her chin and forced her to look at him. With his knuckle, he wiped away the tears that seeped from the outer corner of each eye. Then he lowered his mouth over hers, fully open, and inhaled her breath . . . and with it her soul, she thought sadly, and then forgot to think at all.

The elite of New Orleans was present at the St. Philips Theater that evening for *The Barber of Seville*. The light from a thousand candles shimmered over the diamonds and pearls at the throats and ears of the city's beautiful Creole women. The Creole dandies strutted about in their evening dress of frilled shirt, lace cuffs, and kid gloves.

Daniel arrived at the opera late, just before the candles were snuffed. The sheik had already boarded the vessel that was to sail on the morrow, but Oliver, Seth, and Suzette accompanied Gabrielle and Daniel. With foresight, he had instructed Seth to purchase a subscription to the opera. "I want a parterre box directly across from Marchesseau's. None other."

Every eye in the house was trained on that loge, curious to see who was to occupy it. The usual tension just before a performance pervaded the place. In the orchestra pit, the string section rosined their bows, the brass section loosened their valves, and the reed section adjusted their mouth pieces or ran through the scales.

Daniel chose that moment to pull back the crimson velvet curtain and usher Gabrielle and Suzette into the box ahead of him, Seth, and Oliver. Suzette had elected to wear the badge of her status, a *tignon* of brilliant purple that matched her flowing Greek tunic. Indignation and offense showed on the faces of the Creoles in the audience. They were insulted that she dared to enter their domain, for a balcony was reserved for mulattoes.

Yet the Creoles' indignation evaporated at the sight of Gabrielle on Daniel's arm. Gasps zephyred among them.

"It's the daughter of the Marquis de Marchesseau!"

"Wasn't she supposed to have been abducted?"

"Her escort, he fits the description of the brigand, her abductor! How could there be two men with hair that red?"

"She looks willing enough to me."

"Would you look at that gown she's wearing!"

"Look at her hair. Cropped! Could that be the new style?"

"My dear, I'd wager she is his mistress."

"What do you think Marchesseau will do?"

"The gown is a disgrace!"

"It's indecent!"

Gabrielle, her head carried painfully high, wore a ball gown Daniel had had made especially for that night, a diaphanous muslin of virginal white with a train beaded with tiny seed pearls. To complete the costume, she wore gold-corded sandals.

If Daniel had had the gown's square décolletage cut shamefully low so that the pink buds of her breasts were almost exposed, if he had picked a material that was semitransparent without the modesty of undergarments—well, who could blame everyone for staring? Her long gloves covered more than her gown did.

For himself, he had selected a black broadcloth suit with mere pleatings of linen unadorned with lace. Next to Gabrielle's brilliance, he looked austere and formidable. Seth looked elegant in a white satin waistcoat and cream-colored breeches and coat. Oliver, his hair slicked back with bear grease, merely looked uncomfortable, especially without his turkey-feathered felt hat.

Daniel ignored the stares and mutterings and placed his hands possessively on Gabrielle's bare shoulders. Her flesh was icy cold. Before the eyes of all, he lowered his head and kissed the hollow of her neck.

"Don't," she whispered.

"Smile," he taunted. "Where's your pride?"

Her chin rose stubbornly. Her face was bruised with fatigue. He noticed she avoided glancing toward her father's box. She placed her gloved hand in his, suffering him to lead her to her armchair. He took a quiet pleasure in the whispers that flew behind swishing fans and gloved hands.

Only after Oliver, Seth, and he had seated themselves did he allow his bored gaze to wander over the hundreds of heads—and gradually shift upward to the box across from his. Marchesseau was there, sitting with a little man, whom Daniel had heard was with a Dutch banking firm. Marchesseau was scrambling frantically to meet his notes.

Daniel's gaze met Marchesseau's murderous one. Even at that distance, the veins in the man's temples stood out in a web of blue against the raging white of his skin. Intermission should prove interesting. For eight long years, he had dreamed of tonight.

He nodded slightly at Marchesseau, permitted a social smile to touch the ends of his lips, and turned his attention to the libretto in his hands.

All of the candles but those of the orchestra pit and the stage were snuffed, and the first strains of music quieted the rampant whispers that ran like a hiss through the audience. He reached over and took Gabrielle's hand. "Courage, *mon coeur*."

"You knew my father would be here," she said without looking at him. "I'll never forgive you."

Her voice was low, meant only for his ears, but he knew that behind him Seth, Oliver, and Suzette were aware of what she was suffering and did not approve. "It's not your forgiveness I want."

In the dark of the box, her eyes flashed at him. "What more do you want of me? You have taken my maidenhood, humiliated me, made me beg! What more?"

"I want to hear you say you love me." Why, he didn't know. He admired her courage, her pride in the face of subjugation, but her love should mean nothing to him. She was a Marchesseau.

"Why? Because it's one more way that you seek to humble me?" Tears sparkled like diamonds in her eyes. "Well, I'll surprise you, Daniel du Plessis. Yes, I do love you. But you know nothing of love—or humility, and until you do, you'll never possess my love as you have my body."

"You should have learned by now not to deny me anything, *ma mignonne*. By doing so, you only arouse my determination to take it."

She shot him a withering stare, then averted her attention to the stage and the opera in process. With the first intermission, he leaned over and asked her, "Shall we keep with tradition and parade ourselves through the lobby?"

"Please," Gabrielle said, "I have no wish to leave the box."

"What?" he mocked. "Surely you want to see your father?"

"Not like this; not in front of everyone."

"The first time I met you," he chided, "you were dressed nearly as revealingly."

"You know that's not what I'm talking about. Parading me before my father as your mistress . . . Haven't you humbled us enough already?"

"Not quite," Daniel drawled. "Now come along, or do you wish to hide up here? Cowardice isn't like you, you know."

He had allowed her no choice but to accompany him to the confrontation with her father. Her hand trembled in his, but he noted that her ashen face wore that cool, unapproachable look that had so often frustrated him. Behind them lumbered Oliver, looking like some great watchdog, and Seth and Suzette, farther back. All three had disapproving expressions. On this one subject, their opinions mattered little to him.

Below, the lobby was more crowded than ever before. People chatted and strolled about, but the tension was evident. Everyone waited.

From the lobby's other end, Daniel saw Marchesseau striding toward them. The men and women fell back, giving the two opponents room. That close, Daniel saw the engulfing hatred that filled Marchesseau's eyes.

The marquis held out his hand to his daughter. "Come, Gabrielle," he said stiffly.

He had to give Marchesseau credit; the man had not lost his self-control. "She stays with me," Daniel drawled, and passed her hand, which dug into his sleeve, over to Oliver's keeping. In Oliver's other hand now was a deadly-looking horse pistol.

Marchesseau's jaw clenched. His hand tighted on his beribboned walking stick. Still, he managed a wolfish grin. "You will not escape so easily, du Plessis. When you entered tonight, I immediately sent word to the governor. Even now his troops are on their way to arrest you for treason against first Spain, then France."

"I doubt that seriously. You see, at this moment, a representative of President Jefferson, George Rogers Clark, is closeted with the governor, informing him that as of April thirtieth, France officially sold Louisiana to the United States, the country to which I owe my allegiance."

Words of disbelief passed among the opera-goers. "I don't believe you," Marchesseau sneered.

"Well, while we wait for confirmation, I suggest we repair to the gaming rooms behind here. A game of faro, perhaps?"

"You are insane!"

"So your daughter has told me innumerable times. Nonetheless, I challenge you to a game of cards. The stakes: If you win, I surrender your daughter to you. But if I win . . . Well, you are to surrender Maison Bellecour to me."

Not a person in the lobby breathed. Marchesseau's honor was exposed, as Daniel had calculated. If the marquis refused to risk the wager, he would be admitting his estates were worth more than his daughter. Daniel had nothing to lose; Marchesseau, everything.

Sweat beaded on Marchesseau's upper lip. One lid ticked fiercely. Behind Daniel, Gabrielle let out what could only be described as a sound of grief, or maybe that wounded gasp came closer to being the keening of a wild animal.

Without warning, Marchesseau raised the walking cane and brought it down with a lashing sound across Daniel's shoulder.

Pain vibrated through his body, but he made no motion to retaliate. At his side, Gabrielle strained against Oliver's hold and cried out, "No!" In behalf of her father or himself, he didn't know which.

In an age where honor was everything, the least breach of etiquette, the most venial sin against politeness, the least suspicion indicated of unfair dealing were causes sufficient for a challenge, which none dared refuse.

But to strike a blow was strictly forbidden; thus Daniel was given the privilege of the challenge of the duello. Before the elite of New Orleans, Daniel bowed and said, "Monsieur, shall we meet at dawn in St. Anthony's Garden?"

"Damn you," Marchesseau snarled. "I'll kill you now!"

French honor was normally satisfied by wounds, but no one present was surprised that Marchesseau demanded death; to have settled for a mere drawing of blood as satisfaction for Daniel's dishonor of his daughter would have been considered an act of cowardice.

Daniel smiled coldly. "The choice of weapons is yours."

"The pistol," Marchesseau spat, and turned on his heel. Daniel had expected that choice. Marchesseau, though an expert with the blade, was older than he and would be the first to tire at swordplay.

The gardens behind St. Louis Cathedral were awash with lanterns and torches carried by avid spectators. The Dutch financier agreed to serve as Marchesseau's second, Seth as Daniel's. Someone found a brace of pistols, and the two seconds checked to see that a single ball was provided in each before passing the pistols to the duelists.

Daniel took his pistol, weighed it in the palm of his hand. The crowd shifted restlessly like milling cattle. The *beau monde* of New Orleans was eager for the duel to begin. He ignored them. His whole attention was centered on the unfamiliar pistol. He went through the act of raising his arm, bringing the weapon down in a strong, steady arc, and sighting in, until he was satisfied.

The count was settled on by the seconds—twenty paces and then turn and fire. Seth returned to Daniel and reported the arrangements. "I'm ready," Daniel said, and nodded curtly to Marchesseau, who stood with his entourage of sycophants on the other side of the garden.

"For God's sake!" Gabrielle cried out, and broke loose from a surprised Oliver. She ran to Daniel and fell to her knees, wrapping her arms about his legs. "Don't do this, Daniel. You swore you wanted to humble me. Well, look at me! Before everyone, I'm on my knees, begging you. Don't go through with this!"

He was past being reached by reasoning. His mind was locked on a single act that had taken years to reach this culmination. Nothing outside the perimeter of twenty paces could distract him. His power of focus was directed inward, a total physical and mental concentration on all that he had learned from the weapons master and all that he had experienced and all that he perceived.

He looked down at her, his eyes empty. "You're getting your gown dirty. Get up."

After Oliver loosened her grasp and led her away, Daniel and Marchesseau positioned themselves, back to back. It was after midnight, those hours when nature reckons with itself. A steaming mist rose from the damp earth. Not a breath of wind stirred the oak leaves and red camellia petals. Seth dropped his handkerchief, and Daniel stepped off his paces.

One . . . two . . . three . . . four . . .

Do not impose your will above that of Allah's.

. . . nine . . . ten . . . eleven . . .

The tendons in Daniel's neck bulged like ropes. An even greater battle was taking place within him than the one on the field of honor. The surpassing need to complete his revenge waged a war with a revelation that left him trembling.

. . . fifteen . . . sixteen . . . seventeen . . .

With the raging conflict, sweat sheened his face. To walk away could only invite a bullet in the back, for he knew too well Marchesseau's code of honor. But there was also such a thing as a living death, like that of a leper colony.

In that instant, he flung the pistol from him. The spectators gaped and murmured among themselves in astonishment. As he strode toward them, they fell back from him as if he were the proverbial pariah.

"Du Plessis!" Marchesseau called.

Daniel kept walking. He had almost become the man Marchesseau was.

Almost simultaneously, two shots thundered and reverberated against the buildings surrounding St. Anthony's Garden, rending the dawn.

CHAPTER

54

PAIN WAS ALWAYS PRESENT. BUT sometimes there was another presence, too. Gabrielle, he thought in his more lucid moments, but he wasn't certain. He was simply aware of a woman's soft crooning—her voice? The loving touch of a woman's hands, cooling his burning flesh. Tears bathing his fevered face.

One day, at last, he opened his eyes. He was in the apartment he had let in New Orleans. Oliver was hunkering over him, his fierce visage giving way to a gaped-toothed smile. Then Oliver's face wavered like the heat behind Daniel's eyes and evaporated . . . like a mirage.

Another day, Daniel awakened from his pain-webbed cocoon to catch Suzette bending over him. She smiled. "Welcome back to life, Daniel."

"I need a cigarette."

"You need to rest," she chided. "You've been badly hurt."

Daniel rubbed his fingers through the tangled mat of his hair and winced at the soreness in his shoulder that came with movement. "*Merde!*" he grunted.

"You were shot," Seth said, coming into Daniel's field of vision. "Would a cigar do in place of one of your fiendish Turkish things?"

"No. Marchesseau? He shot me?"

"Afraid so, the scum. Right square in your back."

Daniel frowned. "Gabrielle returned to him?"

"He's dead. He took a ball that went straight through his heart."

Wearily, Daniel closed his eyes, realizing in that moment that the fight had meant more than the victory. His was a Pyrrhic victory. He felt nothing, no triumph.

His eyes snapped open. "Marchesseau's shot took me down. Who fired the second shot?"

"No one knows," Suzette said. "It's a mystery."

"What about Oliver? He had a pistol."

"And he had his hands full just trying to hold Gabrielle back."

"Where is she?" Daniel asked. "She was here, wasn't she?"

Seth looked uneasily at Suzette, who said, "She was. She slept here in the room with you for more than three weeks, and she—"

"Three weeks," Daniel groaned.

"—stayed by your side and refused to let any of us relieve her. Then, when we knew you were going to live . . ."

"Well," Daniel demanded, knowing fully well the answer.

"She left," Seth said.

Daniel struggled to sit up and then fell back, gasping from the effort. "Why in God's name didn't you stop her?"

"Good God, Daniel!" Seth exclaimed. "You've disgraced Marchesseau's daughter, he's dead, Maison Bellecour is yours for the taking. What more do you want?"

Daniel's voice took on the edge of steel. "I want—and will have—Gabrielle."

"Well, she doesn't want you," Suzette snapped. "Why should she, after everything you've done to her—especially after she listened to you barter her for Maison Bellecour the night of the duel? I believe you shattered whatever remained of her love for you."

She turned on Seth and spat, "Men, bah!" and stalked from the bedroom.

"I think I will have to ask her to marry me, if ever I'm to have any peace of mind," Seth said with a wry grimace.

"Get Oliver," Daniel said. "I want him to find Gabrielle."

Seth cocked his blond head. "You love her, don't you? This isn't just a protraction of your revenge?"

The revelation was so sweeping, it stunned him. His pride

rebeled against the admission—to love a Marchesseau, no, never. But he did. He loved Gabrielle . . . her indomitable spirit, her own hardheaded pride, her soft womanliness that touched some soft corner in him and made him more of a man. "*Oui*," he admitted in a low, marveling voice.

"Then God help you," Seth said, "because for once I have to agree with Suzette. Gabrielle might have loved you—and I don't profess to understand women, but I saw her face that night, my friend. As a lawyer, I've been trained to read people and all their nuances of expressions. She'll never forgive you, Daniel."

"I'll find her and make her forgive me, beg her forgiveness."

Seth's brows arched in skepticism. "Beg? That's something new for you. Nevertheless, it'll take more than begging, or I'm not a lawyer."

Over the following days, Oliver came and went from the apartment. His report was invariably the same. He shrugged his big shoulders, twisted his felt hat in his hands, and said, "My men have turned up nothing."

"Impossible," Daniel fumed. "These are the agents who wormed secrets out of whores, fishmongers' wives, seamen, and slaves? Someone has to have seen her. A woman that tall, with hair that color can't go unnoticed. She has to be somewhere, and, by God, I'll find her!"

He dressed that very day, with Oliver's help, and set out, first, for the taverns. Two days of toasting left him with no information and a godawful hangover. Next, he went to the *salle d'armes*. The Creole gentlemen who studied there lived fast—and knew everything. In a way, they were as bad gossips as old women.

Marcel Lassaut still frequented the place. At Daniel's questioning, he effected the expressive Gallic shrug. "When the Vieux Carré isn't talking about the coming of American rule, it's talking about the Marchesseau woman and you. But, *non*, no one has seen her or I would know about it." He kissed his bunched fingertips and added, "I, Marcel, a connoisseur of beautiful women."

Daniel sent Oliver and his team of keelboatmen up and down the river to scout the surrounding towns. One by one, they reported back, their searches unfruitful.

Could she have changed the color of her hair? Daniel wondered.

Still, a woman of her height would have drawn attention. What if she had left the city? Returned to Paris? Or worse, gone to any of a thousand seaports in the world? Three days of careful questioning along the levee revealed that no one had seen a woman of her description during the past month—but a month, who remembers that long? She could have disguised her height by stooping.

With a dismal drizzle to make his mood worse, he sought out the nearest dockside cabaret to formulate his next strategy. His beard-stubbled face and clothes he hadn't bothered to change in a week or more fitted in with the hard-faced ruffians who drank their beer or rum and laughed raucously and swore obscenely. Near the bar, a young man strummed his guitar and sang a song of the *toros*.

Few listened. Even there, the talk was of the coming American rule. To the French Creoles, the Americans were strangers. They spoke another language and had different social and political customs. At least the Spanish, during their tenure of rule in Louisiana, had shared the same language root and culture.

Daniel ignored the cabaret's other customers and sat hunched in a dark corner with his mug, brooding. Had Gabrielle not told him she would find a place to hide where he couldn't find her? The realization that Gabrielle could be anywhere in the world by that time—and the astronomical odds of finding her—frustrated him to near madness.

He vacillated between swearing he would search the world over until he did find her and the alternative of vowing his determination to forget her. Each was an impossibility, and he lifted mug after mug that evening in an attempt to obliterate the dilemma that tore at his heart.

After perhaps a dozen mugs had left their ring stain on the oaken table, he looked up belligerently to find the old sheik before his table. There on the wharves, where seamen of all nationalities strode, the sheik's Arabian regalia went barely noticed—or would have, except that the old man had a commanding presence that drew the attention of everyone.

"I thought you sailed," Daniel growled. He resented any intrusion on his private suffering.

The blue eyes of his former father-in-law smoldered with the tension of his innermost thoughts. Daniel shrank inwardly from the way that sharp gaze seemed to pierce all the way through to his soul. He told himself he had drunk too much.

"I heard of the duel. I have prolonged my stay to see how you fared, my son."

"I lived," Daniel said shortly. He felt a great tiredness such as he had never felt before, not even in those years he had worked the salt pits from sunup until sundown.

"May I sit?" the old man asked gravely. "Only for a few minutes, for my own time is also limited."

"*Oui*," Daniel muttered indifferently. The sheik's relentless stare made him uneasy. Those old eyes were like wells of time.

"Gabrielle—I know where she is."

Daniel's head snapped up. "What?" he demanded, not certain he had heard right. "What did you say?"

"I know where Gabrielle Fabreville is, Daniel."

He had to restrain himself from grabbing the man and shaking him. "Where? Where can I find her?"

"Where you put your pride behind you, where you assume the mantle of humility."

Daniel's last remnants of control shattered. "Tell me!" he commanded, ready to throttle the sheik for the information.

"The quickest way to acquire compassion and humility, my son, is to do exactly what you are afraid to do."

"Damn you, don't speak in riddles!"

The sheik merely stared at him. In an instant's cold sobriety, Daniel knew he'd get not one word more of explanation, though he might beat the old man senseless.

Exhausted after going for weeks with little sleep and depressed by the days of his fruitless search, Daniel trudged back to the apartment through a torrential downpour. Somehow, he would have to learn to live with the secret pain of Gabrielle's absence. He sprawled facedown across his bed, fully dressed, and immediately went to sleep.

But even his utter fatigue did not keep away the nightmare: the fragmentary hands that reached for him, that would imprison him forever . . . his mother's face, her nose denuded of flesh . . . her eyes compassionate, even in his revulsion of her . . .

He bolted upright in the bed. A hoarse scream rattled at the back of his throat. Something cold and damp pulsed beneath his drum-tight skin. His heart throbbed out a furious tattoo against his eardrums. Sweat dripped off his eyelashes—or tears, or both.

And he knew . . .

He knew where he'd find the humility and the compassion of the old man's riddles, where he'd find the courage to forgive himself after more than a quarter of a century—and where he'd find Gabrielle.

A skin-crawl started near the base of his testicles.

It was a ghostly mansion abandoned by a planter who had given up trying to fight the indomitable swamps. The mansion, moldering away on a hump of vine-swathed land in the labyrinth of swamps just outside of New Orleans, was inhabited by bats and owls and rats—and lepers. Long before the turn of the century, the city had set aside the spot as an isolation community for the innumerable lepers who populated the area. Occasionally, a few brave souls ventured close enough to the place to leave donations of clothes or food, usually as rotted as the lepers themselves.

Tropical flowers ran riot in the once well-tended gardens, their intoxicating fragrance overpowering the putrid odor of rotting stumps. This was a place of perpetual banishment and slow, agonizing death, a place of no hope.

Some hobbled about the mansion or its overgrown but lush gardens on feet that had no toes; others stared with glassy eyes in faces that had no cheeks and whose lips and chins had rotted off. Some had only a few sores between their fingers or toes; others had only thickened facial skin to give them away. Then there were the lepers who were too far progressed in the disease to stand and instead sat in filthy corners waiting to die. This was humanity wallowing at its lowest point.

Here at the mansion, no law existed; yet Gabrielle moved among the leprosy-riddled men inviolate. Perhaps at first the haughty way she carried herself had staved off those healthier males still capable of venting their lust; but her compassion as she went among them, dispensing what aid she could, earned their respect and, by the end of the second week, her virtual protection.

Initially, she had been horrified, frightened, repulsed, but the place was her only sanctuary. Anywhere else on the face of the earth, Daniel du Plessis would find her and take her and keep her . . . but never love her.

After almost a month of living among the lepers, her fear had been replaced by indignation that the human race could ignore such suffering, that it didn't even bother to make an effort at alleviating the living conditions of the lepers. Originally, she had planned to stay only until she thought Daniel had grown weary of looking for her—a few weeks at most—but now that she knew the personalities behind the hideous masks, heard their pathetic stories and witnessed their attempts at humor, she put off leaving.

One afternoon, dressed in the homespun skirt and wash-worn cotton blouse from her Natchez days and barefoot, she tended a lovely, fair-headed girl of ten who sat on the gallery steps, bewildered by her situation. She was free of lesions, although her right arm and leg had no feeling. A slight puffiness of the earlobes and redness of the eyes confirmed her plight. Eventually, her sight would dim and her bone would atrophy, and absorption would shrink her fingers and toes until she had only palms left and stubs for feet.

"It's the best of the fruit in the box," Gabrielle said, and held out the pear.

The little girl stared vacantly at the proffered fruit.

"Eat it," Gabrielle urged. "It's good for you."

The girl looked past Gabrielle, past the mutilated and bloated men and women who wandered in the yard, soaking up the sun. Gabrielle turned to follow her gaze and saw the man who pushed aside a web of creepers to stand staring at the wasted human bodies. Veins made a pulsing road map in his forehead. His eyes looked as though he was standing at the outer edge of life, staring at the space beyond.

She rose and stood on the step, fighting the shaking that was vibrating up through her as he waded among the mutilated forms that begged piteously and stretched forth fragmented hands. In contrast, he was so alive, so vital, his mane of extraordinary red hair eclipsing even the opulence of tropical flowers.

Only when he was almost before her did she realize that tears trickled down his beard-stubbled face. Astounded, she watched as he knelt before her in the most humbling of positions. His lips, damp with his tears, brushed the bare toes of one foot. Hesitantly, she touched his heaving shoulders, almost afraid to hope.

He looked up, and in his glistening eyes she saw the answer she looked for. He rose and cupped her face between his powerful hands. "Forgive me." It was a trembling whisper.

She nodded, too filled with her love for him to reply. Instead, she wrapped her arms around him and pressed his glorious red head against the hollow of her shoulder. "The nightmare is over, my love."

In the sultry July sunlight, the robed sheik left St. Louis Cathedral and walked slowly, as old people were wont to do, beneath the majestic oaks of St. Anthony's Garden. At that moment, the wildly pealing bells of St. Louis Cathedral signaled that the wedding was over; Daniel du Plessis had taken Gabrielle Fabreville, the Marquise de Marchesseau, as his wife.

The old sheik would not be attending the reception. He was on his way to the wharves, where he would board a ship that would take him home . . . not to Algeria, but this time back to Perpignan in France.

Still, for just a moment, he paused in the garden, at almost the same spot he had stood in months before . . . when he had fired the shot that saved the life of Reinette's son. It was odd how fate always intervened. So many times when he had writhed at the blows life dealt, fate would step in to turn everything around, somehow tying up all the loose ends, making everything right with age.

Perhaps it was the Arab's fatalism beginning to take hold of him after all these years. Certainly, O'Reilly would appreciate life's trick. How could the Irish mercenary have known when he hauled Reinette's husband out of El Morro to leave him on the battle-torn beach of Algiers, that the Jew would not only survive but, years later, would save the son the mercenary believed to be his own?

For a moment, the sheik thought he smelled the sweet scent of gardenias and tears glistened in his rheumy eyes, remembering the lovely marsh sprite, the *feu follet*, who had been his wife. Then, tucking away the memory to take out later in the lonely years left to him, Daniel's father, Aaron Simon, strode on down the path.

Insh'allah.

ABOUT THE AUTHOR

A favorite of romance readers everywhere, Parris Afton Bonds is the author of thirteen books and the mother of five sons, in addition to being a teacher of creative writing at a local community college. She is co-founder and board member of Romance Writers of America and was the recipient of the Best Novel of 1981 Award given by the Texas Press Women for *Dust Devil*. Some of her previous books include *Deep Purple*, *Lavender Blue*, *Mood Indigo*, and *Blue Moon*.